CORNELL

NATURE-STUDY LEAFLETS

BEING A SELECTION, WITH REVISION, FROM THE
TEACHERS' LEAFLETS, HOME NATURE - STUDY
LESSONS, JUNIOR NATURALIST MONTHLIES AND
OTHER PUBLICATIONS FROM THE COLLEGE OF
AGRICULTURE, CORNELL UNIVERSITY, ITHACA, N.Y.,
1896 - 1904

STATE OF NEW YORK — DEPARTMENT OF AGRICULTURE

NATURE-STUDY BULLETIN NO. 1

❧

ALBANY
J. B. LYON COMPANY, PRINTERS
1904

LETTER OF TRANSMITTAL.

COLLEGE OF AGRICULTURE,
CORNELL UNIVERSITY,
ITHACA, N. Y.

Hon. C. A. WIETING,
Commissioner of Agriculture,
Albany, N. Y.:

SIR.— I submit herewith as a part of the Annual Report of 1903 a number of the nature-study publications for reprinting. Most of these publications are out of print and the call for them still continues. These publications have practically all arisen under your supervision, and under the directorship of Professor I. P. Roberts.

Nature-study work should begin in the primary grades. It is a fundamental educational process, because it begins with the concrete and simple, develops the power of observation, relates the child to its environment, develops sympathy for the common and the near-at-hand. By the time the child has arrived at the fifth or sixth grade he should be well prepared for specific work in the modern environmental geography, in the industries, or in other exacter common-life subjects. Nature-study is a necessary foundation for the best work in biology, physiography and agriculture. Since it is content work, it is also equally important as a preparation in all expression work, as in English, number and reading. In most present-day rural schools it may well continue through the eighth grade ; and, if well taught, it may even take the place very profitably of some of the "science" of some of the higher schools. Its particular sphere, however, in a well-developed school, is below the sixth grade, possibly below the fifth. But even if the term nature-study ceases at the fifth or sixth grade, the nature-study method will persist throughout the school course,— the method of dealing first-hand and in their natural setting with objects, phenomena and affairs, and of proceeding from the simple and undissected to the complex and remote.

The reader should bear in mind that the College of Agriculture has no organic connection with the public school system of New

York State, and that its nature-study work is a propaganda. From first to last the College has been fortunate in having the sympathy, aid, and approval of the State Department of Public Instruction, and now of the new Education Department. The time is now near at hand when nature-study will be adequately recognized in the school system of the State, and then the nature-study work of the College of Agriculture may take new form.

In these reprinted leaflets the reader will find many methods of presentation of a great variety of subject-matter. A wide range has purposely been included, in the hope that any interested teacher may find at least one or two leaflets that will be suggestive in his own work. Our own ideas as to what is a valuable leaflet have changed greatly since the work was begun ; and it is to be expected that they will continue to change with the progress of the work and the development of the schools. It would be an interesting review if we were to summarize our own experiences with our own work. The leaflet that is most praised by the critics may be the least useful in practice. The greatest danger is that of making the work too complete, too rigid and too formidable.

L. H. BAILEY,

Director College of Agriculture.

CONTENTS.

PART I. TEACHERS' LEAFLETS.

4   CONTENTS.

CONTENTS.

PART II. CHILDREN'S LEAFLETS.

PART I.

TEACHERS' LEAFLETS.

PUBLICATIONS DESIGNED TO AID THE TEACHER WITH SUBJECT-MATTER, TO INDICATE THE POINT OF VIEW, AND TO SUGGEST A METHOD OF PRESENTATION.

7

THE SCHOOL HOUSE.

By L. H. BAILEY.

IN the rural districts, the school must become a social and intellectual centre. It must stand in close relationship with the life and activities of its community. It must not be an institution apart, exotic to the common-day lives; it must teach the common things and put the pupil into sympathetic touch with his own environment. Then every school house will have a voice, and will say:

I teach
The earth and soil
To them that toil,
The hill and fen
To common men
That live right here;

The plants that grow,
The winds that blow,
The streams that run
In rain and sun
Throughout the year;

And then I lead,
Thro' wood and mead,
Thro' mold and sod,
Out unto God
With love and cheer.

I teach!

9

LEAFLET I.

WHAT IS NATURE–STUDY ?*

By L. H. BAILEY.

NATURE–STUDY, as a process, is seeing the things that one looks at, and the drawing of proper conclusions from what one sees. Its purpose is to educate the child in terms of his environment, to the end that his life may be fuller and richer. Nature-study is not the study of a science, as of botany, entomology, geology, and the like. That is, it takes the things at hand and endeavors to understand them, without reference primarily to the systematic order or relationships of the objects. It is informal, as are the objects which one sees. It is entirely divorced from mere definitions, or from formal explanations in books. It is therefore supremely natural. It trains the eye and the mind to see and to comprehend the common things of life; and the result is not directly the acquiring of science but the establishing of a living sympathy with everything that is.

The proper objects of nature-study are the things that one oftenest meets. Stones, flowers, twigs, birds, insects, are good and common subjects. The child, or even the high school pupil, is first interested in things that do not need to be analyzed or changed into unusual forms or problems. Therefore, problems of chemistry and of physics are for the most part unsuited to early lessons in nature-study. Moving things, as birds, insects and mammals, interest children most and therefore seem to be the proper objects for nature-study; but it is often difficult to secure such specimens when wanted, especially in liberal quantity, and still more difficult to see the objects in perfectly natural conditions. Plants are more easily had, and are therefore usually more practicable for the purpose, although animals and minerals should by no means be excluded.

---

* Paragraphs adapted from Teachers' Leaflet, No. 6, May 1, 1897, and from subsequent publications.

If the objects to be studied are informal, the methods of teaching should be the same. If nature-study were made a stated part
of a rigid curriculum, its purpose might be defeated. One difficulty with our present school methods is the necessary formal-
ity of the courses and the hours. Tasks are set, and tasks are
always hard. The best way to teach nature-study is, with no hard
and fast course laid out, to bring in some object that may be at
hand and to set the pupils to looking at it. The pupils do the
work,— they see the thing and explain its structure and its meaning. The exercise should not be long, not to exceed fifteen
minutes perhaps, and, above all things, the pupil should never
look upon it as a "recitation," nor as a means of preparing for
"examination." It may come as a rest exercise, whenever the
pupils become listless. Ten minutes a day, for one term, of a
short, sharp, and spicy observation lesson on plants, for example,
is worth more than a whole text-book of botany.

The teacher should studiously avoid definitions, and the setting
of patterns. The old idea of the model flower is a pernicious
one, because it does not exist in nature. The model flower, the
complete leaf, and the like, are inferences, and pupils should
always begin with things and phenomena, and not with abstract
ideas. In other words, the ideas should be suggested by the
things, and not the things by the ideas. "Here is a drawing of a
model flower," the old method says; "go and find the nearest
approach to it." "Go and find me a flower," is the true method,
"and let us see what it is."

Every child, and every grown person too, for that matter, is
interested in nature-study, for it is the natural way of acquiring knowledge. The only difficulty lies in the teaching, for very
few teachers have had experience in this informal method of
drawing out the observing and reasoning powers of the pupil
without the use of text-books. The teacher must first of all feel
in natural objects the living interest which it is desired the pupils
shall acquire. If the enthusiasm is not catching, better let such
teaching alone.

Primarily, nature-study, as the writer conceives it, is not knowledge. He would avoid the leaflet that gives nothing but information. Nature-study is not "method." Of necessity each teacher
will develop a method; but this method is the need of the teacher,
not of the subject.

Nature-study is not to be taught for the purpose of making

the youth a specialist or a scientist. Now and then a pupil will desire to pursue a science for the sake of the science, and he should be encouraged. But every pupil may be taught to be interested in plants and birds and insects and running brooks, and thereby his life will be the stronger. The crop of scientists will take care of itself.

It is said that nature-study teaching is not thorough and therefore is undesirable. Much that is good in teaching has been sacrificed for what we call "thoroughness,"— which in many cases means only a perfunctory drill in mere facts. One cannot teach a pupil to be really interested in any natural object or phenomenon until the pupil sees accurately and reasons correctly. Accuracy is a prime requisite in any good nature-study teaching, for accuracy is truth and it develops power. It is better that a pupil see twenty things accurately, and see them himself, than that he be confined to one thing so long that he detests it. Different subjects demand different methods of teaching. The method of mathematics cannot be applied to dandelions and polliwogs.

The first essential in nature-study is actually to see the thing or the phenomenon. It is positive, direct, discriminating, accurate observation. The second essential is to understand why the thing is so, or what it means. The third essential is the desire to know more, and this comes of itself and thereby is unlike much other effort of the schoolroom. The final result should be the development of a keen personal interest in every natural object and phenomenon.

Real nature-study cannot pass away. We are children of nature, and we have never appreciated the fact so much as we do now. But the more closely we come into touch with nature, the less do we proclaim the fact abroad. We may hear less about it, but that will be because we are living nearer to it and have ceased to feel the necessity of advertising it.

Much that is called nature-study is only diluted and sugar-coated science. This will pass. Some of it is mere sentimentalism. This also will pass. With the changes, the term nature-study may fall into disuse; but the name matters little so long as we hold to the essence.

All new things must be unduly emphasized, else they cannot gain a foothold in competition with things that are established. For a day, some new movement is announced in the daily papers, and then, because we do not see the head lines, we think that the movement is dead; but usually when things are heralded they have only just appeared. So long as the sun shines and the fields are green, we shall need to go to nature for our inspiration and our respite; and our need is the greater with every increasing complexity of our lives.

All this means that the teacher will need helps. He will need to inform himself before he attempts to inform the pupil. It is not necessary that he become a scientist in order to do this. He goes as far as he knows, and then says to the pupil that he cannot answer the questions that he cannot. This at once raises him in the estimation of the pupil, for the pupil is convinced of his truthfulness, and is made to feel — but how seldom is the sensation! — that knowledge is not the peculiar property of the teacher but is the right of any one who seeks it. Nature-study sets the pupil to investigating for himself. The teacher never needs to apologize for nature. He is teaching merely because he is an older and more experienced pupil than his pupil is. This is the spirit of the teacher in the universities to-day. The best teacher is the one whose pupils the farthest outrun him.

In order to help the teacher in the rural schools of New York, we have conceived of a series of leaflets explaining how the common objects can be made interesting to children. Whilst these are intended for the teacher, there is no harm in giving them to the pupil; but the leaflets should never be used as texts from which to make recitations. Now and then, take the children for a ramble in the woods or fields, or go to the brook or lake. Call their attention to the interesting things that you meet — whether you yourself understand them or not — in order to teach them to see and to find some point of sympathy; for every one of them will some day need the solace and the rest which this nature-love can give them. It is not the mere information that is valuable; that may be had by asking someone wiser than they, but the inquiring and sympathetic spirit is one's own.

The pupils will find their regular lessons easier to acquire for this respite of ten minutes with a leaf or an insect, and the school-going will come to be less perfunctory. If you must teach drawing, set the picture in a leaflet before the pupils for study, and then substitute the object. If you must teach composition, let the pupils write on what they have seen. After a time, give ten minutes now and then to asking the children what they saw on their way to school.

Now, why is the College of Agriculture at Cornell University interesting itself in this work? It is trying to help the farmer, and it begins with the most teachable point — the child. The district school cannot teach technical professional agriculture any more than it can teach law or engineering or any other profession or trade, but it can interest the child in nature and in rural problems, and thereby join his sympathies to the country at the same time that his mind is trained to efficient thinking. The child will teach the parent. The coming generation will see the result. In the interest of humanity and country, we ask for help.

How to make the rural school more efficient is one of the most difficult problems before our educators, but the problem is larger than mere courses of study. Social and economic questions are at the bottom of the difficulty, and these questions may be beyond the reach of the educator. A correspondent wrote us the other day that an old teacher in a rural school, who was receiving $20 a month, was underbid 50 cents by one of no experience, and the younger teacher was engaged for $19.50, thus saving the district for the three months' term the sum of $1.50. This is an extreme case, but it illustrates one of the rural school problems.

One of the difficulties with the rural district school is the fact that the teachers tend to move to the villages and cities, where there is opportunity to associate with other teachers, where there are libraries, and where the wages are sometimes better. This movement is likely to leave the district school in the hands of younger teachers, and changes are very frequent. To all this there are many exceptions. Many teachers appreciate the advantages of living in the country. There they find compensations for the lack of association. They may reside at home. Some of the best work in our nature-study movement has come from the rural schools. We shall make a special effort to reach the country schools. Yet it is a fact that new movements usually take root in the city schools and gradually spread to the smaller places. This is not the fault of the country teacher; it comes largely from the fact that his time is occupied by so many various duties and that the rural schools do not have the advantage of the personal supervision which the city schools have.

Retrospect and Prospect after five years' work.*

To create a larger public sentiment in favor of agriculture, to increase the farmer's respect for his own business,—these are the controlling purposes in the general movement that we are carrying forward under the title of nature-study. It is not by teaching agriculture directly that this movement can be started. The common schools in New York will not teach agriculture to any extent for the present, and the movement, if it is to arouse a public sentiment, must reach beyond the actual farmers themselves. The agricultural status is much more than an affair of mere farming. The first undertaking, as we conceive the problem, is to awaken an interest in the things with which the farmer lives and has to do, for a man is happy only when he is in sympathy with his environment. To teach observation of common things, therefore, has been the fundamental purpose. A name for the movement was necessary. We did not wish to invent a new name or phrase, as it would require too much effort in explanation. Therefore, we chose the current and significant phrase "nature-study," which, while it covers many methods and practices, stands everywhere for the opening of the mind directly to the common phenomena of nature.

We have not tried to develop a system of nature-study nor to make a contribution to the pedagogics of the subject. We have merely endeavored, as best we could, to reach a certain specific result,— the enlarging of the agricultural horizon. We have had no pedagogical theories, or, if we have, they have been modified or upset by the actual conditions that have presented themselves. Neither do we contend that our own methods and means have always been the best. We are learning. Yet we are sure that the general results justify all the effort.

Theoretical pedagogical ideals can be applied by the good teacher who comes into personal relations with the children, and they are almost certain to work out well. These ideals cannot always be applied, however, with persons who are to be reached by means of correspondence and in a great variety of conditions, and particularly when many of the subjects lie outside the customary work of the schools.

Likewise, the subjects selected for our nature-study work must be governed by conditions and not wholly by ideals. We are

---

* From Bull. 206, Sixth Report of Extension Work, 1902.

sometimes asked why we do not take up topics more distinctly agricultural or economic. The answer is that we take subjects that teachers will use. We would like, for example, to give more attention to insect subjects, but it is difficult to induce teachers to work with them. If distinctly agricultural topics alone were used, the movement would have very little following and influence. Moreover, it is not our purpose to teach technical agriculture in the common schools, but to inculcate the habit of observing, to suggest work that has distinct application to the conditions in which the child lives, to inspire enthusiasm for country life, to aid in home-making, and to encourage a general movement towards the soil. These matters cannot be forced. In every effort by every member of the extension staff, the betterment of agricultural conditions has been the guiding impulse, however remote from that purpose it may have seemed to the casual observer.

We have found by long experience that it is unwise to give too much condensed subject-matter. The individual teacher can give subject-matter in detail because personal knowledge and enthusiasm can be applied. But in general correspondence and propagandist work this cannot be done. With the Junior Naturalist, for example, the first impulse is to inspire enthusiasm for some bit of work which we hope to take up. This enthusiasm is inspired largely by the organization of clubs and by the personal correspondence that is conducted between the Bureau and these clubs and their members. It is the desire, however, to follow up this general movement with instruction in definite subject-matter with the teacher. Therefore, a course in Home Nature-study was formally established under the general direction of Mrs. Mary Rogers Miller. It was designed to carry on the experiment for one year, in order to determine whether such a course would be productive of good results and to discover the best means of prosecuting it. These experimental results were very gratifying. Nearly 2,000 New York teachers are now regularly enrolled in the Course, the larger part of whom are outside the metropolitan and distinctly urban conditions. Every effort is made to reach the rural teacher.

In order that the work may reach the children, it must be greatly popularized and the children must be met on their own ground. The complete or ideal leaflet may have little influence.

2

For example, I prepared a leaflet on "A Children's Garden" which several people were kind enough to praise. However, very little direct result was secured from the use of this leaflet until "Uncle John" began to popularize it and to make appeals to teachers and children by means of personal talks, letters and circulars. So far as possible, his appeal to children was made in their own phrase. The movement for the children's garden has now taken definite shape, and the result is that more than 26,000 children in New York State are raising plants during the present year. Another illustration of this kind may be taken from the effort to improve the rural school grounds. I wrote a bulletin on " The Improvement of Rural School Grounds," but the tangible results were very few. Now, however, through the work of "Uncle John" with the teachers and the children, a distinct movement has begun for the cleaning and improving of the school grounds of the State. This movement is yet in its infancy, but several hundred schools are now in process of renovation, largely through the efforts of the children.

The idea of organizing children into clubs for the study of plants and animals, and other outdoor subjects, originated, so far as our work is concerned, with Mr. John W. Spencer, himself an actual, practical farmer. His character as "Uncle John" has done much to supply the personality that ordinarily is lacking in correspondence work, and there has been developed amongst the children an amount of interest and enthusiasm which is surprising to those who have not watched its progress.

The problems connected with the rural schools are probably the most difficult questions to solve in the whole field of education. We believe, however, that the solution cannot begin directly with the rural schools themselves. It must begin in educational centres and gradually spread to the country districts. We are making constant efforts to reach the actual rural schools and expect to utilize fully every means within our power, but it is work that is attended with many inherent difficulties We sometimes feel that the agricultural status can be reached better through the hamlet, village, and some of the city schools than by means of the little red school house on the corner. By appeals to the school commissioners in the rural districts, by work through teachers' institutes, through farmers' clubs, granges and other means we believe that we are reaching farther and farther into the very agricultural regions. It is difficult to get consideration for purely agricultural subjects in the rural schools themselves. Often the school does not have facilities for teaching such subjects, often the teachers are employed only for a few months, and there is frequently a sentiment against innovation. It has been said that one reason why agricultural subjects are taught less in the rural schools of America than in those of some parts of Europe, is because of the few male teachers and the absence of school gardens.

We have met with the greatest encouragement and help from very many of the teachers in the rural schools. Often under disadvantages and discouragements they are carrying forward their part of the educational work with great consecration and efficiency. In all the educational work we have been fortunate to have the sympathy and co-operation of the State Department of Public Instruction. We do not expect that all teachers nor even a majority will take up nature-study work. It is not desirable that they should. We are gratified, however, at the large number who are carrying it forward.

This Cornell nature-study movement is one small part of a general awakening in educational circles, a movement which looks towards bringing the child into actual contact and sympathy with the things with which he has to do. This work is taking on many phases. One aspect of it is its relation to the teaching of agriculture and to the love of country life. This aspect is yet in its early experimental stage. The time will come when institutions in every State will carry on work along this line. It will be several years yet before this type of work will have reached what may be considered an established condition, or before even a satisfactory body of experience shall have been attained. Out of the varied and sometimes conflicting methods and aims that are now before the public, there will develop in time an institution-movement of extension agricultural teaching.

The literature issued by the Bureau of Nature-Study is of two general types: that which is designed to be of more or less permanent value to the teacher and the school ; and that which is of temporary use, mostly in the character of supplements and circulars designed to meet present conditions or to rally the teachers or the Junior Naturalists. The literature of the former type is now republished and is to be supplied gratis to teachers in New York State. The first publication of the Bureau of Nature-Study was a series of teachers' leaflets. This series ran to twenty-two numbers. It was discontinued in May, 1901, because it was thought that sufficient material had then been printed to supply teachers with subjects for a year's work. It was never intended to publish these leaflets indefinitely. Unfortunately, however, some persons have supposed that because these teachers' leaflets were discontinued we were lessening our efforts in the nature-study work. The fact is that later years have seen an intensification of the effort and also a strong conviction on the part of all those concerned that the work has permanent educative value. We never believed so fully in the efficiency of this kind of effort as at the present time.

THE NATURE-STUDY MOVEMENT.*

By L. H. BAILEY.

THE nature-study movement is the out-growth of an effort to put the child into contact and sympathy with its own life.

It is strange that such a movement is necessary. It would seem to be natural and almost inevitable that the education of the child should place it in intimate relation with the objects and events with which it lives. It is a fact, however, that our teaching has been largely exotic to the child; that it has begun by taking the child away from its natural environment; that it has concerned itself with the subject-matter rather than with the child. This is the marvel of marvels in education.

Let me illustrate by a reference to the country school. If any man were to find himself in a country wholly devoid of schools, and were to be set the task of originating and organizing a school system, he would almost unconsciously introduce some subjects that would be related to the habits of the people and to the welfare of the community. Being freed from traditions, he would teach something of the plants and animals and fields and people. Yet, as a matter of fact, what do our rural schools teach? They usually teach the things that the academies and the colleges and the universities have taught — that old line of subjects that is supposed, in its higher phases, to lead to "learning." The teaching in the elementary school is a reflection of old academic methods. We really begin our system at the wrong end — with a popularizing and simplifying of methods and subjects that are the product of the so-called higher education. We should begin with the child. "The greatest achievement of modern education," writes

* Reprinted from the Proceedings of the National Educational Association, 1903. Paper read in general session at Boston, July, 1903.

Professor Payne, "is the gradation and correlation of schools, whereby the ladder of learning is let down from the university to secondary schools, and from these to the schools of the people." It is historically true that the common schools are the products of the higher or special schools, and this explains why it is that so much of the common-school work is unadapted to the child. The kindergarten and some of the manual-training, are successful revolts against all this. It seems a pity that it were ever necessary that the ladder of learning be "let down;" it should be stood on the ground.

The crux of the whole subject lies in the conception of what education is. We all define it in theory to be a drawing out and a developing of the powers of the mind; but in practice we define it in the terms of the means that we employ. We have come to associate education with certain definite subjects, as if no other sets of subjects could be made the means of educating a mind. One by one, new subjects have forced themselves in as being proper means for educating. All the professions, natural science, mechanic arts, politics, and last of all agriculture, have contended for a place in educational systems and have established themselves under protest. Now, any subject, when put into pedagogic form, is capable of being the means of educating a man. The study of Greek is no more a proper means of education than the study of Indian corn is. The mind may be developed by means of either one. Classics and calculus are no more divine than machines and potatoes are. We are much in the habit of speaking of certain subjects as leading to "culture;" but this is really factitious, for "culture" is the product only of efficient teaching, whatever the subject-matter may be. So insistent have we been on the employing of "culture studies" that we seem to have mistaken the means of education for the object or result of education. What a man is, is more important than what he knows. Anything that appeals to a man's mind is capable of drawing out and training that mind; and is there any subject that does not appeal to some man's mind? The subject may be Sanskrit literature, hydraulics, physics, electricity, or agriculture — all may be made the means whereby men and women are educated, all may lead to what we ought to know as culture. The particular subject with which the person deals is incidental, for

"A man's a man for a' that and a' that."

Is there, then, to be no choice of subjects? There certainly is.

It is the end of education to prepare the man or woman better to live. The person must live with his surroundings. He must live with common things. The most important means with which to begin the educational process, therefore, are those subjects that are nearest the man. Educating by means of these subjects puts the child into first-hand relation with his own life. It expands the child's spontaneous interest in his environment into a permanent and abiding sympathy and philosophy of life. I never knew an exclusive student of classics or philosophy who did not deplore his lack of touch with his own world. These common subjects are the natural, primary, fundamental, necessary subjects. Only as the child-mind develops should it be taken on long flights to extrinsic subjects, distant lands, to things far beyond its own realm; and yet, does not our geography teaching still frequently begin with the universe or with the solar system?

In the good time coming, geography will not begin with a book at all, as, in fact, it does not now with many teachers. It may end with one. It will begin with physical features in the very neighborhood in which the child lives — with brooks and lakes and hills and fields. Education should begin always with objects and phenomena. We are living in a text-book and museum age. First of all, we put our children into books, sometimes even into books that tell about the very things at the child's door, as if a book about a thing were better than the thing itself. So accustomed are we to the book-route that we regard any other route as unsystematic, unmethodical, disconnected. Books are only secondary means of education. We have made the mistake of considering them primary. This mistake we are rapidly correcting. As the book is relegated to its proper sphere, we shall find ourselves free to begin with the familiar end of familiar things.

Not only are we to begin with common objects and events, but with the child's natural point of contact with them. Start with the child's sympathies; lead him on and out. We are to develop the child, not the subject. The specialists may be trusted to develop the subject-matter and to give us new truth. The child is first interested in the whole plant, the whole bug, the whole bird, as a living, growing object. It is a most significant fact that most young children like plants, but that most youths dislike botany. The fault lies neither in the plants nor in the youths. A youth may study cells until he hates the plant that bears the cells. He may acquire a technical training in cells, but he may be divorced from objects with which he must live, and his life becomes poorer rather than richer.   I have no objection to minute dissection and analysis, but we must be very careful not to begin it too early nor to push it too far, for we are not training specialists : we are developing the power that will enable the pupil to get the most from his own life.   As soon as the pupil begins to lose interest in the plant or the animal itself, stop!

There is still another reason for the study of the common things in variety: it develops the power to grasp the problems of the day and to make the man resourceful.   A young man who has spent all his time in the schoolroom is usually hopelessly helpless when he encounters a real circumstance.   I see this remarkably illustrated in my own teaching, for I have young men from the city and from farms.   The farm boy will turn his hand to twenty things where the city boy will turn his to one.   The farm boy has had to meet problems and to solve them for himself: this is sometimes worth more than his entire school training.   Why does the farm boy make his way when he goes to the city ?

It is no mere incident to one's life that he be able to think in the thought of his own time.   Even though one expect to devote himself wholly to a dead language, in school he should study enough natural science and enough technology to enable him to grasp living problems.   I fear that some institutions are still turning out men with mediæval types of mind.

Now, therefore, I come again to my thesis,— to the statement that the end and purpose of nature-study is to educate the young mind by means of the subjects within its own sphere, by appealing to its own sympathetic interest in them, in order that the person's life may be sweeter, deeper, and more resourceful.   Nature-study would not necessarily drive any subject from the curriculum; least of all would it depreciate the value of the "humanities;" but it would restore to their natural and proper place the subjects that are related to the man.   It would begin with things within the person's realm.   If we are to interest children — or grown-ups, either, for that matter — we must begin by teaching the things that touch their lives.   Where there is one person that is interested in philology, there are hundreds that are interested in engines and in wheat. From the educational point of view, neither the engine nor the wheat is of much consequence, but the men who like the engines and who grow the wheat are immeasurably important and must be reached.   There are five millions of farms in the United States on which chickens are raised, and also thousands of city and village lots where they are grown. I would teach chickens. I would reach Men by means of the Old Hen.

How unrelated much of our teaching is to the daily life is well shown by inquiries recently made of the children of New Jersey by Professor Earl Barnes. Inquiries were made of the country school children in two agricultural counties of the State as to what vocation they hoped to follow. As I recall the figures, of the children at seven years of age 26 per cent desired to follow some occupation connected with country life. Of those at fourteen years, only 2 per cent desired such occupation. This remarkable falling off Professor Barnes ascribes in part to the influence of the teacher in the country schools, who is usually a town or city girl. The teacher measures everything in terms of the city. She talks of the city. She returns to the city at the end of the week. In the meantime, all the beauty and attractiveness and opportunity of the country may be unsuggested. Unconsciously both to teacher and pupil, the minds of the children are turned toward the city. There results a constant migration to the city, bringing about serious social and economic problems ; but from the educational point of view the serious part of it is the fact that the school training may unfit the child to live in its normal and natural environment. It is often said that the agricultural college trains the youth away from the farm ; the fact is that the mischief is done long before the youth enters college.

Let me give another illustration of the fact that dislike of country life is bred very early in the life of the child. In a certain rural school in New York State, of say forty-five pupils, I asked all those children that lived on farms to raise their hands ; all hands but one went up. I then asked those who wanted to live on the farm to raise their hands ; only that one hand went up. Now, these children were too young to feel the appeal of more bushels of potatoes or more pounds of wool, yet they had thus early formed their dislike of the farm. Some of this dislike is probably only an ill-defined desire for a mere change, such as one finds in all occupations, but I am convinced that the larger part of it was a genuine dissatisfaction with farm life. These children felt that their lot was less attractive than that of other children ; I concluded that a flower garden and a pleasant yard would do more to content them with living on the farm than ten more

bushels of wheat to the acre. Of course, it is the greater and
better yield that will enable the farmer to supply these amenities;
but at the same time it must be remembered that the increased
yield itself does not arouse a desire for them. I should make
farm life interesting before I make it profitable.

Of course, nature-study is not proposed merely as a means of
keeping youth in the country; I have given these examples only
to illustrate the fact that much of our teaching is unrelated to
the circumstances in which the child lives — and this is particularly true of teaching in the rural schools. Nature-study applies
to city and country conditions alike, acquiring additional emphasis
in the country from the fact that what we call "nature" forms
the greater part of the environment there. But the need to connect the child with itself is fundamental to all efficient teaching.
To the city child the problems associated with the city are all-
important; but even then I should give much attention to the
so-called "nature subjects;" for these are clean, inspiring, universal. "Back to nature" is an all-pervading tendency of the
time.

We must distinguish sharply between the purposes of nature-
study and its methods. Its purposes are best expressed in the
one word "sympathy." By this I do not mean sentimentalism or
superficiality or desultoriness. The acquiring of sympathy with
the things and events amongst which one lives is the result of a
real educational process — a process as vital and logical and
efficient as that concerned in educating the older pupil in terms
of fact and "science." Nature-study is not "natural history,"
nor "biology," nor even elementary science. It is an attitude, a
point of view, a means of contact.

Nature-study is not merely the adding of one more thing to a
curriculum. It is not co-ordinate with geography, or reading, or
arithmetic. Neither is it a mere accessory, or a sentiment, or an
entertainment, or a tickler of the senses. It is not a "study." It
is not the addition of more "work." It has to do with the whole
point of view of elementary education, and therefore is fundamental. It is the full expression of personality. It is the practical working out of the extension idea that has become so much a
part of our time. More than any other recent movement, it will
reach the masses and revive them. In time it will transform our
ideals and then transform our methods.

The result of all this changing point of view I like to speak of as a new thing. Of course, there is no education that is wholly new in kind; and it is equally true that education is always new, else it is dead and meaningless. But this determination to cast off academic methods, to put ourselves at the child's point of view, to begin with the objects and phenomena that are near and dear to the child, is just now so marked, and is sure to be so far-reaching in its effects, that I cannot resist the temptation to collect these various movements, for emphasis, under the title of the "new education."

"Nature-study" is another name for this new education. It is a revolt from the too exclusive science-teaching and book-teaching point of view, a protest against taking the child first of all out of its own environment. It is a product of the teaching of children in the elementary schools. The means and methods in nature-study are as varied as the persons who teach it. Most of the criticism of the movement — even among nature-study folk themselves — has to do with means and methods rather than with real ideals. We are now in the epoch when we should overlook minor differences and all work together for the good of a common cause. There is no one subject and no one method that is best.

While it is not my purpose to enter into any discussion of the methods of teaching nature-study, I cannot refrain from calling attention to what I believe to be some of the most serious dangers. (1) I would first mention the danger of giving relatively too much attention to mere subject-matter or fact. Nowhere should the acquiring of mere information be the end of an educational process, and least of all in nature-study, for the very essence of nature-study is spirit, sympathy, enthusiasm, attitude toward life. These results the youth gains naturally when he associates in a perfectly free and natural way with objects in the wild. Science-teaching has fallen short of its goal in the elementary schools — and even in the colleges and universities — by insisting so much on the subject-matter that the pupil is overlooked. In standing so rigidly for the letter, we have missed the spirit. President Eliot has recently called attention to this danger: "College professors heretofore have been apt to think that knowledge of the subject to be taught was the sufficient qualification of a teacher; but all colleges have suffered immeasurable losses as a result of this delusion." (2) A second danger is the tendency to make the instruction too long and too laborious. As soon as the child becomes weary of giving attention, the dan-

ger-point is reached; for thereafter there is loss in the spirit and
enthusiasm, however much may be gained in dry subject-matter.
I believe that even in high schools and colleges we make mistakes
by demanding too long-continued application to one subject.
Short, sharp, enthusiastic exercises, with pith and point, of five
to ten minutes' duration, are efficient and sufficient for most purposes, particularly with beginners. (3) A third danger is the
practice of merely telling or explaining. Set the child to work,
and let the work be within his own realm. Pollen, lichens, cap-
sules, lymphatics, integuments — these are not within the child's
range; they smack of the museum and the text-book. Yet it
appears to be the commonest thing to put mere children at the
subject of cross-fertilization; they should first be put, perhaps, at
flowers and insects. I wish that in every schoolroom might be
hung the motto, "Teaching, not telling." (4) A fourth point I
ought to mention is the danger of clinging too closely to the
book habit; this I have already touched on. We are gradually
growing out of the book slavery, even in arithmetic and grammar
and history. This means a distinct advance in the abilities of the
teacher. Of all subjects that should not be taught by the book,
nature-study is chief. Its very essence is freedom from tradition
and "method." I wish that there were more nature-study books;
but they are most useful as sources of fact and inspiration, not as
class texts. The good teacher of nature-study must greatly modify
the old idea of "recitations." I wish to quote again from President
Eliot: "Arithmetic is a very cheap subject to teach; so are spelling and the old-fashioned geography. As to teaching history in
the old-fashioned way, anybody could do that who could hear a
lesson recited. To teach nature-studies, geometry, literature,
physiography, and the modern sort of history requires well-
informed and skillful teachers, and these cost more than the les-
son-hearers did." (5) Finally, we must come into contact with
the actual things, not with museums and collections. Museums
are little better than books unless they are regarded as secondary means. The museum has now become a laboratory. The
living museum must come more and more into vogue,—living
birds, living plants, living insects. The ideal laboratory is the
out-of-doors itself; but for practical school purposes this must
be supplemented. The most workable living laboratory of any
dimensions is the school garden. The true school garden is a
laboratory plat; time is coming when such a laboratory will be as

much a part of a good school equipment as blackboards and charts and books now are. It will be like an additional room to the school building. Aside from the real school garden, every school premises should be embellished and improved as a matter of neighborhood and civic pride; for one cannot expect the child to rise above the conditions in which he is placed. All these dangers cannot be overcome by any "system" or "method;" they must be solved one by one, place by place, each teacher for himself. Whenever nature-study comes to be rigidly graded and dressed and ordered, the breath of life will be crushed from it. It is significant that everywhere mere "method" is giving way to individualism.

In time, the methods of teaching nature-study will crystallize and consolidate around a few central points. The movement itself is well under way. It will persist because it is vital and fundamental. It will add new value and significance to all the accustomed work of the schools; for it is not revolutionary, but evolutionary. It stands for naturalness, resourcefulness, and for quickened interest in the common and essential things of life. We talk much about the ideals of education; but the true phiiosophy of life is to idealize everything with which we have to do.

LEAFLET III.

AN APPEAL TO THE TEACHERS OF NEW YORK STATE.*

By L. H. BAILEY.

THE kernel of modern educational development is to relate the school-training to the daily life. Much of our education is not connected with the conditions in which the pupils live and is extraneous to the lives that they must lead. The free common schools are more recent in development than universities, colleges and academies and they are even yet essentially academic and in many ways undemocratic. They teach largely out of books and of subjects that have little vital relation with things that are real to the child. The school work is likely to be exotic to the pupil. The child lives in one world, and goes to school in another world.

Every subject has teaching-power when put into pedagogic form. The nearer this subject is to the child, the greater is its teaching power, other conditions being comparable; and the more completely does it put him into touch with his environment and make him efficient and happy therein. In time, all subjects in which men engage will be put in form for teaching and be made the means of training the mind. The old subjects will not be banished, but rather extended ; but the range of subjects will be immensely increased because we must reach all people in terms of their daily experience. How all these subjects are to be handled as school agencies, we cannot yet foresee, nor is it my purpose now to discuss the question ; but it is certain that the common things must be taught. And the common subjects

*Supplement to Home Nature-Study Course, March, 1904. (Vol. V, No. 6.)

are as capable of being made the means of developing the
imagination and the higher ideals as are many of the traditional
subjects.

Great numbers of our people are in industrial and agricultural
environments. By means of the industrial and agricultural trades
they must live. These trades must be made more efficient; and
the youth must be educated to see in them more than a mere
livelihood. These industrial and agricultural subjects must be put
more and more into schools. My own interest lies at present more
with the agricultural subjects, and these are the occasion for this
appeal. The so-called "industrial" and commercial subjects have

*Fig. 1. Junior Gardeners beginning the work of cleaning up a New York school
ground.*

already been put into schools with good effect: the agricultural
subjects now must come within the school horizon.

Probably one million and more of the people of New York State
live on farms. This is approximately one in seven of our entire
population. Moreover, every person is interested in the out-of-
doors and in the things that grow therein. The future agricultural efficiency of New York State will depend on the school
training more than on any other single factor; and on the agricultural efficiency of the State will depend, to an important extent,
its economic supremacy. New York is the fourth State in total
agricultural wealth, being exceeded only by Illinois, Iowa and

Ohio. All the country children should be reached in terms of the country. Most of our school books are made for the city and town rather than for the country. The problem of the development of the rural school is the most important single educational problem now before us; and it is essentially an agricultural problem.

My appeal, therefore, is to every teacher in New York State, whether in country or city — for the city teacher makes public

Fig. 2. Junior Gardeners at work in a New York school ground. The grounds are now ready for planting. The mail carrier now calls and the pupils take the mail home.

opinion, helps to set educational standards, and many of the country children go to school in the cities. I do not wish to press agriculture into the schools as a mere professional subject, but I would teach — along with the customary school work — the objects and phenomena and affairs of the country as well as of the city. The schools lead away from the country rather than towards it. All this I do not regard as a fault of the schools, but merely as a limitation due to the fact that the schools are still in process of

3

evolution. It requires time to adapt a means to an end, and the schools are not to be criticised. But we must do our best to hasten the evolution. Schools, colleges and universities have only begun to reach the people effectively : these institutions must eventually touch every vital and homely problem, for they are to be the controlling factors in our civilization. Any subject that is worthy a person's attention out of school is also worthy his attention in school.

Fig. 3.   Sugar beets and a fourteen-year-old experimenter.
(Supt. Kern, Illinois.)

I heard a good story the other day of an occurrence of many years ago illustrating the fact that school training may be wholly exotic to the pupil. The story was told in Ogdensburg, and Heuvelton is near by. The class in geography was on exhibition, for there were visitors. The questions were answered quickly: "How far is it from Rome to Corinth?" "From Rome to Constantinople?" "From Paris to Rome?" A visitor was asked whether he had any questions to propound. He had one : "How far is it from Heuvelton to Ogdensburg?" No one answered ; yet the visitor said that none of the pupils would be likely to go from Rome to Constantinople, but that every one of them would go from Heuvelton to Ogdensburg.

Not only must the school teach in terms of its own environment, but more and more it must become the intellectual and social center of the neighborhood or district. Every modern rural school building should be attractive enough to induce clubs of many kinds to hold meetings in it. In the old "lyceum" days the school house was an important gathering place. These days are mostly past, but better days should be coming · the school should connect at every point with the life of the community. Any event, however small, that centers the attention of the people at the school house is a beginning and is worth while. A year ago the children and teacher in one of our district schools began the work of "cleaning up" the premises. The picture (Fig. 1) shows them at work. Later, when the grounds were renovated and ready for the planting, boxes were placed for the reception of the mail for those who do not live on the carrier's route : this is the beginning of a centering of attention at the school house. I think that the boxes might have been more attractive and perhaps better placed, but this will come in time : a beginning has been made. When once the people of any community come to think of the school house as a meeting-place for old folks as well as for children, what may we not expect of the rural school ? We need adult education as well as juvenile education.

I have now no course of study to propose for agricultural or country-life subjects in the schools, but I would like to know how many teachers in the State desire to take up certain work of this nature as an experiment. The College of Agriculture will be glad to suggest the kind of work, if need be. The western states are undertaking this work : we must not be behind. It is endorsed by Superintendent Skinner, as will be seen from the letter published at the close of this pamphlet.

To be effective and meaningful, this work should deal directly with the things,— handling the things, studying the things, learning from the things. This is nature-study. To commit to memory something about things is of little consequence. We are too closely committed to books. We are often slaves to books. Books are only secondary or incidental means of educating, particularly in nature-study subjects. We have known the book-way of educating for so long a time that many of us have come to accept it as a matter of course and as the only way. A New York school man recently told me an incident that illustrates this fact singularly well. In the Cattaraugus Indian Reservation he opened a school in which at first he employed only manual-training and nature-study work. Soon one of the children left school. The teacher sought the mother and asked why. The mother replied that there was no use in sending the child to school because the

Fig. 4. *Prize corn and a ten-year-old experimenter in one of Supt. Kern's districts, Illinois.*

teacher had given it no books to study. So slavishly have we followed the book-route that even the Indian accepts it as the only road to schooling !

School-Gardens.

Many lines of work might be suggested for an occasional period. Perhaps the best one for spring is a school-garden. In time, every good school will have its garden, as it now has charts and blackboards and books. A school-garden is a laboratory-room added to the school house. It may be five feet square or ten times that much. The children prepare the land,— lessons in soils, soil physics; sow the seed, — lessons in planting, germination, and the like ; care for the plants,— lessons in transplanting, struggle for existence, natural enemies, conditions that make for the welfare of the plants.   The older pupils may be organized into experiment clubs, as they are being organized in parts of Illinois (see article on "Learning by Doing," by Supt. O. J. Kern, Review of Reviews, Oct., 1903, p. 456).   We can help you in this school-gardening work.

Fig. 5.   " Learning by doing."   A new kind of school work in Illinois, under the direction of Supt. Kern.

OTHER WORK.

If not school-gardens, take up other lines of work,— study the school premises, the nearby brook or field, an apple tree, or any other common object or phenomenon.   If there is any special agricultural industry in the neighborhood, discuss it and set the pupils at work on it.   Any of these common-day subjects will interest the children and brighten up the school work ; and the pursuit of them will teach the children the all-important fact that so few of us ever learn,— the fact that the commonest and home-liest things are worthy the best attention of the best men and women.

Improving the School Grounds.

Just now, the improving of school grounds is a pressing subject. As a preliminary to the actual improving of the grounds, suppose that the following problems were set before the pupils:

1. *Exercises on the Grounds.*

1. *Area.*— Measure the school grounds, to determine the lengths and widths. Draw an outline map showing the shape. The older pupils may compute the square surface area. The distances may be compared, for practice, in feet, yards and rods. (Arithmetic.)

Fig. 6. Using the Babcock milk test at Professor Hollister's School, Corinth, N. Y.

2. *Contour.*— Is the area level, or rough, or sloping? Determine how great the slope is by sighting across a carpenter's level. In what direction does the ground slope? Is the slope natural, or was it made by grading? The older pupils may draw a cross-section line, to a scale, to show what the slope is. (Geography.)

3. *Fences.*— What parts of the area are fenced? What kind of fence? Total length of fence? Give opinion whether this fence is needed, with reasons. Is the fence in good repair? If not, what should be done to remedy it? (Arithmetic, language.)

4. *Soil.*— What is the nature of the soil — clay, sand, gravel, field loam? Was subsoil spread on the surface when the grounds were graded? Is the soil poor or rich, and why do you think so?

Is it stony? What can be done to improve the soil? (Geography, language.)

5. *Ground cover.*— What is on the ground — sod or weeds, or is it bare? What do you think would be the best ground cover, and why? (Geography, language.)

6. *Trees and bushes.*— How many trees and bushes are there on the ground? Were they planted, or did they come up of themselves? Make a map showing where the principal ones are. Name all the kinds, putting the trees in one list and the bushes in another. Do any of the trees need pruning, and why? State whether any of them have been injured or are unhealthy. (Geography, language.)

7. *Tenants.*— What animals live or have lived on the school premises? What birds' nests do you find (these may be found in winter)? Hornets' nests? Perhaps you can find cocoons or egg-masses of insects in winter, and the active insects themselves in spring and fall. What birds visit the place? Do rabbits or mice or moles or frogs inhabit the premises? (Geography, language.)

8. *Natural features.*— Describe any strong natural features, as rocks, ponds, streams, groves. What views do you get from the school grounds? (Geography, language.)

2. *Exercises on the School Structures.*

9. *Buildings.*— How many buildings are on the grounds, including sheds, etc.? Give the sizes in lengths and widths. Brick or wood? Color? Make a map or chart showing the position of these structures, being careful to have the buildings properly proportioned with reference to the entire area. (Language, geography.)

10. *Repairs needed.*— Describe what condition the structures are in. Tell whether repairs are needed on foundations, side walls, roof, belfry, chimney, steps, doors, windows, paint. (Language.)

11. *Flag pole.*— Where is your flag pole? Could it be in a better place? How tall is it above ground? How much in diameter at the base? What kind of wood? Painted? How deep in the ground? When was it put up? What repairs does it need? (Language.)

3. *General Exercises.*

12. *History.*— When was the land set aside for a school? When was the school house built? Who built it? (History, language.)

13. *Cost.*— Try to find out what the land cost. What the building cost. Are they worth as much now? (History, language.)

14. *Government.*—Determine what officers have general control of the school. How did they come to be officers? How long do they hold office? What are the duties of each? Determine whether your school receives any aid from the State. (Government.)

15. *Improvement.*—Tell what you think should be done to improve the school grounds and the school structures. (Language.)

16. *Photographs.*— The teacher or some pupil should photograph the school premises, and send the picture to us. We want at least one picture of every rural school house and grounds in the State. Even a very poor photograph is better than none.

Experiment Garden.—Every school ground should have at least one small plat on which the children can grow some plant that is useful in that community. Just now alfalfa is demanding much attention from farmers, and it is certain soon to become a very important farm crop in New York State. It is used for pasturage and for hay. When once established, it lives for years. It is allied to clover and is a handsome plant for any school grounds. Will not the teacher suggest to the children that they make an alfalfa bed along one side of the school grounds? It will be attractive and will teach many lessons to pupils and parents even if it is only a few square feet in size. We want to put an alfalfa plat on every rural school ground in the State. *We will supply the seed free.* Alfalfa is easy to grow if only a few essential principles are kept in mind. We will send full directions to any one who applies From year to year we will give nature-study lessons on these alfalfa plats.

We are anxious to start work of the above kind. It can be done at any time of the year. We are already in touch with more than 400 school grounds, but we want to reach every rural school ground in the State. *Will not the teacher send to us the best piece of work done by any pupil in any of the foregoing sixteen problems?* These papers we will file, as showing the conditions of the premises of the particular school. They will enable us to see the progress that is being made from year to year in the improvement of your school premises. They will also enable us better to give advice, when called upon to do so. Sometimes we can send to the particular school a man to give advice on the spot. Sending the best reports to the University will be a reward to the most diligent pupils. Send all reports to John W. Spencer, Nature-Study Bureau, Ithaca, N. Y.

We desire to put in the rural school houses of the State some good pictures of country and farm scenes. These pictures will be artistic reproductions of meritorious photographs, and large enough to hang on the walls of the school room. With each picture will be sent instructions for framing in order to make the picture more attractive. We shall choose eight such pictures for distribution the present school year. *We will send one of these pictures free to any rural school in the State that takes up two of the problems given above; and all of them to schools that take up the sixteen problems.* We expect to publish lists of all schools, with teachers' names, that take up this work in improving the premises of rural schools.

Fig. 7. Junior Naturalists making ready for planting. Tompkins Co., N. Y.

To one who is not teaching in the public schools, all this work seems to be simple enough. Such persons are likely to be impatient that more rapid progress is not made in introducing agricultural and common-life subjects into the schools. But the teacher knows that all this work requires patience and skill. It cannot as yet be forced into the schools and still retain spontaneity and vitality. It must come gradually, and prove itself as it goes. Probably all public school teachers are now agreed that the schools should be put closely in line with the life of their various communities. The questions now to be solved are chiefly those of means and methods, and of arousing the school constituencies to the new points of view. A full and free discussion of the whole subject is now needed. The time is hardly yet ripe for very definite courses of study in these new fields. Many schools are already teaching these new subjects with entire success : these schools can serve the cause by making their experience public.

LETTERS ON THE SUBJECT.

However, this circular is merely an appeal. It is an inquiry for suggestions and co-operation. I desire to know what can be

Fig. 8. Junior Gardeners at work in one of the New York Schools.

accomplished in the schools of New York State in the direction of inspiring and useful work for children that live in the country or are interested in the country. I am sure that something needs to be done : just what is most feasible and best the teachers must largely determine. As further suggestions, I append two letters from New York teachers:

From A. M. Hollister, Principal of the Corinth Public Schools, Saratoga Co., N. Y.

"I am sending you under separate cover a picture of my class at work with the Babcock test machine (Fig. 6). We have used the machine both as a means of instruction in physics and chemistry and as a general demonstration before the different classes in the school. It beautifully illustrates some very important principles of physics and chemistry. The most marvellous effect, however, has been shown in the quality of the milk sold in the village. Milk was sold showing a test as low as 2.9 per cent butter fat. Almost as soon as the first testing was reported, the milk showed 3.8 per cent butter fat. Milk has been sent to the school from a number of dairymen with request for a test on particular cows that the parties might base their purchases of cows on the results of the test.

"In regard to the gardening with some of our boys, I would say that both boys and parents are much interested in the subject. We shall doubtless start about forty gardens of one-tenth acre each. The boys are to keep an exact account of all expenses to study methods, and to do all the work. I am anticipating results in a number of directions. The boys will be given something to do and to interest themselves in, which of itself is an important thing for a village boy. It will also develop a power of observation and ingenuity. We wish to get all the information we can on potato, tomato and squash culture. Other things will be suggested during the winter."

Approval of the Superintendent of Public Instruction.

(Published by permission.)

"For many years I have been making earnest efforts to induce teachers, pupils and patrons to improve and beautify the school buildings and school surroundings of our State. Some progress has been made, but much remains to be done.

"I heartily welcome the coöperation of every agency which can contribute to this result. We must interest parents and teachers in this work, but to obtain the best results I have always found that we must first interest the children. Once a spirit of enthusiasm is awakened in the children, it is easy to keep them interested and busy.

"I have long appreciated the earnest assistance of representatives of Cornell University in arousing the interest of pupils, and I heartily commend the plan outlined by the College of Agriculture to make a study of the schoolhouse and school grounds a practical part of the daily education of the child. A child's surroundings have much to do with his education. The result of such systematic study as is suggested must surely be a steadily increasing determination to remedy defects and correct any evil which may exist. When the attention of children is directed to existing conditions which bring discomfort, it will not be difficult to induce them to devise ways and means to improve matters.

"I shall watch the result of your efforts with deep interest, and stand ready to coöperate with you in every way.

"Very sincerely yours,
"CHARLES R. SKINNER,

"Albany, *Dec.* 17, 1903.   *State Superintendent."*

WHAT IS AGRICULTURAL EDUCATION?*

By L. H. BAILEY.

AGRICULTURAL EDUCATION has made great progress within the past few years. Methods are crystallizing and at the same time the field is enlarging. We once thought of agricultural education as wholly special or professional, but we now conceive of it as an integral part of general and fundamental educational policy. As a college or university subject it is necessarily technical and semi-professional; but college work must articulate with the common-school work, as language and science now articulate with the schools. That is, agricultural subjects are now to be considered as a part of primary and secondary school work, leading naturally to special work in the same subjects for those who desire technical training. In the schools the subjects are to be treated non-professionally, as primary means of educating the child. The reason for using these subjects as means of educating lies in the principle that the child should be educated in terms of its own life rather than wholly in subjects that are foreign to its horizon and experience. It is most surprising that, while the theory of education is that the person shall be trained into efficiency, we nevertheless have employed subjects that have little relation to the individual child's effectiveness.

Not long since my father showed me a letter that he received from a school girl in 1851. It read as follows: "I seat myself expressly for the purpose to finish this letter which has been long begun. I go to school room to Mr. Wells and study parsing mental Philosophy grammar and penciling." This sounds as if it came from "The Complete Letter-Writer." This person lived on a farm. She lives on a farm to this day. Her parents and grandparents lived on a farm. The family had no expectation

---

*Cornell Countryman, June, 1904.

of living elsewhere than on a farm. Yet, in her entire school life, I presume there was not a single hour devoted to any subject directly connected with the farm or with the country. If her studies touched life in any way that she could comprehend, it was probably in habits of thought of the city and of the academician rather than in anything that appealed to her as related to the life she was to lead. It is small wonder that the farm has been devoid of ideals, and that the attraction has been to leave it. The direction of the stream determines the course of the river.

The future course of education will develop many means of training the child mind. Heretofore these means have been few and the result has been narrow. We shall see agricultural, commercial, social subjects put into pedagogic form and be made the agencies whereby minds are drawn out. These will be at least as efficient as the customary methods that we happen thus far to have employed. How much of one or how much of another is a detail that must be left to the future. Nor does it follow that the old-time subjects are to pass away. They will be an important part of the system, but not the whole system. These new subjects are now coming into the schools as rapidly, perhaps, as they can be assimilated. It is a general feeling that our schools already are overcrowded with subjects; and this may be true. The trouble is that while we are introducing new ideas as to subjects, we are still holding to old ideas as to curriculums and courses of study. We will break up our schools into different kinds; we will employ more teachers; we will not endeavor to train all children alike; we will find that we may secure equal results from many kinds of training; we will consider the effect on the pupil to be of much greater importance than the developing of the particular subject that he pursues; there are many men of many minds; some system will be evolved whereby individual capabilities will be developed to the full; the means will be related to the pupil: one of the factors will be subjects making up the environment of the pupil that lives in the country.

My plea, therefore, is that agricultural and country life subjects become the means of educating some of the pupils of at least some of the schools. To be sure, we have already introduced "natural science" into many of the schools, but, for the most part, this has worked down from the college and, necessarily, it usually stops at the high school. We need something much more vital for the secondary schools than science as commonly taught.

The great nature-study movement is an expression, as yet imperfect, of the feeling that there should be some living connection between the school life and the real life.

A college of agriculture, therefore, is as much interested in the common schools as a college of arts and sciences is. It should be a part of a system, however informal that system may be, not an establishment isolated from other educational agencies. But even as a college it will reach more persons than it has ever reached in the past. In any self-sustaining commonwealth it is probable that one-third of the people must be intimately associated with the soil. These people need to be as well-trained as those who follow the mechanic trades or the professions. It is immensely difficult to put these agricultural subjects into teachable form and to reach the agricultural people in a way that will mean much to them, because agriculture is a compound of many wonderfully diverse trades in every conceivable kind of natural conditions. Nor can one institution in each large state or province hope eventually to reach all these people, any more than one institution can reach all those who would best be taught in terms of books. But there must be at least one institution that is well equipped for the very highest kind of effort in these fields ; Congress long ago recognized this fact in the establishment of the land-grant colleges, and all persons who are informed on agricultural education also now recognize it. The agricultural colleges have been handicapped from the first for lack of funds. It is now coming to be recognized that the highest kind of effort in these colleges cannot be sustained on a farm that pays for itself nor by means that are copied from the customary college work in "humanities" and "science." If it is to be efficient, agricultural education of a university grade is probably more expensive to equip and maintain than any other kind of education.

Once it was thought that the agricultural college should be wholly separate from any "classical" institution. The oldest of the existing American agricultural colleges, the Michigan institution, is established on this principle. So are the Massachusetts, Iowa and Pennsylvania colleges and a number of others. It is natural that this should have been the feeling in the original movement for the establishment of these colleges, for the movement was itself a protest and revolt from the existing education. Time, however, has put agricultural subjects on an equal pedagogical plane with other subjects, and there is no more reason why the agriculture should be segregated by itself than that the architecture or law or fine arts should be. The agricultural colleges connected with universities are now beginning to grow rapidly. This is illustrated in the great development of the agricultural colleges at the universities in Illinois, Wisconsin, Minnesota, Nebraska, Missouri, Ohio, and elsewhere. It was once thought that the agricultural student would be "looked down upon" in a university or in a college with other departments. This was once true. It was true once, also, of the student in natural science and mechanic arts. Pioneers are always marked men. The only way to place agricultural students on an equality with other students is to place them on an equality.

These remarks are made in no disparagement of the separate agricultural colleges, but only to illustrate the character of the growth of agricultural education. No doubt the separate colleges blazed the way. They stand for an idea that we would not like to dispense with. Every state and territory has one college founded on the land grant, and in the Southern states there are two, one for the whites and one for the blacks; in nearly half of the states these colleges are separate institutions. But the fact remains that the college connected with the university is to have the broader field in the future. Its very connection dignifies it and gives it parity. It draws on many resources that the separate college knows not of, unless, indeed, the separate college develops these resources for itself. The tendency, therefore, is for every ambitious separate college to develop the accessory resources, in the way of equipment in general science, literature, the arts; for agricultural education is constantly coming to be of a higher grade. The separate agricultural and mechanical colleges are rapidly becoming essentially industrial universities, giving general training but with the emphasis on the technical subjects.

It is strange how far this principle of education by isolation has been carried in the development of the agricultural colleges. Not only have the colleges been separated from other educational enterprises, but in many cases they have been planted far in the open country, partly on the theory that the farm boy, of all others, should be removed from temptation and from the allurements of other occupations. It was the early theory, also, that the agricultural student must be compelled to do manual labor in order that he be put in sympathy with it and that his attention be isolated from tendencies that might divert him from farming. These methods seem to have rested on the general theory that if you would make a man a farmer you must deprive him of everything but farming. It would be interesting to try to estimate how much this general attitude on the part of the agricultural colleges was itself responsible for the very inferiority of position that the agricultural student was supposed to occupy. This attitude tended to maintain a traditional class distinction or even to create such a distinction. Agricultural education must be adapted to its ends ; but it must also be able to stand alone in competition with all other education without artificial props. It is no longer necessary that the agricultural student wear blinders.

On the other hand, the farm point of view must be kept constantly before the student, as the engineering point of view is kept before the student in a college of civil engineering ; but we are coming to a new way of accomplishing this. Mere teaching of the sciences that underlie agricultural practice will not accomplish it ; nor, on the other hand, will drill in mere farm practice accomplish it. It is not the purpose of an agricultural college to make men farmers, but to educate farmers. We are not to limit the student's vision to any one occupation, but to make one occupation more meaningful and attractive than it has ever been before. From the farmer's point of view a leading difficulty with the college course is that it sometimes tends to slacken a man's business energy. One cannot at the same time pursue college studies and commercial business ; and yet farming is a business. In a four years' course some students are likely to incur certain habits of ease that are difficult to overcome upon their return to the farm. How much this is a fault of the courses of instruction and how much a personal equation of the student is always worth considering. But if this is a fault of college work it is generic and not peculiar to colleges of agriculture. Experience has now shown that a compulsory labor system is no preventive of this tendency, at least not with students of college and university age. Student labor is now a laboratory effort, comparable with laboratory work in medicine or mechanic arts. The mature student must have some other reason for laboring than merely a rule that labor is required. However, it is yet largely an unsolved problem with the agricultural colleges as to just how the stirring business side of farming can be sufficiently correlated with the courses of study to keep the student in touch and sympathy with affairs. With

4

the passing of compulsory student labor there has no doubt been a reaction in the direction of too little utilization of the college farm in schemes of education ; but we shall now get back to the farm again, but this time on a true educational basis.

Nothing is more significant of the development of the agricultural colleges than the recent splitting up of the professorships. From agricultural chemistry as a beginning, in one form or another, there have issued a dozen chairs, first one subject and then another being separated as a teachable and administrative entity. Even the word "agriculture" is now being dropped from the professorships, for this is a term for a multitude of enterprises, not for a concrete subject. Horticulture was one of the first protuberances to be lopped off ; and even this must very soon be divided into its component parts, for there is little relationship between the effort that grows apples and that grows orchids or between the market garden and landscape gardening. Even the chair of agronomy, the newest department of the colleges, must soon be separated into its units. Forty years ago mechanic arts was undivided. Who then would have prophesied such professorships as experimental engineering, electrical engineering, marine engineering, railroad engineering, naval architecture, machine design ? The progress of the dividing up of the mechanic arts and civil engineering marks the rate of our progress, in the terms of the Land Grant Act, "to promote the liberal and practical education of the industrial classes in the several pursuits and professions in life." All trades, classes and professions are to be reached with a kind of education that is related to their work. One by one we are reaching persons in all walks and all places. Socially, there are centuries of prejudice against the farmer. When education is finally allowed to reach him in such a way as to be indispensable to him, it will at last have become truly democratic.

In this spirit agriculture is divided into its teachable units. The lists of divisions of the teaching force or curriculum in the larger agricultural colleges illustrate this admirably. In Illinois, for example, the title of professors and instructors are associated with such divisions as thremmatology, agronomy, pomology, olericulture, floriculture, soil physics, dairy husbandry, dairy manufacture, horses, beef cattle, swine husbandry, farm crops. At Cornell the coördinate departments of instruction in the College of Agriculture are classified as agricultural chemistry, economic entomology, soils, agronomy, horticulture, animal husbandry with its sub-department of poultry husbandry, dairy industry, agricultural engineering and architecture, the farm home, rural economy and sociology, out-door art (including landscape gardening), nature-study for teachers, besides miscellaneous courses — making altogether thirteen divisions. The courses now offered in the Cornell College of Agriculture, not including the winter-courses, are 76, of which 71 are to be given in the next academic year. Nearly all these courses comprise a half-year's work.

While all this subdividing represents progress there are disadvantages attending it, because it tends to give a partial view of the subject. The larger number of farmers must engage in general "mixed husbandry" rather than in specialties. Farming is a philosophy, not a mere process. The tendency of the inevitable subdividing of the subjects is to force the special view rather than the general view, as if, in medicine, students were to become specialists rather than general practitioners. The farm-philosophy idea was represented by the older teachers of agriculture. Of these men Professor Roberts is a typical example, and his work in making students to be successful, all-around farmers is not yet sufficiently appreciated. Much of this farm philosophy is now coming into the courses of instruction under the titles of rural economy, rural economics, rural sociology and the like. I have sometimes thought that the time may come when we will again have professors of "agriculture" who will coördinate and synthesize the work of the agronomist, soil physicist, chemist, dairyman and others. However, the dividing has not yet worked any harm, and perhaps my fears are ungrounded; and it is certain that with increasing knowledge and specialization the courses of instruction must still further divide.

Another most significant development in agricultural education is the change in attitude towards the college farm. Once it was thought that the college estate should be run as a "model farm." However, a farm that sets a pattern to the farmer must be conducted on a commercial basis; yet it is manifest that it is the province of a college to devote itself to education, not primarily to business. A farm cannot be a "model" for all the kinds of farming of the commonwealth; and if it does not represent fairly completely the agriculture of the state, it misses its value as a pattern. At all events the pattern-farm idea is practically given up. It is then a question whether the farm shall be used merely to "illustrate,"— to display kinds of tools, examples of fences and fields, breeds of stock. This conception of the college farm is comparable with the old idea of "experiments" in agricultural chemistry : the teacher performed the experiments for the students to see. The prevailing idea of the college farm is now (or at least, I think, soon must be) that it shall be used as a true laboratory, as the student in chemistry now works first-hand with his materials instead alone of receiving lectures and committing books. Is a student studying cattle? The herds are his for measurements, testing as to efficiency, studying in respect to heredity, their response to feeding, their adaptability to specific purposes, and a hundred other problems. Cattle are as much laboratory material for the agricultural student as rocks are for the geological student or plants for the botanical student. Technical books were once kept only in libraries ; now they are kept also in laboratories and are laboratory equipment. College museums were once only for display ; now they are also for actual use by the student. Barns are laboratories, to be as much a part of the equipment of a college of agriculture as shops are of mechanic arts. They should be in close connection with the main buildings, not removed to some remote part of the premises. Modern ideas of cleanliness and sanitation are bound to revolutionize the construction and care of barns. There is no reason why these buildings should be offensive. It was once thought that dissecting rooms and hospitals should be removed from proximity to other buildings ; but we have now worked these laboratories integrally into the plans of colleges. Time has now come for a closer assembling of the college barns with the college classrooms. Likewise the entire farm is no doubt to be used in the future as a laboratory, at least in the institutions of university grade — except such part as is used for pure investigation and research. Where, then, shall the student go to see his model barn ? To these farms themselves ; here a stock farm ; there a fruit farm ; elsewhere a dairy farm. The shops in the colleges of mechanic arts have long since come to be true laboratories ; they do not engage in railroading or manufacturing. They do not try to "pay their way ; " if they do pay their way this fact is only an incidental or secondary consideration. A college of agriculture is a teaching institution : it must have equipment and laboratories.

It will be seen that the word "agriculture" has taken on a new and enlarged meaning. The farmer is not only a producer of commodities : he is a citizen, a member of the commonwealth, and his efficiency to society and the state depends on his whole outlook. Also his personal happiness depends on his outlook. He must concern himself not alone with technical farming, but also with all the affairs that make up an agricultural community : good roads, organizations, schools, mail routes, labor movements, rural architecture, sanitation, the æsthetic aspect of the country. One will be struck with the new signification of " agriculture " if he scan the titles of publications that issue from governmental agricultural departments, agricultural experiment stations, agricultural nature-study bureaus, agricultural colleges.

I cannot close this sketch without calling attention to the fact that the college of agriculture has obligations to the farmers of its commonwealth. The very fact that every college of agriculture in North America is supported by public funds imposes this obligation. Moreover, the colleges of agriculture and mechanic arts stand for true democratic effort, for they have a definite constituency that they are called upon to aid. It is desirable that as many persons as possible shall assemble at the college itself, but those who cannot go to college still have the right to ask for help. This is particularly true in agriculture, in which the interests are widely separated and incapable of being combined and syndicated. Thereupon has arisen the great " extension " movement that, in one way or another, is now a part of the work of every agricultural college. Education was once exclusive ; it is now in spirit inclusive. The agencies that have brought about this change of attitude are those associated with so-called industrial education, growing chiefly out of the forces set in motion by the Land Grant Act of 1862. This Land Grant is the Magna Charta of education : from it in this country we shall date our liberties.

LEAFLET V.

SUGGESTIONS FOR NATURE-STUDY WORK.*

By ANNA BOTSFORD COMSTOCK.

SUGGESTIONS for nature-study must necessarily be more or less general. Nature-study should be a matter of observation on the part of the pupils. The teacher's part is to indicate points for observation and not to tell what is to be seen.

After the child has observed all that it is possible for him to see, the remainder of the story may be told him or may be read.

The objects of nature-study should be always in the teacher's mind. These are, primarily, to cultivate the child's power of observation and to put him in sympathy with out-of-door life.

Having these objects clearly in mind, the teacher will see that the spending of a certain amount of time each day giving lessons is not the most important part of the work. A great amount of nature-study may be done without spending a moment in a regular lesson. In the case of all the things kept in the school-room — *i. e.*, growing plants, insects in cages and aquaria, tame birds and domestic animals — the children will study the problems for themselves. The privilege of watching these things should be made a reward of merit.

The use of nature-study readers should be restricted. The stories in these should not be read until after the pupils have completed their own observations on the subjects of the stories.

Stories about adventures of animals and adventures with animals may always be read with safety, as these do not, strictly speaking, belong to nature-study. They belong rather to liter-

---

*Syllabus of Lectures : Nature-Study (Animal and Plant Life), Mrs. A. B. Comstock.

ature and may be used most successfully to interest the child in nature.

Blackboard drawings and charts should be used only to illustrate objects too small for the pupil to see with the naked eye. The pupil must also be made to understand that the object drawn on the board is a real enlargement of the object he has studied with his unaided eye.

The use of a simple lens often contributes much interest to the work of observation. The compound microscope may be used to show some exceptionally interesting point, as the compound eyes of insects, the scales on the butterfly's wing, or the viscid thread of the spider. But this is by no means necessary. Nature-study work does not actually require the use of either microscope or lens, although the latter is a desirable adjunct.

The great danger that besets the teacher just beginning nature-study is too much teaching, and too many subjects. In my own work I would rather a child spent one term finding out how one spider builds its orb web than that he should study a dozen different species of spiders.

If the teacher at the end of the year has opened the child's mind and heart in two or three directions nature-ward, she has done enough.

In teaching about animals, teach no more of the anatomy than is obviously connected with the distinctive habits of each one; *i. e.*, the hind legs of a grasshopper are long so that it can jump, and the ears of a rabbit are long so that it can hear the approach of its foes.

While it is desirable for the teacher to know more than she teaches, in nature-study she may well be a learner with her pupils since they are likely any day to read some page of nature's book never before read by human eyes. This attitude of companionship in studying with her pupils will have a great value in enabling her to maintain happy and pleasant relations with them. It has also great disciplinary value.

Reasons for and against graded courses in nature-study.

The question whether there should be a graded course in nature-study is decidedly a query with two answers.

The reasons why there should not be a graded course, are:

1st. The work should be spontaneous and should be suggested each day by the material at hand. Mother Nature follows no schedule. She refuses to produce a violet one day, an oriole the next, and a blue butterfly on the third.

2d. A graded course means a hard and fast course which each teacher must follow whether or not her tastes and training coincide with it.

3d. There is no natural grading of nature-study work. A subject suited for nature-study may be given just as successfully in the first as in the fifth grade.

There is only one reason why a nature-study course should be graded, and that is so cogent that it outweighs all the reasons on the other side : the training of the grade teacher in nature-study is at present so limited in subject-matter that if the course were ungraded the same work would be given over and over in the successive grades until the pupils became utterly weary of it. To many a pupil in the lower grades to-day, nature-study means the sprouting of beans and peas and nothing more. As a matter of experience, we believe that after a nature-study subject is once studied it should be dropped entirely, the pupil should not again meet it in the schoolroom until he finds it in its respective science in the high school or college. On this account, we have been persuaded that a graded course, or at least a consecutive course, is necessary.

The following suggestions about grading the course are given with a hope of being helpful, and not because we believe that the courses indicated are necessarily the best courses possible. We have graded each subject so that a teacher may follow her own tastes and inclinations, and may not be forced to teach zoology when her interests are entirely with botany, or vice versa.

We have tried to give a distinctive trend to the observations for each year, and have suggested a line along which the work may be done.

As a matter of fact, however, the time to study any living thing is when you chance to find it. If you find an interesting caterpillar or cricket or bird, study it, whatever your grade of work. The probabilities are that it may be long before you chance upon these same species again.

It has been the experience of most teachers that the lower grades are much more interested in nature-study than are the higher. Especially are the seventh and eighth grades difficult to interest. Therefore, we have made this part of the course economic in its bearing, hoping that this may appeal to the grown-up feeling of pupils of these grades.

INSECTS.

First Grade.

The first year of work with insects may well be restricted to familiarizing the pupils with the three most striking phases in the life of insects with complete metamorphosis, *i. e.*, the larvæ, the pupæ, and the winged insects. Moths and butterflies are especially adapted for this work with the small children.

Fall work.— In September there are still many caterpillars feeding. Bring them in the schoolroom and feed them in breeding cages. For different forms of cheap breeding cages, see Insect Life, pp. 326–330 ; Cornell Teachers' Leaflet, No. 5 (No. XIX, this volume) ; Lessons in Nature-Study, p. 45. *p. 227*

During October many of the hairy caterpillars will be found hurrying along in quest of suitable winter quarters. These should be brought in and put in box cages having sand or dirt in the bottom. They are seeking secluded corners in which to curl up and hide during the cold weather. Some of them pass the winter in their cocoons, and some do not. Insect Life, pp. 239–241 ; Manual for Study of Insects, pp. 317–324 ; Moths and Butterflies, (*b*), pp. 191–198.

Bring in as many cocoons as possible. November or December, after the leaves have fallen from the trees, is the best time in which to hunt for the cocoons of *Cecropia*, *Promethea*, and *Cynthia*. Insect Life, pp. 194–196 ; Moths and Butterflies, (*b*), pp. 119–180.

Teach the pupils the difference between the cocoon and the pupa. The pupa is the quiescent form of the insect. The cocoon is the silken bag covering it, and is always made by the caterpillar before it changes to a pupa.

If possible bring in some butterfly larvæ. In September many may be found. The cabbage butterfly especially is always with us. Insect Life, p. 245. Also the larvæ of the black swallow-tail may be easily found. Insect Life, p. 243 ; Everyday Butterflies, p. 130 ; Moths and Butterflies, (*b*), p. 39.

Show the children (do not tell them) that the butterfly caterpillars do not make cocoons, but that the naked pupa is suspended by a silk button, and in some cases also by a silk thread.

Many teachers complain that but few of the moths are able to get out of the cocoons. The usual reason for this is that in the heated atmosphere of the schoolroom the cocoons become too dry.

To obviate this, the cocoons should be dipped in water every week or two.

Spring work.— During the spring term use the apple-tree tent-caterpillars. Cornell Teachers' Leaflet, No. 5 (No. XIX, this volume); Moths and Butterflies, (*b*), p. 201. Show the four stages of the insect : egg, caterpillar, pupa, and moth. Pay especial attention to the way in which the caterpillars grow.

Summary of methods.— This whole year's work may be done with no regular "lessons," and all the time required will be the care of the breeding cages and the time given to hunting for the caterpillars and cocoons. The child's reading may be selected from the many stories of the caterpillars, moths and butterflies. Yet be very careful to make each child understand that he himself is studying out the especial story of each caterpillar and cocoon in the schoolroom.

Second Grade.

The plan for the second year is to continue the study of the life-histories of insects. The pupil, having learned the different stages of the moths and butterflies, should learn that all insects do not experience such marvelous changes of form.

Fall work.— Arrange a breeding cage like figs. 288, 289, Insect Life, p. 329, placing fresh sod in the flower pot and covering the lamp chimney with a square of wire netting. Push the glass chimney down into the earth so as to allow no crevices through which the insects may escape. In such a cage, place grasshoppers and crickets of all sizes, and study their growth. Insect Life, pp. 33–37.

Show the pupils that the young grasshopper looks like the old one except that the wings are shorter ; the same is true of crickets. Keep the sod damp so the grass will not become dry ; and when it gets too old replace it with other sod. A good way to keep these insects alive and to keep the children interested in them is to plant wheat and grass seed in several flower pots, and then to move the glass chimney from pot to pot, giving the insects fresh pasturage when needed.

As early as possible start some aquaria. Cornell Teachers' Leaflet, No. 11 (No. XII, this volume) ; Insect Life, pp. 330–332.

The mosquito is one of the most available insects for study in the aquarium. Insect Life, pp. 131–136 ; Lessons in Nature-Study, p. 12.

The nymphs of dragon flies and damsel flies and many others may be studied during the entire winter. Insect Life, pp. 140–142 ; Cornell Teachers' Leaflet, No. 11 (No. XII, this volume) ; Outdoor Studies, p. 54. Those that have cannibalistic habits should be kept apart, each one in a separate jar. They may be fed by dropping into the jar a bit of raw beefsteak tied to the end of a string The purpose of the string is that the uneaten meat may be withdrawn before it decays. It should not be left in the water more than twenty-four hours. The insects do not need feeding more than twice a week.

Spring work.— In the spring get new material for the aquaria. In pools where there are many dead leaves look for the caddice worms that build the log cabin cases, for these may be kept in aquaria that have no running water. Insect Life, p. 149.

While we advise the introduction of the aquaria during the second year, their use should be continued during the following four grades ; there are always new things to study in ponds and streams, and nothing so fascinates a child as watching the movements of these little denizens of the water.

Summary of methods.— There need be no set lessons in the work of the second year, unless the teacher in a few words, now and then, chooses to call attention to certain things as the occasion seems to demand. The object of the year's work is to teach the pupil the life histories of insects which have no quiescent or pupa stage, and this should be accomplished by simple observation of specimens bred in the schoolroom.

THIRD GRADE.

The general subject of this year's work may well be the Homes of Insects. This is a most interesting topic, and if well taught will inspire the pupils to much individual observation and collecting.

The questions to be asked concerning insect homes are :

Of what material are they made ? How are they made ? What is the purpose of the home ? Is it made by the insect for itself to live in, or is it made by the mother for the protection of her young ? Is it made as a protection for the insects while they are eating, or do they go out to feed and come back only to rest and spend the night or day ?

Fall work.— Leaf rollers : Insect Life, p. 206 ; Ways of the Six-Footed, p. 119.

Leaf miners : Insect Life, p. 208 ; Ways of the Six-Footed, p. 29.

Galls : Insect Life, p. 210 ; Outdoor Studies, pp. 18, 38–39.

Fall web worm : Insect Life, p. 200.

Scallop shell moth : Insect Life, p. 201.

Nests of silver spotted skipper : Insect Life, p. 203 ; Every-day Butterflies, p. 190.

Bag worms : Insect Life, p. 204. Ant lions : Outdoor Studies, p. 81.

Carpenter bees : Ways of the Six-Footed, p. 108.

Tiger beetle larvæ : Insect Life, pp. 270–272.

All kinds of cocoons are found by the children. Ask concerning the cocoons : Where did you find them ? Were they in protected places ? Why ?

Of these nests there are many more than those mentioned above. In fact, to one who sees what he looks at, every plant, every tree, every fence corner and every foot along the country path contains many most interesting homes. The leaf rollers and leaf miners are the most common and most easily found of all.

Spring work.— The spring work in this subject may be to study the way in which caddice worms make their houses ; take a cad-dice worm out of its house and watch it build another. This is a new phase of the study of caddice worms. Ways of the Six-Footed, p. 133.

Study the homes of beetles under sticks and stones, and find the homes of the engraver beetles under bark. Insect Life, p. 216. This work must necessarily be done by the pupils out of school hours, and their discoveries and specimens of homes should be made topics for lessons for the whole school.

During this term begin a butterfly calendar, made on the same plan as the bird calendar. A collection of butterflies might be started for the schoolroom in connection with the calendar. Study the specimens caught and determine whether they hibernated as adults or chrysalids. If their wings are battered and torn, they spent the winter as adults. If they are bright in colors and their wings perfect, they spent the winter in the chrysalis state.

Hints for collecting insects : Cornell Teachers' Leaflet, No. 7 (No. XVIII, this volume) ; Insect Life, pp. 283–314 and pp. 48–49. How to Know the Butterflies.

Summary of methods.— The work in the third grade, as outlined, requires a lesson period now and then when single specimens are brought in by individual pupils. Each pupil should examine the specimen, and after that the lesson may be given.

FOURTH GRADE.

After having studied Insect Homes, the pupils will be ready to take up the broader subject, How Insects Live. The work of this year may be given on this subject.

In order to study the life-histories of insects, the pupils should know some things about insect anatomy. If the work as indicated in the previous grades has been followed, the pupils know the number of legs, wings, and compound eyes most insects have, without ever having killed a specimen or having received a special lesson in insect anatomy. Now teach the children how insects breathe and how they eat. Show the spiracles on the body of any caterpillar which is not hairy ; they may be seen on the abdomen of a grasshopper or of a butterfly that has not too many large scales to cover them.

After they have seen these spiracles or breathing pores, give a lesson, illustrated by chart or blackboard, showing that these holes lead to the breathing tubes of the body. Manual for the Study of Insects, pp. 73–75.

To show how insects eat, allow the pupils to watch the following insects in the breeding cages while feeding : a grasshopper ; a leaf beetle (potato beetle is a good example) ; any caterpillar ; an ant ; and a wasp. Show that all these have mouth parts made for biting. Let the pupils see an aphid sucking the juice of a plant ; this may be done by bringing in a twig infested by aphids. Let the pupils see the water bugs in the aquarium eat. Insect Life, pp. 123–131, and pp. 137–140. Let them watch a fly, a honey bee, and, if possible, a butterfly or moth, eat. All these have mouth parts made for sucking. All this work should be original investigation on the part of the pupils.

After the pupils find out how insects breathe and eat, let them see how each insect lives a life adapted to its own peculiar needs. Try to feed some cabbage worms on clover or grass. Then try turnip or mustard leaves, and watch the result. Change the potato beetle larvæ to some other plant, and watch the result.

Let the pupils first find out how the insects breathe in the water. Each insect in the aquarium tells a different story as to its way of getting air. The teacher will find all these stories indicated in the chapters in Insect Life devoted to pond and brook insects.

Call especial attention to protective coloring of insects. Show that when an insect resembles its surroundings in color it is thereby enabled to escape its enemies ; or, if need be, is enabled to creep upon its prey unobserved.

Note the color of the grasshopper in the road ; color of meadow grasshopper ; color of the caterpillars of the cabbage butterfly (green and hard to find). Notice the shape and color of walking sticks ; color of the katydids. Note the bright color of the larvæ of potato beetle. Why ? (They are distasteful to birds, and their colors advertise the fact.) Study the Monarch butterfly and the Viceroy. Everyday Butterflies, p. 95 and p. 297 ; Ways of the Six-Footed, p. 39. Bring out strongly in all this work that the insect in order to live must have its special food plant and must escape notice of its enemies. This is the proper place to begin the study of the valuable work done by birds in destroying insects.

In addition to this general work, study especially the wasps.

Solitary Wasps : Mud daubers. Bring in their nests and examine them. Ways of the Six-Footed, p. 96. How are the nests provisioned, and for what purpose were they made ? Find, if possible, nests of other solitary wasps. Insect Life, p. 218, p. 262, p. 264.

Social Wasps : Bring in a deserted nest of yellow-jackets. Of what is it made ? How ? What for ? Do the wasps store honey ? Do they live as a colony during the winter ? All these questions may be answered by a pupil who knows of a yellow-jackets' nest in the fall and watches it during the winter. For the teacher there are discussions of these insects in Manual for Study of Insects, pp. 660–664. Wasps and their Ways.

Continue the butterfly collection and the butterfly calendar.

Spring work.— In the spring, begin a collection of moths for the schoolroom. Insect Life, p. 50. Caterpillars and Moths.

In the spring, notice when the first house-flies appear. What happens to the house-fly in winter ? (Send for Circular No. 35, second series, Div. of Entomology of Department of Agriculture, Washington, D. C., for the life-history of the house-fly.) Explain that one female destroyed early in the season means thousands fewer late in the season.

Encourage the children to bring to the schoolroom all sorts of flies and compare them with the house-fly. The object of this is to teach something of the wonderful variety of forms among small and inconspicuous insects. Make a collection of flies for the schoolroom. For description of flies, see Insect Life, pp. 83–84.

A good plan for the spring work is to keep the pupils interested in the first appearance, after the vicissitudes of winter, of each insect which it is possible for them to find. Note that insects do not appear before their food plants appear.

Summary of objects and methods.— The questions to be answered during the whole year's work are : How do the Insects live,— on what do they feed? How do they escape their enemies? What happens to them in winter? How are the new broods started in the spring? The work is chiefly observation, but occasional lessons may be given and stories may be told to keep the interest in the work from flagging.

Fifth Grade.

Fall work.— Study the Bees and Ants.

Fit up ants' nests. Insect Life, p. 278.

Teach the whole life-history by allowing the pupils to colonize the nests. Manual for Study of Insects, pp. 633–639 ; Insect Life, p. 271. Make observations upon the *eggs, pupæ, workers, males, females.* What are the winged forms that appear in swarms in June and July.

Let the pupils observe the relation of ants to aphids. This may be done on almost any shrub or roadside plant. Home Nature-Study Lesson 1904, No. 8.

The teacher should read Sir John Lubbock's "Ants, Bees and Wasps."

Many stories on these subjects may be told and read, especially those concerning the habits of exotic ants and ant-wars which the children are not likely to see ; also of the slave-making ants. These slave-making ants are quite common in New York State ; their nests may be found under stones. They resemble the brown mound-builder ant ; the slaves are black.

Spring work.— In the spring work in this grade, study the habits of the honey bee. An observation hive is desirable but not necessary. Bring in the honeycomb filled with honey. If there are apiarists in your neighborhood, they will gladly give you specimens of brood in the comb. Read The Bee People and the Manual for Study of Insects, p. 673.

Develop all the facts of the wonderful life in the hive by letting the pupils observe them as far as possible. Then give them the many interesting stories :

Story of the Workers.

Story of the Queen.

Story of the Drone.

Story of the Bee Larva.

Story of Honey Making.

Story of Wax and Comb Making.

Story of the Swarm.

In connection with the study of the honey bee, study the bumble bee. Manual for Study of Insects, pp. 672–673 ; Insect Life, p. 256. Begin with the study of the big queen that appears in May or June. Show that she is of great benefit to us and must not be harmed or frightened. Let the bumble bee's nest be a problem for summer observation, and finish the study in the next grade in the fall.

Summary of objects and methods.— The work of this year should have for its objects the harmonious life of social insects ; their unselfish work for each other ; their devotion to their respective colonies ; their ways of building and of defending their habitations.

The work should be based upon observations made by the pupils in and out of the schoolroom. Many lessons should be given, mostly in the form of stories. Ways of the Six-Footed, pp. 55–94.

SIXTH GRADE.

Fall work.— Study the spiders. Lessons in Nature-Study, p. 103 ; Insect Life, pp. 223–232. Cornell Teachers' Quarterly, final number (No. XV, this volume).

In order to study spiders, they need not be handled with bare hands. While all spiders are venomous to the same extent, perhaps, that a mosquito or a bee is venomous, there is only one species in the eastern United States (and that is very rare) the bite of which need be feared by human beings.

The use of spiders in nature-study does not have to do with handling living specimens, but rather with the habits of the different species and the building of the webs. In catching spiders to bring into the schoolroom, use the method indicated by Professor Kellogg in Nature-Study Lessons. Capture the specimen by the use of a pill box : take the box in one hand and the cover in the other, and catch the spider by suddenly closing the box over it.

The pupils should be made to observe the chief differences between spiders and insects ; *i. e.*, spiders have two regions of the body instead of three as in insects ; eight legs instead of six,

5

simple eyes instead of compound. Compare spiders with daddy-long-legs.

If the teacher chooses to kill a specimen and show the arrangement of the eyes and the spinnerets under the microscope, she may do so. This is not necessary, although I have seen it done successfully in the sixth grade. Diagrams and blackboard drawings may be used instead of the microscope.

Let the pupils observe the uses of silk by the spider :
1. Snare for prey. 2. To enwrap prey when first entangled. 3. Nests for eggs. 4. Lining for habitations. 5. Means of locomotion.

Introduce the grass spider into the schoolroom in glass jars containing grass sod, and let the pupils observe it at work.

Encourage a study of cobwebs. Capture the owner of an orb web, and bring it in a glass jar to the schoolroom. Try to give it its natural environment ; i. e., some sort of frame or branch of tree on which it may fasten its web.

The orb web : 1. How is it made? 2. Of how many kinds of silk ? 3. The way the spiral thread is arranged as shown by drawings. 4. The position of the spider on the web. 5. The way the spider passes from one side of the web to the other. 6. The way it treats its prey when the victim is once entangled.

The engineering ability shown in making this web is one of the most marvelous things in all the realm of animal life. These observations may well cover two months of this term.

Study the ballooning spiders, the jumping spiders, the running spiders, and the crab spiders. Study as many egg-sacs of spiders as possible.

Another topic for study during the fall term is the Songs of Insects. Insect Life, p. 235. Bring in the katydids, crickets, and meadow grasshoppers, place them in cages containing green sod, and observe them while they are singing. Note that only the males sing. Show the ears of the crickets, katydids, and meadow grasshoppers in the elbows of their front legs. The ear of the grasshopper is on the side of the segment of the abdomen next to the thorax. Ways of the Six-Footed, pp. 3–27.

Study snowy tree cricket. Manual for Study of Insects, p. 118.

If possible, get a cicada as these insects continue to sing through the warm days of September. Show the cover to the drums on the lower side of the common cicada. Cornell Nature-Study Bulletin, No. 1, p. 24 (No. VI, this volume). This can be made a most interesting subject, and pupils should be encouraged to do observation work outside of school.

Begin a general collection for schoolroom.

Spring work.—Continue making a general collection for the schoolroom, and specialize in this direction. When an insect is brought in and added to the collection, if the teacher knows the insect, a lesson should be given on its life and habits. This connecting of the life and habits of the insects with the collection of dead specimens is of greater value from a nature-study point of view than the collection itself.

Summary of methods.—While this year's work must be based on the observations of the pupils in the schoolroom and out-of-doors, yet many interesting lessons may be given by the teacher.

Seventh Grade.

The study of this entire year may be the relation of insects to flowers. Most of the references are given in the Plant-life work for this grade.

The insect work may be limited to : What insects visit flowers? How do they carry pollen? How does each kind of insect reach the nectar? Which insects are robbers, and which are true pollen carriers? The use of pollen by insects. Outdoor Studies, pp. 7–12.

Take up the study of golden rod and its insect visitors, *i. e.,* let the pupils watch a bunch of golden rod and note all the insect visitors. For directions concerning this work see Outdoor Studies, pp. 29–46.

In the same way take up the study of asters and the late flowers, and their insect visitors. Describe the visitor ; what it does ; what part of the plant it visits.

Summary of objects and methods.—The object of this whole year's work is to show the beautiful inter-relation between insects and flowers. The studies must necessarily be made in the field. But many delightful lessons may be given on the structure of flowers, that make of greatest use to the flowers the work of insect visitors.

Eighth Grade.

The object of this year's work is the economic side of insect-study. Many pupils do not continue these studies to high school or college. Yet if they have homes with gardens or trees in city or country, they must learn to cope with the many insect enemies

that feed upon cultivated plants. They should also learn to discriminate between insect friends and foes. They should learn the
best methods of combating the foes and preserving the friends.

Explain first that in fighting an insect enemy we must know how
it eats. If it inserts its beak in the stem of the plant there is no
use trying to kill it by putting poison on the leaves.

Common Insect Foes.

To be studied in the schoolroom :

Fall work.—Codlin-moth. Insect Life, p. 180. Show work on
an apple, and give methods of destroying it.

Plum curculio. Insect Life, p. 182.

The pomace flies. Insect Life, p. 184.

Scale insects. Manual for Study of Insects, pp. 165–174.

Potato beetle. Manual for Study of Insects, p. 176.

Spring work.— Tussock moths and canker worms. Circular No.
9, 2d Series, Dept. Agr., Div. of Ent., Washington, D. C.; Cornell
Teachers' Circular, No. 1.

Cabbage worms. How to Know the Butterflies.

Currant worms. Manual for Study of Insects, pp. 613–614.

Plant lice or aphids. Insect Life, pp. 177–178.

Carpet beetle. Circular No. 5, 2d Series, Dept. Agr., Washington, D. C.; Manual for Study of Insects, p. 539.

Clothes moth. Manual for Study of Insects, pp. 257–258; Circular No. 36, 2d Series, Dept. Agr., Washington, D. C.

Tent caterpillar. Cornell Teachers' Leaflet, No. 5 (No. XIX,
this volume).

A study of spraying should be made. Insects and Insecticides,
pp. 39–56. Spray Calendar, distributed free by the Cornell Agricultural Experiment Station.

Important Insecticides. Farmers' Bulletin No. 127, Dept. Agr.,
Washington, D. C.

Insect Friends.

Fall work.— Lady bugs. Insect Life, p. 179.

Aphis lions. Insect Life, p. 178; Ways of the Six-Footed,
p. 125.

Red clover and the bumble bee.

Parasitic insects. Manual for Study of Insects, pp. 621–630.

Spring work.— Bees and orchard in blossom.

Summary of methods.— The observations may be made in the
schoolroom or out-of-doors. There should be observations of

experiments in spraying. This may be accomplished in most localities by encouraging the pupils to visit orchards undergoing the operation of spraying. However, by means of syringe or watering pot, the infested plants brought into the schoolroom may be sprayed and the results noted. Lessons should be given on the importance of preserving insect friends while we are destroying insect enemies.

OTHER ANIMALS ADAPTED FOR NATURE-STUDY.

The Toad and Frog. The study of either of these two species is delightful spring work for any grade. Cornell Teachers' Leaflet, No. 9 (No. XVI, this volume); Wilderness Ways, p. 25.

Salamanders or Efts. Familiar Life of the Roadside.

Fishes. Observations upon goldfish or minnows kept in an aquarium should be made the basis of lessons upon the life of fishes. Study : (1) The shape of the body ; see how it is especially adapted to rapid movement through the water. (2) The shape and arrangement of the fins, and their uses. (3) How the fish propels itself through the water. (4) How the fish breathes. (5) The shape of the fish's mouth, and how and what it eats. (6) Experiment to ascertain the ability of the fish to see and hear. Cornell Teachers' Leaflet, No. 21 (Nos. XIII and XXXVI, this volume).

Encourage observations of habits of different species of fish common in our ponds and streams. Study their eggs and the places where they are found. Teach the children the reason for the game laws, and impress upon them a true respect for those laws. Food and Game Fishes.

Mice. Some house mice in an improvised cage may be placed in the schoolroom, and the habits of the little creatures observed. Give them paper to see how they make their nests. Note how and what they eat, and how they clean themselves. Note shape of teeth and their use. If possible, study the wild mice. Squirrels and Other Fur Bearers, p. 111 ; Wild Life, p. 171.

Squirrels and Chipmunks. The work on these animals must be based on out-of-door observations. Try to get the pupils to discover for themselves answers to the following questions : How and where do they travel? What do they eat? Where and how do they carry their food? Do they store it for winter? If so, where? What do they do in winter? Squirrels and Other Fur Bearers, p. 15, p. 134 ; Wild Neighbors, p. 1.

Rabbits.— A domesticated rabbit should, if possible, be kept in the schoolyard so that the pupils may make their own observations upon its habits. Let them study : How and what it eats. The shape of its teeth. The form and use of the ears. How does it travel? What sort of tracks does it make, and why? From these observations lead the pupils to think of the life of the wild rabbit, how it is adapted to escape from its enemies and to get its food. Ways of Wood Folk, p. 41 ; Story of Raggylug.

Guinea pigs.— These little animals are easily kept in the schoolroom, and, though not particularly interesting in their habits, they prove attractive to the smaller children and may be studied in the same way as the other animals.

Domestic animals.— These need not be studied in the schoolroom, as the pupils, if they have opportunity, can make the observations at home. Studies of the horse, cow, pig, sheep, and goat, and also the cat and dog may be made most interesting. Such questions as these may be asked concerning each : What is the characteristic form of the animal? What is its clothing? What does it eat? How are its teeth adapted to its food? What is its chief use to man? How does it travel, slow or fast? How are its feet adapted to its way of running or walking? Has it a language? How many emotions can it express by sound? How many can it express by action? How does it fight, and what are its weapons? What sort of life did its wild ancestors live? How did they get their food, and how did they escape from their enemies?

Summary of methods of nature-study of animals.— Study only so much anatomy as is clearly adapted to the animal's ways of living. Observations made by the pupils should be arranged into lessons by either pupil or teacher. Such lessons make excellent English themes, and they may be adapted to any grade.

BIRDS.

Begin the study of birds by the careful study of some domesticated species that may be observed closely and for a long period. The hen is perhaps the best for this purpose. Study carefully all of the adaptations of her anatomy to her life necessities. Study shape of her body ; the feathers ; the bill ; her food; how she eats ; drinks ; the shape of her feet ; their covering ; how she sees ; hears ; smells ; sleeps ; study the life of a chick ; study the language of chick, hen and cock ; embryology of a chick. Study a robin or some bird that builds near houses. Note all its habits from the time it appears in spring until autumn.

Bird houses and bird protection. Usefulness of birds. Our Native Birds, Lange. Publications of U. S. Dept. Agr.

Summary of methods.— It is much more important that the pupil know the habits of one species than that he should know by name many species. Therefore encourage patient watching and careful observation concerning the things which birds do. Such observations may be made into lessons by pupil or by teacher for the benefit of all the pupils. First Book of Birds, and Second Book of Birds ; Bird Lore ; The Story of the Birds ; Bird Neighbors.

PLANTS.

First Grade.

Fall term.— Let the children study the different forms and the colors of leaves. By no means teach the botanical terms for all the shapes of leaves ; simply let the children gather and bring in all the different kinds of leaves they can find. Let them draw the different forms in their blank books. Press leaves and mount them.

The object of this work is to give the child an idea of the great number of leaf forms and colors, and to get him interested in observing them. References : Botany, Bailey, pp. 90–100 ; Lessons with Plants, pp. 79–90 ; Gray's How Plants Grow, chapter on Leaves and Forms of Leaves ; Elements of Botany, pp. 89–93.

Winter and spring terms.— Let the children study vegetables. The following questions should be answered concerning a vegetable. What part of the plant is it ? Does it grow below or above ground ? What sort of leaf has it ? What sort of flower ? What sort of fruit or seed ? Lessons with Plants, pp. 353, 356, 364 ; First Studies, pp. 50, 51, 174 ; Botany, Bailey, pp. 31–37 ; Cornell Teachers' Quarterly, No. 7 (No. XXXIX, this volume).

Second Grade.

Teach the use of the flower. Do this by bringing in all flowers possible, and show that as the flower fades the fruit becomes evident. Let the pupils observe for themselves the fact that the flower exists for the sake of the fruit. Interest the pupils in all kinds of fruits and seeds. This is not the place to teach seed dispersion, but simply the forms and colors of fruits and seeds. Let the pupils also observe that insects carry pollen from flower to flower. Do not give the explanation of this to children of this age, but let them see the bees at work.

For this work see Plant World, by Mrs. Bergen, pp. 80–107.

Let the pupils observe the following things in plant physiology :

Flowers sleep : Botany, Bailey, p. 50 ; Lessons with Plants, p. 402 ; Plants, Coulter, pp. 9, 10, 48 ; Elements of Botany, p. 98.

Plants turn toward the light : Elements of Botany, p. 100 ; Botany, Bailey, p. 50 ; First Studies, p. 136.

Effect of frost on flowers and leaves.

Winter and spring work.— Seed germination : First Studies, pp. 1–24 ; Lessons with Plants, pp. 316–331 ; Botany, Bailey, pp. 164–171 ; Cornell Teachers' Leaflet, No. 1 (No. XXVIII, this volume) ; Plants, p. 307 ; Lessons in Nature-Study, p. 22.

Let the pupils observe in the field : Position of leaves when first open. A Reader in Botany, by Newell, Part I, p. 84.

Position of leaves and flowers in the rain. First Studies, p. 135 ; Elements of Botany, pp. 175–176 ; Plants, p. 51.

THIRD GRADE.

Fall work.— The fall work of this grade may be (1) The way flowers make fruit, *i. e.*, the way the fruit is formed from the flower. (2) The dispersion of seeds.

Fruits. First Studies, pp. 168–171 ; Lessons with Plants, pp. 251–310 ; Botany, Bailey, pp. 147–157.

Seed dispersion. First Studies, p. 176 ; Plant World, pp. 133–156 ; Little Wanderers, by Morley ; Seed Dispersal, by Beal ; Cornell Teachers' Quarterly, No. 2 (No. VIII, this volume) ; Seed Travelers, by Weed ; Botany, Bailey, p. 158.

Let the pupils observe : " How some plants get up in the world." First Studies, p. 150 ; Lessons with Plants, p. 396 ; Botany, Bailey, p. 108.

Spring work.— Opening of the buds. Lessons with Plants, pp. 48–63 ; First Studies, p. 33.

Arrangement of buds. Lessons with Plants, pp. 63–69.

Expansion of bark. Lessons with Plants, pp. 69–72.

FOURTH GRADE.

The object of this year's work may be the teaching of the value of earth, air, light, and water upon plants.

Fall work.— Experiments to show these to be carried on in schoolroom. Experiments to show value of earth to plants :

(1) Plant seeds in fertile earth ; poor earth ; clean sand or sawdust.

(2) Plant seeds in sawdust and on cotton batting placed on water in a jar.

Experiments to show use of light to plants :

(1) Sow seeds in two boxes of earth prepared just alike. Place one in the window, one in a dark closet, and note results.

(2) Place house plants from greenhouse in a window, and note change of position of leaves.

(3) The story of the sunflower.

Experiments showing use of water to plants :

(1) Place a very much wilted cut plant in water, and note result.

(2) Place seeds in earth which is dry, and in earth which is kept moist.

(3) Plant seeds on batting floating on a tumbler of water, and note results.

These experiments should extend over several weeks.

Winter and spring work.— Begin the study of trees. Choose some tree in the schoolyard, if possible, and make this the basis of the work. The following is an outline for the study of a maple tree : Begin observations in January. Make drawings of the tree, showing the relations of branches to trunk and general outline. Note the following details : The color of trunk and branches in January, and the color in February and March ; when the buds begin to swell ; the arrangement of buds ; watch closely to determine whether a bud develops into a blossom or a leaf ; the peculiarities of bark on trunk and branches ; do the leaves or the blossoms appear first ; the shape and color of the blossoms ; draw them and study them thoroughly ; the color and position of the leaves when they first appear ; draw the different stages of the unfolding of the leaves ; keep a calendar of all the year's history of the tree ; when in full leaf make another drawing of the whole tree ; study the tree from below, and if possible from above, to show arrangement of leaves in reference to light ; make drawings of the fruit when it is formed ; study how it travels ; when the first autumn tints appear ; make colored drawings of the tree in its autumn foliage, and note when leaves begin to fall and when the branches are finally bare ; note different form of maple in the open and maple in the forest.

In connection with the year's history of the tree, study the tree from an economic point of view. Make a special study of sugar-making in connection with the maple tree. Study maple wood. To do this get a quarter section of a piece of maple log and study the grain lengthwise and in cross sections. Study all the industries possible in which maple is used. Devote one notebook to all the work on the maple tree, and at the end summarize the observations. For drawing of trees, see Cornell Teachers' Leaflet, No. 12 (Nos. XXIX and XXX, this volume). Home Nature-Study, Vol. V, Nos. 2, 5.

FIFTH GRADE.

The work during this grade may be devoted to plant physiology. For this work use First Studies of Plant Life, Atkinson. The experiments described in this book are simple and excellent; they give the pupil definite knowledge of the life processes of plants, and the use to the plant of roots, stems, leaves, flowers, and fruit.

Continue studies of trees. Select some other species than the one studied during the last grade. Study it in the same way Note the differences between the two. Two or three contrasting species may thus be studied.

SIXTH GRADE.

Having studied in the previous year the uses of different parts of the plant, the pupil will be fitted now to take up the general subject of weeds.

Take some common forms and let the pupils observe that they grow where other plants do not grow, or that they drive out other plants; then study the special reasons why each kind of weed is able to do these things. Botany, Bailey, pp. 214–222; Elements of Botany, pp. 196–205.

During the autumn another subject for study in this grade is *Mushrooms*. Lead the pupils to see how these flowerless plants produce seed, and let them bring in as many forms as possible. Do not try to teach which mushrooms are poisonous. Lessons with Plants, p. 347; Mushrooms, by Atkinson.

Winter work.— Evergreen trees. Cornell Teachers' Leaflet, No. 13 (No. XXXIII, this volume).

Spring work.— The spring work may well be the making of a calendar for trees and plants. Keep a record each day of the leafage of plants, the appearance of weeds, and the appearance of blossoms of fruit trees and all common flowers. Record which appear first, leaves or blossoms.

This work will be good preparation for the study of the "struggle for existence," which comes in the next grade.

SEVENTH GRADE.

The work for this year, both fall and spring, may be the study of the cross fertilization of flowers. Choose a few of the common flowers, and let the pupils study the means by which pollen is carried from flower to flower.

In studying any flower fertilized by insects always ask : Where is the nectary ? Where in relation to the nectary are the stigma and the anthers ? What path must the insect follow in order to get the nectar ? Do the flowers attract insects by color ? By fragrance ? What insects do you find visiting the flowers studied ? Lessons with Plants, pp. 224–245 ; Plants, Coulter, pp. 109–137 ; Elements of Botany, pp. 182–196 ; Readers in Botany, Newell, Part II, p. 86 ; Plant World, Bergen, pp. 57–127 ; Ten New England Blossoms, Weed.

The cross fertilization of flowers is only one adaptation for succeeding in the struggle for existence.

Study as many other ways of insuring the continuance of a plant as is possible. Botany, Bailey, pp. 197–217 ; Lessons with Plants, pp. 15–20 ; Elements of Botany, pp. 199–212.

Study plant communities. Botany, Bailey, pp. 219–227 ; Plant Relations, pp. 146, 162, 168 ; Plant Structures, p. 313 ; Cornell Teachers' Leaflet, No. 19 (No. XXXV, this volume).

EIGHTH GRADE.

It seems to be the experience of most teachers that pupils of the seventh and eighth grades are with difficulty kept interested in nature-study. This is probably due to the fact that the methods suited to earlier grades are not suited to these. Pupils of this age, now feeling " grown up," are attracted only by more mature work. They may be interested in some of the following subjects :

Horticulture and Gardening.— Cornell Teachers' Leaflets. Garden-Making ; The Pruning-Book ; The Principles of Fruit-Growing ; The Principles of Vegetable-Gardening, all by Bailey. Plant Culture, by Goff.

Forestry.— Relations of forests to preservation of rain-fall and streams. Preservation of Forests. Use of Forests. Reforesting waste lands, etc. A Primer of Forestry by Pinchot, United States Department Agriculture. A First Book of Forestry, Roth.

Ferns.—Study and make collections of all the ferns of the locality. Make drawings of each fern and its fruiting organs. and press and mount the specimens with full accounts of habits and locality of the plant. How to Know the Ferns, Mrs. Parsons ; Gray's Botany ; Our Ferns, Clute.

BIBLIOGRAPHY.*

INSECTS.

Every Day Butterflies. S. H. Scudder. Houghton, Mifflin & Co. $2.00.

Insect Life. J. H. Comstock. D. Appleton & Co. $1.25.

Lessons in Nature-Study. Jenkins & Kellogg. W. B. Harrison. $1.00.

Manual for Study of Insects. J. H. Comstock. Comstock Pub. Co. $3.75.

Moths and Butterflies. (*a*) Julia P. Ballard. Putnam's Sons. $1.50.

Moths and Butterflies. (*b*) Mary C. Dickerson. Ginn & Co. $2.50.

Stories of Insect Life. Weed & Murtfeldt. Ginn & Co. 35 cents.

Outdoor Studies. James B. Needham. American Book Co. 40 cents.

Bee People. Margaret W. Morley. A. C. McClurg. $1.25.

The Butterfly Book. W. J. Holland. Doubleday, Page & Co. $3.00.

Caterpillars and Their Moths. Eliot and Soule. The Century Co. $2.00.

Wasps and Their Ways. Margaret W. Morley. Dodd, Mead & Co. $1.50.

The Ways of the Six-Footed. Anna Botsford Comstock. Ginn & Co. 40 cents.

How to Know the Butterflies. J. H. and Anna Botsford Comstock. D. Appleton & Co. $2.25.

ANIMALS OTHER THAN INSECTS.

Animal Life. Jordan & Kellogg. D. Appleton & Co. $1.25.

---

* This list comprises some of the books that have been helpful to me. It is not intended to be complete. Good new books are constantly appearing. The teacher should endeavor to keep up with the new books.

Familiar Fish.   Eugene McCarthy.   D. Appleton & Co. $1.50.

Story of the Fishes.   James N. Baskett.   D. Appleton & Co.
65 cents.

Familiar Life of the Roadside.   Schuyler Mathews.   D. Appleton & Co. $1.75.

Squirrels and Other Fur Bearers.   John Burroughs.   Houghton, Mifflin & Co. $1.00.

Wild Life in Orchard and Field.   Harper & Bros.   Wild
Neighbors.   The Macmillan Co.   Ernest Ingersoll. $1.50 each.

Kindred of the Wild.   Roberts.   L. C. Page. $2.00.

Wild Life Near Home.   Dallas Lore Sharp.   The Century Co.
$2.00.

Four Footed Americans.   Wright.   The Macmillan Co. $1.50.

American Animals.   Stone & Cram.   Doubleday, Page & Co.
$4.00.

Food and Game Fishes.   Jordan & Evermann.   Doubleday,
Page & Co. $4.00.

Various books that deal with animals from the story or narrative
point of view will be found to be interesting and helpful.   They
are often useful in arousing an interest in the subject.   There are
many good animal books not mentioned in the above list.

Birds.

Bird Homes.   A. R. Dugmore.   Doubleday, Page & Co. $2.00.

Bird Life (with colored plates).   Frank M. Chapman.   D. Appleton & Co. $5.00.

Bird Neighbors.   Neltje Blanchan.   Doubleday, Page & Co.
$2.00.

Birds of Village and Field.   Florence Merriam.   Houghton,
Mifflin & Co. $2.00.

First Book of Birds.   Olive Thorne Miller.   Houghton, Mifflin
& Co. $1.00.

Second Book of Birds.   Olive Thorne Miller.   Houghton, Mifflin & Co. $1.00.

Our Native Birds.   D. Lange.   The Macmillan Co. $1.00.

Story of the Birds.   James N. Baskett.   D. Appleton & Co.
65 cents.

How to Attract the Birds.   Neltje Blanchan.   Doubleday, Page
& Co. $1.35.

The Bird Book.   Eckstorm.   D. C. Heath & Co.   80 cents.

The Relations of Birds to Man.   Weed & Dearborn.   Lippin-
cott. $2.50.

The Woodpeckers. F. H. Eckstorm. Houghton, Mifflin & Co. $1.00.

Bird Lore. A magazine. The Macmillans. Houghton, Mifflin & Co. $1.00.

PLANT LIFE.

Botany ; an Elementary Text for Schools. L. H. Bailey. The Macmillan Co. $1.00.

Corn Plants. F. L. Sargent. Houghton, Mifflin & Co. 60 cents.

Elements of Botany. J. Y. Bergen. Ginn & Co. $1.10.

Familiar Flowers of Field and Garden. S. Mathews. D. Appleton & Co. $1.75.

First Studies in Plant Life. George F. Atkinson. Ginn & Co. 70 cents.

Flowers and Their Friends. Margaret W. Morley. Ginn & Co. 60 cents.

Flowers of Field, Hill and Swamp. C. Creevey. Harper & Bros. $2.50.

Glimpses at the Plant World. Fanny D. Bergen. Ginn & Co. 35 cents.

A Guide to the Wild Flowers. Alice Lounsberry. Frederick A. Stokes Co. $2.50.

How Plants Grow. Asa Gray. American Book Co. 80 cents.

How to Know the Ferns. Mrs. Frances Theodore Parsons. Chas. Scribner's Sons. $1.50.

Our Ferns in Their Haunts. Clute. Stokes Co. $2.00.

How to Know the Wild Flowers. Mrs. Wm. Starr Dana. Chas. Scribner's Sons. $2.00.

Lessons With Plants. L. H. Bailey. The Macmillan Co. $1.10.

Little Wanderers. Margaret W. Morley. Ginn & Co. 35 cents.

Mushrooms. George F. Atkinson. Andrus & Church, Ithaca, N. Y. $3.00.

Plants ; a text-book of botany. J. M. Coulter. D. Appleton & Co. $2.00.

Plants and Their Children. Mrs. Wm. Starr Dana. American Book Co. 65 cents.

Reader in Botany. J. H. Newell. 2 vols. Ginn & Co. 70 cents.

Seed Dispersal. W. J. Beal. Ginn & Co. 40 cents.

Ten New England Blossoms. Clarence M. Weed. Houghton, Mifflin & Co. $1.25.

With the Wild Flowers, $1.00 ; Field, Forest and Wayside Flowers, $1.50. Maud Going. Baker, Taylor & Co.

Flowers and Their Insect Visitors. Gibson. Newson & Co. $1.00.

Trees.

A Guide to the Trees. Alice Lounsberry. Frederick A. Stokes Co. $2.50.

Familiar Trees and Their Leaves. S. Mathews. D. Appleton & Co. $1.75.

Our Native Trees. Our Native Shrubs. Harriet Keeler. Chas. Scribner's Sons. $2.00 each.

A Primer of Forestry. Pinchot. U. S. Dept. Agri.

Getting Acquainted with the Trees. J. H. McFarland. Outlook Co. $1.75.

The First Book of Forestry. Roth. Ginn & Co. $1.00.

Among Green Trees. Julia E. Rogers. Mumford. $3.00.

Trees, Shrubs and Vines. Parkhurst. Chas. Scribner's Sons. $1.50.

Practical Forestry. John Gifford. D. Appleton & Co. $1.20.

The Nature-Study Idea. L. H. Bailey. Doubleday, Page & Co. $1.00.

Science Sketches. David Starr Jordan. McClurg & Co. $1.50.

Poetry of the Seasons. Mary I. Lovejoy. Silver, Burdette & Co. 60 cents.

Nature in Verse. Mary I. Lovejoy. Silver, Burdette & Co. 60 cents.

Nature Pictures by American Poets. The Macmillan Co. $1.25.

Arbor Day Manual. Charles Skinner. Bardeen & Co. $2.50.

Songs of Nature. John Burroughs. McClure, Phillips & Co. $1.50.

Among Flowers and Trees. Wait & Leonard. Lee & Shepherd. $2.00.

LEAFLET VI.

A SUMMER SHOWER.*

BY R. S. TARR.

A RAINSTORM comes, the walks are wet, the roads are muddy. Then the sun breaks through the clouds and soon the walks are no longer damp and the mud of the road is dried. Where did the water come from and where has it gone? Let us answer these questions.

A kettle on the stove is forgotten and soon a cracking is heard; the housewife jumps to her feet for the kettle is dry. The kettle was filled with water, but it has all boiled away; and where has it gone? Surely into the air of the room, for it can be seen issuing as "steam" and then disappearing from view, as if by magic. The heat of the fire has changed the liquid water to a gas as invisible as the air itself. This gas is *water vapor*.

Do you wish to prove that the water vapor is there, although unseen? Then, if the day is cool, watch the window and notice the drops of water collect upon it. Or, if the day is warm, bring an ice-cold glass or pitcher into the room and see the drops collect upon it (Fig. 9). People sometimes say, when drops of water collect on a glass of cold water, that the glass is "sweating;" but see whether the same thing will not happen with a cold glass that does not contain water.

Fig. 9. A glass of cold water on which vapor has condensed in drops.

These two simple observations teach us two very important facts: (1) That heat will change liquid water to an invisible vapor, or gas, which will float about in the air of a room; and (2) that cold will cause some of the vapor to change back to liquid water.

Let us observe a little further. The clothes upon the line on

---

*Teachers' Leaflet, No. 14: Cornell Nature-Study Bulletin, June, 1899.

wash day are hung out wet and brought in dry. If the sun is shining they probably dry quickly; but will they not dry even if the sun is not shining? They will, indeed; so here is another fact to add to our other two, namely (3) that the production of vapor from water will proceed even when the water is not heated.

This change of water to vapor is called *evaporation.* The water evaporates from the clothes; it also evaporates from the walks after a rain, from the mud of the road, from the brooks, creeks and rivers, and from ponds, lakes, and the great ocean itself. Indeed, wherever water is exposed to the air some evaporation is taking place. Yet heat aids evaporation, as you can prove by taking three dishes of the same kind and pouring the same amount of water into each, then placing one on the stove, a second in the sun, and a third in a cool, shady place, as a cellar, and watching to see which is the last to become dry.

About three-fourths of the earth's surface is covered by water, so that the air is receiving vapor all the time. In fact, every minute thousands of barrels of water-vapor are rising into the atmosphere from the surface of the ocean. The air is constantly moving about, forming winds, and this load of vapor is, therefore, drifted about by the winds, so that the air you are breathing may have in it vapor that came from the ocean hundreds or even thousands of miles away. You do not see the vapor, you are perhaps not even aware that it is there; yet in a room 10 feet high and 20 feet square there is often enough vapor, if it could all be changed back to water to fill a two-quart measure.

There is a difference in the amount of vapor from time to time. Some days the air is quite free from it, and then clothes will dry rapidly. On other days the air is damp and humid; then people say it is "muggy," or that the "humidity is high." On these muggy days in summer the air is oppressive because there is so much vapor in it. Near the sea, where there is so much water to evaporate, the air is commonly more humid or moist than in the interior, away from the sea, where there is less water to evaporate.

We have seen that there is some vapor in all air, and that there is more at some times than at others. We have also seen how it has come into the air, and that cold will cause it to condense to liquid water on cold window panes and on water glasses. There are other ways in which the vapor may be changed to liquid.

After a summer day, even when there has been no rain, soon

after the sun sinks behind the western horizon the grass becomes so damp that one's feet are wet in walking through it. The dew is "falling." During the daytime the grass is warmed by the sun; but when the sun is gone it grows cooler, much as a stove becomes cool when the fire is out. This cool grass chills the air near it and changes some of the vapor to liquid, which collects in drops on the grass, as the vapor condenses on the outside of a glass of ice water.

In the opposite season of the year, on a cold winter's day, when you step out of a warm house into the chilly air, a thin cloud, or fog, forms as you expel the air from your lungs, and you say that you can "see your breath." What you really see are the little drops of water formed as the vapor-laden breath is chilled on passing from the warm body to the cold air. The vapor is condensed to form a tiny mist.

Fig. 10. A wreath of fog settled in a valley with the hilltops rising above it.

Doubtless you have seen a wreath of fog settling in a valley at night; or in the morning you may have looked out upon a fog that has gathered there during the night (Fig. 10). If your home happens to be upon a hillside, perhaps you have been able to look down upon the fog nestled there like a cloud on the land, which it really is. Such a fog is caused in very nearly the same way as the tiny fog made by breathing. The damp air in the valley has been chilled until the vapor has condensed to form tiny mist or fog particles. Without doubt you can tell why this fog disappears when the sun rises and the warm rays fall upon it.

On the ocean there are great fogs, covering the sea for hundreds of miles; they make sailing dangerous, because the sailors cannot see through the mist, so that two vessels may run together, or a ship may be driven upon the coast before the captain knows it.

Once more, this is merely condensed vapor caused by chilling air that has become laden with vapor. This chilling is often caused when warm, damp winds blow over the cold parts of the ocean.

This leads the way to an understanding of a rain storm ; but first we must learn something about the temperature of the air. The air near the ground where we live is commonly warmer than that above the ground where the clouds are. People who have gone up in balloons tell us so ; and now scientific men who are studying this question are in the habit of sending up great kites, carrying thermometers and other instruments, in order to find out about the air far above the ground.

Fig. 11. Fog clouds among the valleys in the mountains, only the mountain peaks projecting above them.

It is not necessary, however, to send up a kite or a balloon to prove this. If your home is among mountains, or even among high hills, you can prove it for yourself ; for often, in the late autumn, when it rains on the lower ground, it snows upon the mountain tops, so that when the clouds have cleared away the surface of the uplands is robed in white (Fig. 12). In the spring-time, or in the winter during a thaw, people living among these highlands often start out in sleighs on a journey to a town, which is in the valley, and before they reach the valley their horses are obliged to drag the sleigh over bare ground. It is so much warmer on the lower ground that the snow melts away much more quickly than it does among the hills.

The difference in temperature is, on the average, about one degree for every three hundred feet, so that a hill top rising twelve hundred feet above a valley would have an average temperature about four degrees lower than the valley. Now some mountains, even in New York, rise thousands of feet above the surrounding country. They rise high into the regions of cold air,

Fig. 12. A mountain whitened by snow on the top, while there is no snow at the base.

so that they are often covered with snow long before any snow has fallen on the lowlands ; and the snow remains upon them long after it has disappeared from the lower country (Fig. 12).

Fig. 13. A mountain peak snow capped, and covered on the very crest by a cloud.

Some mountains are so lofty that it never rains upon them, but snows instead ; and they are never free from snow, even in mid-summer. If one climbs to the top of such peaks he finds it always very cold there. While he is shivering from the cold he can look down upon the green fields where the birds are singing, the flowers blossoming and the men, working in the fields, are complaining of the heat.

One who watches such a mountain as this, or in fact any mountain peak, will notice that it is frequently wrapped in clouds (Fig. 13). Damp winds blowing against the cold mountains are chilled and the vapor is condensed. If one climbs through such a cloud, as thousands of people have done when climbing mountains, he often seems to pass through nothing but a fog, for really many clouds are only fogs high in the air. (Fig. 14).

But very often rain falls from these clouds that cling to the mountain sides. The reason for this is easy to understand. As the air comes against the cold mountains so much vapor is condensed that some of the tiny fog particles grow larger and larger until they become mist particles, which are too heavy to float in the air. They then begin to settle; and as one particle strikes against another, the two unite, and this continues until perhaps a dozen have joined together so as to form a good-sized drop, which is so heavy that it is obliged to fall to the ground as rain.

Fig. 14. Clouds clinging to the mountain sides. If one were climbing these mountains he would find himself, in passing through the clouds, either in a fog or a mist.

Let us now look at our summer storms. These do not form about mountain peaks; yet what has been said about the mountains will help us to understand such showers.

It is a hot summer day. The air is muggy and oppressive, so that the least exertion causes a perspiration, and even in the shade one is uncomfortably hot. Soon great banks of clouds appear (Fig. 15),—the "thunder heads,"— and people say "a thunder shower is coming, so that we will soon have relief from this oppressive heat." The clouds draw near, lightning is seen and thunder heard, and from the black base of the cloud, torrents of water fall upon the earth. If we could have watched this cloud from the beginning, and followed it on its course, we would have seen some facts that would help explain it. Similar clouds perhaps began to form over your head in the early afternoon and drifted away toward the east, developing into thunder storms many miles to the east of you.

On such a day as this, the air near the ground is so damp that it gives up vapor easily, as you can prove by allowing a glass of ice water to stand on a table and watching the drops of water gather there, causing the glass to "sweat" (Fig. 9). The sun beats down upon the heated ground and the surface becomes like a furnace, so that the air near the ground is warmed.

Air that is warm is lighter than cool air, and, being lighter, will rise, for the heavy cool air will settle and push it up, as a chip of

Fig. 15. A " thunder head," or cumulus cloud.

wood will rise in a pail of water, because it is lighter than the water which pushes it to the top. This is why the warm air rises from a furnace, or a stove, or a lamp. It is the reason why the hot air rises through a house chimney ; undoubtedly you can find other illustrations, as ventilation, and can find abundant opportunity to prove that warm air will rise.

The warm, moist air near the ground becomes so light that the heavy air above settles down and pushes it up, so that an uprising current of air is formed above the heated ground, much as an uprising current of hot air rises through the chimney when the stove is lighted. Rising thousands of feet into the sky the warm air reaches such a height, and finally comes to a place so cool, that some of the vapor must be condensed, forming fog particles, which in turn form a cloud.

On such a day, if you will watch a cloud, you will notice that its base is flat (Fig. 15); and this flat base marks the height above ground where the temperature of the atmosphere is low enough to change the vapor to fog particles. Of course the air still rises somewhat above this base and continues to get cooler, and to have more and more vapor condensed. This makes a pile of clouds resting on a level base, but with rounded tops (Fig. 15). Some-

times the base of these summer clouds, called cumulus clouds, is a mile above the ground and their tops fully a mile higher than this.

Just as on the mountain side, where the drops grow larger until they must fall, so here, fog particles grow to drops of such a size that they are too heavy to float. This growth is often aided by the violent currents of air, which sometimes tumble and toss the clouds about so that you can see the commotion from the ground. These currents blow one particle against another, forming a single drop from the collision of two; then still others are added until the rain drop is so heavy that it must fall.

Fig. 16. *Photograph of a lightning flash.*

But sometimes the air currents are so rapid that the drops are carried on up, higher and higher, notwithstanding the fact that they are heavy. Then they may be carried so high, and into air so cold, that they are frozen, forming hail. These "hailstones" cannot sink to the ground until they are thrown out of the violent currents, when they fall to the ground, often near the edge of the storm.

Some hailstones are of great size; you will find it interesting to examine them. If you do this, notice the rings of clear and clouded ice that are often to be seen. These are caused when the hail, after forming, settles to a place where it melts a little, then is lifted again by another current, growing larger by the addition of more vapor. This continues until finally the ice ball sinks to the ground.

There is thunder and lightning in such storms. Few things in nature are grander than these, and those who will watch the lightning flash will see many beautiful and interesting sights (Fig. 16). Sometimes the flash goes from cloud to cloud, again from the cloud to the ground. No one knows exactly why the lightning comes; but we do know that it is an electric spark, something like that which one can often see pass from the trolley to the wire of an electric car line. The main difference is that the spark in a thunder storm is a powerful lightning bolt that passes over a space of thousands of feet and often does great damage where it strikes.

The thunder is a sound which may be compared to the crack heard when a spark passes from the trolley, though of course the noise is very much louder. The crack of the lightning echoes and reverberates among the clouds, often changing to a great rumble; but this rumbling is mainly caused by the echo, the sound from the lightning being a loud crack or crash like that which we sometimes hear when the lightning strikes near by.

Some of the vapor of the air, on condensing, gathers on solid objects like grass, or glass; but some, as fog, floats about in the air. Really this, too, is often gathered around solid objects. Floating about in the air are innumerable bits of "dust" which you can see dancing about in the sunlight when a sunbeam enters a dark room. Some of these "dust" particles are actual dust from the road, but much of it is something else, as the pollen of plants, microbes, and the solid bits produced by the burning of wood or coal.

Each bit serves as a tiny nucleus on which the vapor condenses; and so the very "dust" in the air aids in the formation of rain by giving something solid around which the liquid can gather. The great amount of dust in the air near the great city of London is believed to be one of the causes for the frequent fogs of that city.

That there is dust in the air, and that the rain removes it, is often proved when a dull hazy air is changed to a clear, bright air by a summer shower. Watch to find instances of this. Indeed, after such a hazy day, when the rain drops first begin to fall, if you will let a few drops fall upon a sheet of clean white paper, and then dry it, you will find the paper discolored by the dust that the rain brought with it. So the rain purifies the air by removing from it the solids that are floating in it.

These are only a few of the things of interest that you can see for yourself by studying the air. Watch the sky; it is full of interest. See what you can observe for yourself. Watch especially the clouds, for they are not only interesting but beautiful (Fig. 17). Their forms are often graceful, and they change with such rapidity that you can notice it as you watch them. Even in the daytime the colors and shadows are beautiful; but at sunrise and at sunset the clouds are often changed to gorgeous banks of color.

Watch the clouds and you will be repaid; look especially for the great piles of clouds in the east during the summer when the sun is setting (Fig. 18). Those lofty banks, tinged with silver and gold, and rising like mountains thousands of feet into the air, are really made of bits of fog and mist. Among them vapor is still

Fig. 17.   A sky flecked with clouds high in the air.

changing to water and rain drops are forming, while violent currents are whirling the drops about, and perhaps lifting them to such a height that they are being frozen into hailstones. Far off to the east, beneath that cloud, rain is falling in torrents, lightning is flashing and thunder crashing, though you cannot hear it because it is so far away.

You see the storm merely as a brightly lighted and beautifully

colored cloud mass in the sky; but the people over whom it is hanging find it a threatening black cloud, the source of a furious wind, a heavy rain, and the awe-inspiring lightning. To them it may not be beautiful, though grand in the extreme; and so, too, when the summer thunder shower visits you in the

Fig. 18.   The cloud banks of a thunder storm on the horizon.

early evening, you may know that people to the west of you are probably looking at its side and top and admiring its beauty of form and color.

The storm passes on, still to the eastward, and finally the cloud mass entirely disappears beneath the eastern horizon ; but if you watch, you will see signs that it is still there, though out of sight ; for in the darkness of the night you can see the eastern horizon lighted by little flashes, the source of which cannot be seen. You call it " heat lightning," but it is really the last signal that we can see of the vanishing thunder storm, so far away that the sound of the crashing thunder cannot be heard.

You watch the mysterious flashes ; they grow dimmer and dimmer and finally you see them no more. Our summer shower is gone. It has done what thousands of others have done before, and what thousands of others will do in the future. It has started, moved off, and finally disappeared from sight ; and as it has gone it has told us a story. You can read a part of this story if you will ; and in reading it will find much that interests.

LEAFLET VII.

A SNOW STORM.*

By ANNA BOTSFORD COMSTOCK.

The snow had begun in the gloaming,
And busily all the night
Had been heaping field and highway
With a silence deep and white.
Every pine and fir and hemlock
Wore ermine too dear for an earl,
And the poorest twig on the elm-tree
Was ridged inch deep with pearl.
From sheds new-roofed with Carrara
Came Chanticleer's muffled crow
The stiff rails were softened to swan's-down
And still fluttered down the snow.
                                    — *Lowell.*

 HE storm which Lowell describes so delightfully is the first soft, gentle snow fall that comes in November or early December. "The silence deep and white" settles like a benediction over the brown, uneven landscape, and makes of it a scene of enchantment. Very different from this is the storm that comes when the winter cold is most severe and winter winds most terrific. Then the skies are as white as the fields, with never a sign of blue ; if the sun appears at all, it shines cold instead of warm, and seems but a vague white spot behind the veil of upward, downward whirling snowflakes ; the wild wind takes the " snow dust " in eddies across the fields and piles it at the fences in great drift billows with overhanging crests. On such a day the snow is so cold and dry, the clouds so low and oppressive, the bare trees so brown and bleak,

---

*Home Nature-Study Course, December, 1903.

that we shiver even though we gaze on the dreary scene from the window of a warm and comfortable room.

But another change is sure to come. Some February day the wind will veer suddenly to the south and breathe warm thawing breaths over the white frozen world. Then will the forests appear in robes of vivid blue-purple against the shining hills ; and in the

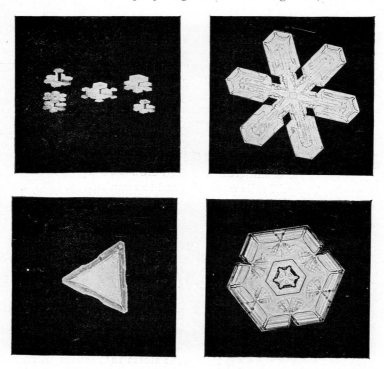

Fig. 19.   Snow crystals enlarged.

mornings the soft blue of the horizon will shade upward into rose-color and still upward into yellow and beryl green ; these hues are never seen on the forest or in the sky except when the snow covers the earth to the horizon line. The eye that loves color could ill afford to lose from the world the purples and blues which bring contrast into the winter landscape.

The snow storm to our limited understanding, begins with a miracle — the miracle of crystallization. Why should water freezing freely in the air be a part of geometry, the six rays of the snow

crystal growing at an angle one to another, of sixty degrees? Or
as if to prove geometry divine beyond cavil, sometimes the rays
include angles of twice sixty degrees. Then why should the
decorations of the rays assume thousands of intricate, beautiful
forms, each ray of a flake ornamented exactly like its five sisters?
And why should the snowflake formed in the higher clouds of the
upper air be tabular in shape but still, in cross section, show that

Fig. 20. Snow crystals enlarged.

it is built on the plan of six radii? Look at it as we will, the
formation of a crystal is a beautiful mystery and is as unfathom-
able as is the mystery of life.

I am indebted to the courtesy of Mr. R. G. Allen, Section Director
for New York of the U. S. Weather Bureau, for suggestions in making out the following questions. The beautiful pictures of snow
crystals illustrating this lesson were made from photographs taken
by Mr. W. A. Bentley of Jericho, Vt. It is our desire to interest all

teachers in the natural history of a snow storm, to the end that "they may love the country better and be content to live therein."

A thermometer hung in a sheltered, open place away from the warmth of the house is a necessary preliminary to the proper observation of the phenomena of a snow storm.

Dark woolen cloth is the best medium on which to catch and observe snow crystals.

Fig. 21. " With a silence deep and white."

QUESTIONS ON A SNOW STORM.

1. What causes snow?
2. At what temperature do snow crystals form?
3. How do the clouds appear before a snow storm?
4. What is the temperature of the air before the storm?
5. What is the direction of the wind before the storm?
6. Does the storm come from the same direction as the wind?

7. What are the conditions of the wind and temperature when the snow crystals are most perfect in form?

8. What are these conditions when the snow crystals are matted together in great flakes?

9. What are these conditions when the snow crystals appear sharp and needle-like?

10. Are the snow crystals of the same storm similar in structure and decoration?

11. What is the difference in structure between a snowflake and a hail stone?

12. What is sleet?

13. What is the difference between hoar frost and snow?

14. Does the temperature rise or fall during a snow storm?

15. Is it colder or warmer after a snow storm has passed than it was before it began?

16. What are the conditions of weather which cause a blizzard?

17. Why does a covering of snow prevent the ground from freezing so severely as it would if bare?

18. Why is snow a bad conductor of heat?

19. Pack snow in a quart cup until it is full and let it melt; then tell how full the cup is of water. What do you infer from this?

20. Have you ever observed the grass to be green beneath snow drifts? Tell why.

21. Does snow evaporate as well as melt?

22. How does snow benefit the farmer and the fruit grower?

23. Do the snow storms in your locality come from one general direction all winter?

7

LEAFLET VIII.

A HANDFUL OF SOIL: WHAT IT IS.*

BY R. S. TARR.

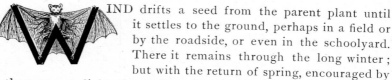

IND drifts a seed from the parent plant until it settles to the ground, perhaps in a field or by the roadside, or even in the schoolyard. There it remains through the long winter; but with the return of spring, encouraged by the warm sunlight, the seed awakens from its dormant condition, breaks open the seed-cover and sends leaves into the air and roots into the ground. No one planted the seed; yet the plant has made its way in the world and it thrives until it has given to other seeds the same opportunity to start in life.

Had the seed fallen upon a board or a stone it might have sent out leaves and roots; but it could never have developed into a plant, for something necessary would have been lacking. What is there in the soil that is so necessary to the success of plant life? How has it come to be there? What is this soil that the plants need so much? These are some of the questions which we will try to answer.

One readily sees that the soil furnishes a place in which the plants may fix themselves,— an anchorage, as it were. It is also easy to see that from the soil the plants obtain a supply of water; and, moreover, that this water is very necessary, for the vegetation in a moist country suffers greatly in time of drought, and few plants are able to grow in a desert region because there is so little water. You can make a desert in the schoolroom and contrast it with moist soil by planting seeds in two dishes of soil, watering one, but furnishing no water to the other.

That water is necessary to plants is also proved by the plant itself. The sap and the moisture which may be pressed out of a grass stem or an apple are principally water taken from the soil by the roots. But there is more than water, for the juice of an apple is sweet or sour, while the sap and juice of other plants may be sweet or bitter. There are substances dissolved in the water.

*Nature-Study Quarterly, No. 2: Leaflet 15.

It is these dissolved substances that the plants need for their
growth, and they find them ready for use in the soil. There is a
plant-food which the roots seek and find, so that every plant
which sends roots into the soil takes something from it to build up
the plant tissue. The sharp edges of some sedges, which will cut
the hand like a dull knife, and the wood ashes left when a wood
fire is burned, represent in part this plant-food obtained from the
soil.

Let us take a handful of soil from the field, the schoolyard, or
the street and examine it. We find it to be dirt that "soils" the
hands; and when we try to brush off the dirt, we notice a gritty

*Fig. 21. A boulder-strewn soil of glacial origin with one of the large erratics on the
right similar to those which early attracted attention to the drift. See page 105.*

feeling that is quite disagreeable. This is due to the bits of
mineral in the soil; and that these are hard, often harder than a
pin, may often be proved by rubbing soil against a piece of glass,
which the hard bits will often scratch, while a pin will not.

Study this soil with the eye and you may not see the tiny bits,
though in sandy soils one may easily notice that there are bits of
mineral. Even fine loamy and clay soils, when examined with a
pocket lens or a microscope, will be found to be composed of tiny
fragments of mineral. It is evident that in some way mineral has
been powdered up to form the soil; and since the minerals come
from rocks, it is the rocks that have been ground up. That powdered rock will make just such a substance as soil may be proved

by pounding a pebble to bits, or by collecting some of the rock dust that is made when a hole is drilled in a rock. Much the same substance is ground from a grindstone when a knife is sharpened on it, making the water muddy like that in a mud hole.

It will be an interesting experiment to reduce a pebble to powder and plant seeds in it to see whether they will grow as well as in soil; but in preparing it try to avoid using a sandstone pebble, because sandy soils are never very fertile.

Not only is soil made up of bits of powdered rock, but it everywhere rests upon rock (Fig. 25). Some consider soil to be

Fig. 22. A glacial soil, containing numerous transported pebbles and boulders, resting on the bed rock.

only the surface layers in which plants grow; but really this is, in most places, essentially the same as the layers below, down even to the very rock, so that we might call it all soil; though, since a special name, *regolith* (meaning stone blanket), has been proposed for all the soft, soil-like rock-cover, we may speak of it as regolith and reserve the word soil for the surface layers only.

In some places there is no soil on the bare rocks; elsewhere the soil-cover is a foot or two in depth; but there are places where the regolith is several hundred feet deep. In such places, even the wells do not reach the bed rock; nor do the streams cut down to it ; but even there, if one should dig deep enough, he would reach the solid rock beneath.

How has the hard rock been changed to loose soil ? One of the ways, of which there are several, may be easily studied whenever a rock has been exposed to the air. Let us go to a stone wall or among the pebbles in a field, for instance, and, chipping off the surface, notice how different the inside is from the outside. The outer crust is rusted and possibly quite soft, while the interior is harder and fresher. Many excellent examples of this may be found in any stony field or stone wall.

Fig. 23. The bed of a stream at low water, revealing the rounded pebbles that have been worn and smoothed by being rolled about, thus grinding off tiny bits which later are built into the flood-plains.

As hard iron rusts and crumbles to powder when exposed to the weather ; so will the minerals and the rocks decay and fall to bits ; but rocks require a very much greater time for this than does iron. It happens that the soil of New York has not been produced by the decay of rock ; and, therefore, although the soils in many parts of the world have been formed in this way, we will not delay longer in studying this subject now, nor in considering the exact way in which rocks are enabled to crumble.

Another way in which rocks may be powdered may be seen in most parts of New York. The rains wash soil from the hillsides causing the streams to become muddy. In the streams there are also many pebbles, possibly the larger fragments that have fallen into the stream after having been broken from the ledges. The current carries these all along down the stream, and, as they go, one piece striking against another, or being dragged over the rocks in the stream bed, the pebbles are ground down and smoothed (Fig. 23), which means, of course, that more mud is supplied to the stream, as mud is furnished from a grindstone when a knife or scythe is being sharpened on it. On the pebbly beaches of the

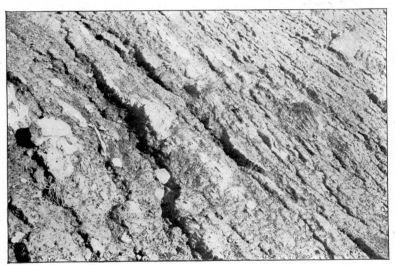

Fig. 24. Near view of a cut in glacial soil, gullied by the rains, and with numerous transported pebbles embedded in the rock flour.

sea or lakeshore much the same thing may be seen ; and here also the constant grinding of the rocks wears off the edges until the pebbles become smooth and round.

Supplied with bits of rock from the soil, or from the grinding up of pebbles and rocks along its course, the stream carries its load onward, perhaps to a lake, which it commences to fill, forming a broad delta of level and fertile land, near where the stream enters the lake. Or, possibly, the stream enters the sea and builds a delta there, as the Mississippi river has done.

But much of the mud does not reach the sea. The greatest supply comes when the streams are so flooded by heavy rains or

melting snows that the river channel is no longer able to hold the water, which then rises above the banks, over-flowing the surrounding country. Then, since its current is checked where it is so shallow, the water drops some of its load of rock bits on the flood-plain, much as the muddy water in a gutter drops sand or mud on the sidewalk when, in time of heavy rains, it overflows the walk.

Fig. 25. A scratched limestone pebble taken from a glacial soil.

Many of the most fertile lands of the world are flood-plains of this kind, where sediment, gathered by the streams farther up their courses, is dropped upon the flood-plains, enriching them by new layers of fertile soil. One does not need to go to the Nile, the Yellow, or the Mississippi for illustrations of this ; they abound on every hand, and many thousands of illustra-tions, great and small, may be found in the State of New York. Doubt-less you can find one.

There are other ways in which soils may be formed ; but only one more will be considered, and that is the way in which most of the soils of New York have been made. To study this let

Fig. 26. The grooved bed rock scratched by the movement of the ice sheet over it.

us go to a cut in the earth, such as a well or a stream bank (Figs. 22 and 24). Scattered through the soil numerous pebbles and boulders will doubtless be found ; and if these are compared with the bed rock of the country, which underlies the soil

(Fig. 22), some of them will be found to be quite different from it. For instance, where the bed rock is shale or limestone, some of the pebbles will no doubt be granite, sandstone, etc. If you could explore far enough, you would find just such rocks to the north of you, perhaps one or two hundred miles away in Canada ; or, if your home is south of the Adirondacks, you might trace the pebbles to those mountains.

On some of these pebbles, especially the softer ones, such as limestone, you will find scratches, as if they had been ground forcibly together (Fig. 25). Looking now at the bed rock in some place from which the soil has been recently removed, you will find it also scratched and grooved (Fig. 26) ; and if you take the direction of these scratches with the compass, you will find that they extend in a general north and south direction, pointing, in fact, in the same direction from which the pebbles have come.

All over northeastern North America and northwestern Europe the soil is of the same nature as that just described. In our own country this kind of soil reaches down as far as the edge of the shaded area in the map (Fig. 27), and it will be noticed that all of New York is within that area excepting the extreme southwestern part near the southern end of Chautauqua lake.

Not only is the soil peculiar within this district, but there are many small hills of clay or sand, or sometimes of both together (Figs. 33 and 34). They rise in hummocky form and often have deep pits or kettle-shaped basins between, sometimes, when the soil is clayey enough to hold water, containing tiny pools. These hills extend in somewhat irregular ranges stretching across the country from the east toward the west. The position of some of these ranges is indicated on the map (Fig. 27).

For a long time people wondered how this soil with its foreign pebbles and boulders, altogether called " drift," came to be placed where it is ; they were especially puzzled to tell how the large boulders, called erratics (Fig. 21), should have been carried from one place to another. It was suggested that they came from the bursting of planets, from comets, from the explosion of mountains, from floods, and in other ways equally unlikely ; but Louis Agassiz, studying the glaciers of the Alps and the country round about, was impressed by the resemblance between the " drift " and the materials carried by living glaciers.

Agassiz, therefore, proposed the hypothesis that glaciers had carried the drift and left it where we now find it ; but for many

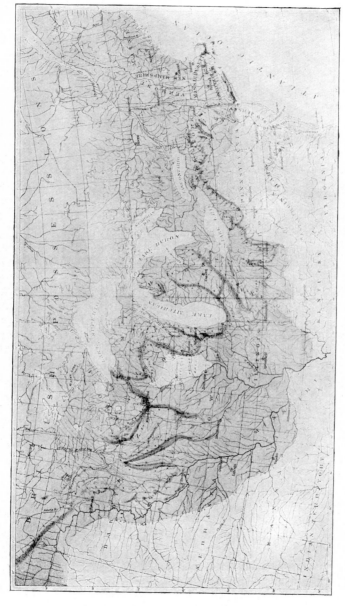

Fig. 27. *Map showing the extent of the ice sheet in the United States. Position of some of the moraines indicated by the heavily shaled lines. (After Chamberlain.)*

years his glacial hypothesis met with a great deal of opposition because it seemed impossible that the climate could have changed so greatly as to cover what is now a temperate land with a great sheet of ice.   Indeed, even now, although all who have especially studied the subject are convinced, many people have not accepted Agassiz's explanation, just as years ago, long after it was proved that the earth rotated each day, many people still believed that it was the sun, not the earth, that was moving.

The glacial explanation is as certain as that the earth rotates. For some reason, which we do not know, the climate changed and allowed ice to cover temperate lands, as before that time the climate had changed so as to allow plants like those now growing as far south as Virginia to live in Greenland, now ice covered. When the ice of the glacier melted away it left many signs of its presence ; and when

Fig. 28.   A view over the great ice plateau of Greenland, with a mountain peak projecting above it.

the temperate latitude plants grew in Greenland they left seeds, leaves and tree trunks which have been imbedded in the rocks as fossils.   One may now pick the leaves of temperate climate trees from the rocks beneath a great icecap.

To one who studies them, the signs left by the glacier are as clear proof as the leaves and seeds.   From these signs we know that the climate has changed slowly, but we have not yet learned why it changed.

There are now two places on the earth where vast glaciers, or ice sheets, cover immense areas of land, one in the Antarctic, a region very little known, the other in Greenland, where there is an ice sheet covering land having an area more than ten times that of the State of New York. Let us study this region to see what is being done there, in order to compare it with what has been done in New York.

In the interior is a vast plateau of ice, in places over 10,000 feet high, a great icy desert (Fig. 28), where absolutely no life of any kind, either animal or plant, can exist, and where it never rains, but where the storms bring snow even in the middle of summer.

Fig. 29. The edge of a part of the great Greenland ice sheet (on the left) resting on the land, over which are strewn many boulders brought by the ice and left there when it melted.

Such must have been the condition in northeastern America during the glacial period.

This vast ice sheet is slowly moivng outward in all directions

Fig. 30. A scratched pebble taken from the ice of the Greenland glacier.

from the elevated center, much as a pile of wax may be made to flow outward by placing a heavy weight upon the middle. Moving toward the north, east, south and west, this glacier must of course come to an end somewhere. In places, usually at the heads of bays, the end is in the sea, as the end of our glacier must have been off the shores of New England. From these sea-ends, icebergs constantly break off; these floating away toward the south, often reach, before they melt, as far as the path followed by the steamers from the United States to Europe. Between the bays where the glacier ends in the sea, the ice front rests on the land (Fig. 29), as it did over the greater part of New York and the states further west. There it melts in the summer, supplying streams with water and filling many small ponds and lakes. The front stards there year after year, sometimes moving a little ahead, again melting further back so as to reveal the rocks on which it formerly rested.

The bed rock here is found to be polished, scratched and grooved just like the bed-rock in New York ; and the scratches extend in the direction from which the ice moves. Resting on the rock are boulders and pebbles (Fig. 22), sometimes on the bare rock, sometimes imbedded in a clay as they are in the drift. As we found when studying the soil in our own region, so here the pebbles are often scratched, and many of them are quite different from the rock on which they rest.

Fig. 31. *A part of the edge of the Greenland glacier, with clean white ice above, and dark discolored bands below where laden with rock fragments. In the foreground is a boulder-strewn moraine.*

Going nearer to the ice we find the lower part loaded with pebbles, boulders and bits of clay very like those on the rocks near by. Fig. 30 shows one of these, scratched and grooved, which I once dug from the ice of this very glacier. The bottom of the ice is like a huge sandpaper, being dragged over the bed rock with tremendous force. It

Fig. 32. *Hummocky surface of the boulder-strewn moraine of Greenland.*

carries a load of rock fragments, and as it moves secures more by grinding or prying them from the rocks beneath. These all travel on toward the edge of the ice, being constantly ground finer and finer as wheat is ground when it goes through the mill. Indeed the resemblarce is so close that the clay produced by this grinding action is often called *rock flour.*

Dragged to the front of the ice, the rock bits, great and small, roll out as the ice melts, some, especially the finest, being carried away in the water, which is always muddy with the rock flour it carries; but much remains near the edge of the ice, forming a *moraine* (Figs. 31 and 32). This moraine, dumped at the edge of

Fig. 33. A view over the hummocky surface of a part of the moraine of the great American ice sheet in Central New York.

the glacier, very closely resembles the hummocky hills of New York (Figs. 33 and 34), mentioned above, which are really moraines formed at the ice-edge during the glacial period. While their form is quite alike, the New York moraines are generally less pebbly than the Greenland moraines, because the Greenland glacier carries less rock flour than did the glacier which covered New York.

In the Greenland glacier, as you can see in Fig. 31, there is much dirt and rock; in the glacier of the glacial period there was even more. When it melted away the ice disappeared as water, but the rock fragments of course fell down upon the rock beneath and formed soil. If over a certain region, as for instance over your home, the ice carried a great load of drift, when this gradually settled down, as the ice melted, it formed a deep layer of soil; but if the glacier had only a small load a shallow soil was left. Again, if the ice front remained for a long time near a certain place, as near your home, it kept bringing and dumping rock fragments to form moraines, which, of course, would continue to grow higher so long as the ice dumped the rock fragments, much as a sand pile will continue to grow higher so long as fresh loads are brought and dumped.

There are other causes for differences in the glacial soils, but most of them cannot be considered here. One of them is so important, however, that it must be mentioned. With the melting of so much ice, vast floods of water were caused, and these came from the ice, perhaps in places where there are now no streams, or at best only small ones. These rapid currents carried off much of the rock flour and left the coarser and heavier sand, gravel, or pebbles, the latter often well rounded, with the scratches removed by the long-continued rolling about in the glacial stream bed.

One often finds such beds of sand or gravel in different parts of the State, telling not only of ice where it is now absent, but of water currents where is now dry land. The rock flour was in some cases carried to the sea, elsewhere to lakes, or in still other places deposited in the flood-plains of the glacier-fed rivers. Now some of this rock flour is dug out to make into bricks.

Enough has been said to show that the soils of New York were brought by a glacier, and to point out that there are many differences in thickness as well as in kind and condition of the soil. The agriculture of the State is greatly influenced by these differences. In some cases one part of a farm has a deep, rich soil, another part a barren, sandy, pebbly or boulder-covered soil (Fig. 21), while in still another part the bed rock may be so near the surface that it does not pay to clear the forest from it. Moreover, some farms are in hummocky moraines, while others, near by, are on level plains (Fig. 34), where a broad glacial stream built up a flood-plain in a place where now the stream is so small that it never rises high enough to overflow the plain.

There are even other differences than these, and one who is familiar with a region is often puzzled to explain them ; but they are all due to the glacier or to the water furnished by its melting,

and a careful study by a student of the subject of Glacial Geology
will serve to explain them. Each place has had peculiar conditions and it would be necessary to study each place much more
carefully than has been done here in order to explain all the
differences.

Not only is agriculture influenced greatly by the differences in
the soil from place to place, but also by the very fact that they
are glacial soils. Being made up of partly ground-up rock fragments the soils are often stony and difficult to till. Unlike the
soil of rock decay, the particles of which the glacial soil is made
have been derived by mechanical grinding, not by chemical
decay and disintegration. There has been less leaching out of

*Fig. 34.   Hummocky moraine hills in the background and a level gravel plain
— an ancient glacial-stream flood-plain — in foreground.*

the soluble compounds which make plant foods. These are
stored up in the rock fragments ready for use when decay causes
the proper changes to produce the soluble compounds which
plants require.

Slowly the glacial soils are decaying, and, as they do so, are
furnishing plant-food to the water which the roots greedily draw
in. So the glacial soil is not a mere store house of plant-food,
but a manufactory of it as well, and glacial soils are therefore
"strong" and last for a long time. That decay is going on, especially near the surface, may often be seen in a cut in the soil,
where the natural blue color of the drift is seen below, while near

the surface the soil is rusted yellow by the decay of certain minerals which contain iron.

Few materials on the earth are more important than the soil; it acts as the intermediary between man and the earth. The rocks have some substances locked up in them which animals need ; by decay, or by being ground up, the rocks crumble so that plants may send roots into them and extract the substances needed by animals. Gifted with this wonderful power the plants grow and furnish food to animals, some of which is plant-food obtained from the rocks ; and so the animals of the land, and man himself, secure a large part of their food from the rocks. It is then worth the while to stop for a moment and think and study about this, one of the most marvelous of the many wonderful adjustments of Nature, but so common that most persons live and die without even giving it more than a passing thought.

8

LEAFLET IX.

A HANDFUL OF SOIL: WHAT IT DOES.*

By L. A. CLINTON.

THE more one studies the soil, the more certainly it will be found that the earth has locked up in her bosom many secrets, and that these secrets will not be given up for the mere asking. As mysterious as the soil may appear at different times, it always is governed by certain laws. These principles once understood, the soil becomes an open book from which one may read quickly and accurately.

USES OF THE SOIL.

The soil has certain offices to perform for which it is admirably fitted. The most important of these offices are :

1. To hold plants in place ;
2. To serve as a source of plant-food ;
3. To act as a reservoir for moisture ;
4. To serve as a storehouse for applied plant-food or fertilizer.

Some soils are capable of performing all these offices, while others are fitted for only a part of them. Thus a soil which is pure sand and almost entirely deficient in the essential elements of plant-food, may serve, if located near a large city, merely to hold the plants in position while the skillful gardener feeds the plants with specially prepared fertilizers, and supplies the moisture by irrigation.

Early in the study of soils an excursion, if possible, should be made into the woods. Great trees will be seen and under the trees will be found various shrubs and possibly weeds and grass. It will be noticed that the soil is well occupied with growing plants. The surface will be found covered with a layer several inches thick of leaves and twigs. Beneath this covering the soil is dark, moist, full of organic matter, loose, easily spaded except as roots or stones may interfere, and has every appearance of being fertile.

---

* Nature-Study Quarterly, No. 2: Leaflet 15, October, 1899.

SOIL CONDITIONS AS FOUND IN MANY FIELDS.

After examining the conditions in the forest, a study should be made of the soil in some cultivated field. It will be found that in the field the soil has lost many of the marked characteristics noticed in the woodland. In walking over the field, the soil will be found to be hard and compact. The surface may be covered with growing plants, for if the seeds which have been put into the soil by the farmer have not germinated and the plants made growth, nature has quickly come to the rescue and filled the soil with other plants which we commonly call weeds. It is nature's plan to keep the soil covered with growing plants, and from nature we should learn a lesson. The field soil, instead of being moist, is dry ; instead of being loose and friable, it is hard and compact, and it appears in texture entirely different from the woodland soil. The cause of the difference is not hard to discover. In the woods, nature for years has been building up the soil. The leaves from the trees fall to the ground and form a covering which prevents washing or erosion, and these leaves decay and add to the humus, or vegetable mould, of the soil. Roots are constantly decaying and furnish channels through the soil and permit the circulation of air and water.

In the field, nature's lesson has been disregarded and too often the whole aim seems to be to remove everything from the soil and to make no returns. Consequently the organic matter, or humus, has been used up ; the tramping of the horses' feet has closed the natural drainage canals ; after the crop is removed, the soil is left naked during the winter and the heavy rains wash and erode the surface, and remove some of the best plant-food. After a few years of such treatment, the farmer wonders why the soil will not produce as liberally as it did formerly.

Experiment No. 1.— The fact that there is humus, or vegetable mould, in certain soils can be shown by burning. Weigh a potful of hard soil and a potful of lowland soil, or muck, after each has been thoroughly dried. Then put the pots on the coals in a coal stove. After the soil is thoroughly burned, weigh again. Some of the difference in weight may be due to loss of moisture, but if the samples were well dried in the beginning, most of the loss will be due to the burning of the humus.

Conditions Which Affect Fertility.

There are certain conditions which affect soil fertility and of these the most important are :

Texture ;

Moisture-content ;

Plant-food ;

Temperature.

Texture and Its Relation to Fertility.

By texture is meant the physical condition of the soil. Upon good texture, more than upon any other one thing, depends the productivity of the soil. When the texture is right the soil is fine, loose, and friable ; the roots are able to push through it and the feeding area is enlarged. Each individual particle is free to give up a portion of its plant-food, or its film of moisture. The conditions which are found in the woods' soil are almost ideal.

Experiment No. 2.— The importance of good texture may be well shown in the class room. Pots should be filled with a soil which is lumpy and cloddy, and other pots with the same kind of material after it has been made fine and mellow. After seeds are planted in the different pots, a careful study should be made of the length of time required for germination and of the health and vigor of the plants.

Experiment No. 3.— The greater part of our farming lands do not present ideal conditions as regards texture. Clay soils are especially likely to be in bad condition. If samples of the various soils can be collected, as sand, loam, clay, etc., it may be clearly shown how different soils respond to the same kind of treatment. With a common garden trowel, the soils should be stirred and worked while wet, and then put away to dry. After drying, the conditions presented by the soils should be noted, also the length of time required for the soils to become dry. Whereas the sand and the loam will remain in fairly good condition when dry, the clay will have become "puddled," *i. e.*, the particles will have run together and made a hard, compact mass. Thus it is found in practice that clay soils must be handled with far more care and intelligence than is required for the sand and loams, if the texture is to be kept perfect.

Experiment No. 4.— If, in the experiment above suggested, the clay soil is mixed with leaf-mould, or humus soil, from the woods, it will be found to act very differently. The vegetable matter thus mixed with the mineral matter prevents the running together of the particles of clay.

Two principles, both important as relating to soil texture, now have been illustrated. Soils must not be worked when they are so wet that their particles will cohere, and organic matter, or humus, must be kept mixed with the mineral matter of the soil. In practical farm operations, if the soil can be made into a mud ball it is said to be too wet to work. The required amount of humus is retained in the soil by occasionally plowing under some green crop, as clover, or by applying barn manures.

Fig. 35.   The glass of water at the right has received lime and the clay has been flocculated ; the other was not treated.

Clay soils are also frequently treated with lime to cause them to remain in good condition and be more easily tilled. Lime causes the fine particles to flocculate, or to become granular, *i. e.*, several particles unite to form a larger particle, and these combinations are more stable and do not so readily puddle, or run together. A mud-puddle in clay soil will remain murky until the water has evaporated entirely. Let a little water-slaked lime be mixed with the muddy water, and the particles of clay will be flocculated and will settle to the bottom ; thus the water will become clear.

Experiment No. 5.— Into two glasses of water put some fine clay soil ; thoroughly stir the mixture (Fig. 35). Into one glass thus prepared put a spoonful of water-slaked lime ; stir thoroughly, then allow both glasses to remain quiet that the soil may settle. Notice in which glass the water first becomes clear, and note the appearance of the sediment in each.

The Moisture in the Soil.

In Leaflet VI has been given the history of a thunder shower. We are not told much about the history of the water after it reaches the earth. If we go out immediately after a heavy shower, we find little streams running alongside the road. These little streams unite to make larger ones, until finally the creeks and rivers are swollen, and, if the rain was heavy enough, the streams may overflow their banks. In all these streams, from the smallest to the largest, the water is muddy. Where did this mud come from? It was washed largely from the cultivated fields, and the finest and best soil is certain to be the first to start on its voyage to the valleys or to the sea. If the farmer had only learned better the lesson from nature and kept his fields covered with plants, a large part of the loss might have been prevented. A rain gauge should be kept in every school yard, so that every shower can be measured. It can then be easily determined by the pupils how

Fig. 36. *a. Soil too dry.* *b. Soil in good condition.* *c. Soil too wet.*

many tons of rain fall upon the school grounds, or how much falls upon an acre of land. It will be a matter of surprise that the amount is so great.

Not all the water which falls during a summer shower is carried off by surface drainage, since a considerable part sinks into the soil. As it passes down, each soil grain takes up a portion and surrounds itself with a little film of water, much as does a marble when dipped into water. If the rain continues long enough, the soil will become saturated and the water which cannot be retained, will, under the influence of gravity, sink down to the lower layers of soil until it finally reaches the level of the free water. From this free water, at varying depths in the soil, wells and springs are supplied. If the soil were to remain long saturated, seeds would not germinate, and most cultivated plants would

not grow because all the air passages of the soil would be filled
with water (Fig. 36). The water which sinks down deep into the
soil and helps to supply our wells is called free water. That part
which is held as a film by the soil particles (as on a marble) is
called capillary water. After the rain is over and the sun shines,
a part of the moisture which is held by the particles near the
surface is lost by evaporation. The moisture which is below
tends to rise to restore the equilibrium ; thus there is created
a current toward the surface, and finally into the air ; the moisture which thus escapes aids in forming the next thunder storm.

Experiment No. 6.— Humus enables the soil to take up and
hold large quantities of water. To illustrate this, two samples of
soil should be obtained, one a humus, or alluvial, soil, rich in
organic matter, and the other a sandy soil. Put the two samples
where they will become thoroughly air dry. Procure, say five
pounds each of the dry soils, and put each into a glass tube over
one end of which there is tied a piece of muslin, or fine wire
gauze. From a graduated glass pour water slowly upon each sample until the water begins to drain from the bottom of the tube.
In this way it can be shown which soil has the greater power of
holding moisture. Both samples should then be set away to dry.
By weighing the samples each day, it can be determined which
soil has the greater power of retaining moisture. This experiment
may be conducted not only with sand and humus, but with clay,
loam, gravel, and all other kinds of soil.

Experiment No. 7.— A finely pulverized soil will hold more film-
moisture than a cloddy soil. To illustrate the importance of
texture as related to moisture, soil should be secured which is
cloddy, or lumpy. One tube should be filled, as heretofore
described (Exp. No. 6), with the lumpy soil, and the other tube
with the fine soil which results from pulverizing the lumps, equal
weights of soil being used in each case. From a graduated glass
pour water upon each sample until the drainage begins from the
bottom. Notice which soil possesses greater power of absorbing
moisture. Put the samples away to dry, and by careful weighing,
each day, it can be determined which soil dries out more readily.

The prudent farmer will take measures to prevent the escape
of this moisture into the air. All the film-moisture (on the soil
particles) needs to be carefully conserved or saved, for the plants
will need very large amounts of moisture before they mature,
and they can draw their supply only from this film-moisture.

We can again apply the lesson learned in the woods. The soil there is always moist ; the leaves form a cover, or blanket, which prevents the evaporation of moisture. Underneath an old plank or board, the soil will be found moist. If we can break the connection between the soil and the air, we can check the escape of moisture. A layer of straw over the soil will serve to prevent the loss of moisture ; yet a whole field cannot be thus covered. It has been found that the surface soil, if kept loose,

Fig. 37. " Foot-prints on the sands of time."

say about three inches of the top soil can be made to act as a blanket or covering for the soil underneath. Although this top layer may become as dry as dust, yet it prevents the escape, by evaporation, of moisture from below. It is a matter of common observation that if tracks are made across a freshly cultivated field, the soil where the tracks are will become darker (Fig. 37). This darker appearance of the soil in the foot-marks is due to the moisture which is there rising to the surface. The implement of

Fig. 38. A cross section through one of the foot-prints.

tillage makes the soil loose, breaking the capillary connection between the lower layers of soil and the surface ; thus the upward passage of the water is checked. Where the foot-print is, the soil has been again pressed down at the surface, the particles have been crowded closer together, and capillarity is restored to the surface so that the moisture is free to escape (Fig. 38). In caring for flower-beds, or even in growing plants in a pot in the school-room, it is important that the surface of the soil be kept loose and mellow. Far better in a flower garden is a garden rake than a watering pot.

Experiment No. 8.— To show the importance of the surface mulch, fill several pots with a sandy loam soil, putting the same weight of soil into each pot. In one pot, pack the soil firmly ; in another pot, pack the soil firmly and then make the surface loose. These pots of soil may then be put away to dry; by daily weighing each it can be readily determined what effects the various methods of treatment have upon the moisture-holding power of soils.

Experiment No. 9.— The above experiment may be varied by covering the soil in some of the pots with leaves, or straw, or paper, care being taken that the added weight of the foreign matter is properly accounted for.

SOIL TEMPERATURE.

If a kernel of corn be placed in the ground in early spring before the soil has become warm, the seed will not germinate.

Fig. 39.   The moss-grown lawn or grass plot.

Abundance of moisture and oxygen may be present, but the third requisite for germination, proper temperature, is lacking. The soil is very slow to become warm in the spring, and this is due to the large amount of water which must be evaporated. During the winter and spring, the rain and melting snow have saturated the soil. The under-drainage is deficient so there is no way for the escape of the surplus water except by evaporation, and evaporation is a cooling process. A well-drained soil is thus warmer than a poorly-drained one.

The atmosphere is much quicker to respond to changes in temperature than is the soil. In the spring, the air becomes warm while the soil continues cold, and the rains which fall during this time are warmed by passing through the warm air. Then in sinking through the soil the rain-water parts with some of its heat which makes the soil warmer. During mid-summer the soil becomes very warm, and it is not affected by cool nights, as is the atmosphere. Consequently as a summer rain may be several degrees cooler than the soil, the water in passing through the soil takes up some of the heat ; thus the soil conditions are made more favorable for plant growth. Therefore, soil temperature is regulated somewhat by the rainfall.

Experiment No. 10.— The color of a soil also affects its temperature, a dark soil being warmer than a light colored soil. By having thermometers as a part of the school room equipment, interesting experiments may be conducted in determining the effect of color and moisture upon the temperature of soils

AIR IN THE SOIL.

Although that part of the plant which we can see is entirely surrounded by air, it is also necessary that the soil be in such a

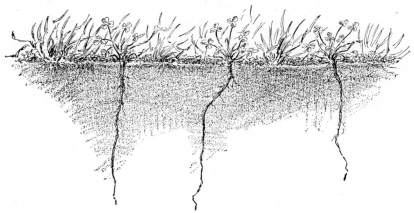

Fig. 40. *The clover roots penetrate the soil deeply.*

condition that it can be penetrated by the air. Indeed, growth cannot begin in a soil from which the air is excluded.

Experiment No. 11.— To prove this, put clay soil in a pot and plant seeds ; then wet the surface of the soil and puddle or pack the clay while wet and watch for the seeds to germinate and grow. At the same time put seeds in another pot filled with loose, mellow, moist soil.

Frequently, after the farmer has sown his grain, there comes a heavy, beating rain, and the surface of the soil becomes so packed that the air is excluded and the seeds cannot germinate. If plants are grown in pots and the water is supplied at the top, the soil may become so hard and compact as to exclude the air and the plants will make a sickly growth. The surface soil must be kept loose so that the air can penetrate it.

On many lawns it may be noticed that the grass is not thriving. It has a sickly appearance, and even the application of fertilizer

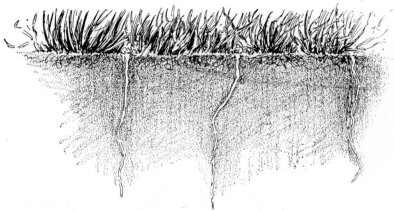

Fig. 41. After the clover dies the soil is in better condition for its having lived.

does not seem to remedy the conditions. Perhaps the ground has become so hard that the air cannot penetrate and the grass is being smothered. If the surface of the soil can be loosened with a garden rake, and clover seed sown, much good may be accomplished. The clover is a tap-rooted plant, sending its main root deep into the soil.

After the death of the plant, the root decays, and the nitrogen which is stored in it can be used as food by the other plants. Most useful of all, however, in such cases, the decay of the tap-root of the clover makes a passage deep into the soil and thus allows the air to enter. Consult Figs. 39–41.

LEAFLET X.

THE BROOK.*

By J. O. MARTIN.
Introduction By L. H. BAILEY.

A BROOK is the best of subjects for nature-study. It is near and dear to every child. It is a world in itself. It is an epitome of the nature in which we live. In miniature, it illustrates the forces which have shaped much of the earth's surface. Day by day and century by century, it carries its burden of earth-waste which it lays down in the quiet places. Always beginning and never ceasing, it does its work as slowly and as quietly as the drifting of the years. It is a scene of life and activity. It reflects the sky. It is kissed by the sun. It is caressed by the winds. The minnows play in the pools. The soft weeds grow in the shallows. The grass and the dandelions lie on its sunny banks. The moss and fern are sheltered in the nooks. It comes one knows not whence ; it flows one knows not whither. It awakens the desire of exploration. It is a realm of mysteries. It typifies the flood of life. It goes "on forever."

In many ways can the brook be made an adjunct of the schoolroom. One teacher or one grade may study its physiography ; another its birds ; another may plat it. Or one teacher and one grade may devote a month or a term to one phase of it. Thus the brook may be made the center of a life-theme.

L. H. B.

---

* Nature-Study Quarterly, No. 5 : Leaflet 18. June, 1900.

I. A BROOK AND ITS WORK.

On a rainy day most of us are driven indoors and thus we miss some of nature's most instructive lessons, for in sunshine or rain the great mother toils on, doing some of her hardest labor when her face is overcast with clouds. Let us find our waterproofs,

raise our umbrellas, bid defiance to the pattering rain, and go forth to learn some of the lessons of a rainy day.

Along the roadside, the steady, down-pouring rain collects into pools and rills, or sinks out of sight in the ground. The tiny streams search out the easiest grade and run down the road, digging little gullies as they go. Soon these rills meet and, joining their muddy currents, flow on with greater speed down the hillside until they reach the bottom of the valley and go to swell the brook which flows on, through sunshine or rain. The water which sinks into the ground passes out of sight for a time, but its journey is also downward toward the brook, though the soil, acting as a great sponge, holds it back and makes it take a

Fig. 42.   The brook may be made the center of a life-theme.

slower pace than the rushing surface water.   This slower-moving underground water percolates through the soil until it comes to a layer of rock, clay, or other impervious substance, along the slope of which it flows until it is turned again to the surface in the form of a spring.   Perhaps this spring is one of those clear, cold pools, with the water bubbling up through its sandy bottom, from which we love to drink on a hot summer's day ; or, again, it is a swampy spot on the hillside where the cat-tails grow. In whatever form it issues from the ground, a tiny rill carries away its overflow, and this sooner or later joins the brook.

The brook, we see, is simply the collected rainfall from the hillsides, flowing away to join the river. It grows larger as other brooks join it, and becomes a creek and finally a river. But where is the dividing line between brook, creek, and river? So gradually does the brook increase in volume that it would be difficult to draw any dividing line between it and the larger streams. And so with the rills that formed the brook : each is a part of the river, and the names rill, brook, creek, and river are merely relative terms.

Brooks are but rivers on a small scale ; and if we study the work that a brook is doing, we shall find it engaged in cutting down or building up, just as the river does, although, owing to the smaller size of the brook, we can see most of these operations in a short distance. Let us take our way through the wet grass and dripping trees to the brookside and see what work it is doing.

The countless rain-born rills are pouring their muddy water into the brook and to-day its volume is much greater than when it is fed, as it is in fair weather, by the slower-moving underground water of the springs. It roars along with its waters no longer clear but full of clay and sand ("mud" as we call it).

If we should dip up a glassful of this muddy water, we should find that when it had settled there remained on the bottom of the glass a thin deposit of sediment. The amount of this sediment is small, no doubt, for a single glassful, but when we think of the great quantity of water constantly flowing by, we can see that considerable sediment is going along with it. But this sediment in suspension is not all the load that the brook is moving. If you will roll up your sleeve, plunge your hand to the bottom of the brook and hold it there quietly, you will feel the coarser gravel and small stones rolling along the bottom.

All this load of sand and gravel comes, as we have seen, from the valley sides, the banks of the brook, and from its bed. It is moving downward away from its original resting place ; and what is the result? For thousands upon thousands of years, our brook may have been carrying off its yearly load of sediment ; and though each day's labor is small, yet the added toil of centuries.

has been great.   The result of this labor we can see in the great
trough or valley through which the brook flows.   Tennyson
speaks of the ceaseless toil of the brook in the following words :

> "I chatter, chatter, as I flow
>   To join the brimming river,
> For men may come and men may go,
>   But I go on forever."

We have seen how the rills and torrents bring into the brook
their loads of sand, clay, and gravel ; now let us walk along the bank

Fig. 43.   A brook cutting under its bank and causing a landslide.

and see what the brook is doing to increase this load.   Just here
there is a sudden turn in the channel and so sharp is the curve
that the rushing stream is not able to keep in mid-channel, but
throws itself furiously against the outer bank of the curve, eating
into the clay of which it is composed, until the bank is undermined, allowing a mass of clay to slide down into the stream bed,
where it is eaten up and carried away by the rushing water (Fig.
43).   Farther on, the brook dashes down a steep, rocky incline,
and if we listen and watch we may hear the thud of boulders
hurled along, or even see a pebble bound out of the muddy
foaming water.   These moving pebbles strike against each other

and grind along the bottom, wearing out themselves as well as the large unmovable boulders of the rocky bed of the brook. Thus the larger stones are ground down, rounded at first but in time reduced to sand, adding in this way to the moving burden of the brook. By this slow process of cutting and grinding, the deep rock gorges of New York state, like those at Watkins, Ithaca, Au Sable Chasm, and even the mighty gorge of Niagara, have been made. The Grand Canyon of the Colorado, over a mile in depth, is one of the greatest examples of stream cutting to be found in the world.

Now the brook leads us into a dripping woodland, and just ahead we can hear the roar of a little waterfall, for at this point the cutting stream flows upon the bed rock with its alternating bands of hard and soft rock through which the busy brook is cutting a miniature gorge. Here is a hard layer which the stream has undermined until it stands out as a shelf, over which the water leaps and falls in one mass with a drop of nearly ten feet. Watch how the water below boils and eddies ; think with what force it is hammering its stone-cutting tools upon the rocky floor. Surely here is a place

Fig. 44. A pile of brook debris deposited by the checking of the current.

where the brook is cutting fast. Notice that swirling eddy where the water is whirling about with the speed of a spinning top ; let us remember this eddy and when the water is lower we will try to see what is happening at its bottom.

On the other side of the woods our brook emerges into a broad meadow ; let us follow it and see what becomes of its load, whether it is carried onward, or whether the tired brook lays

9

it down occasionally to rest. Out of the woods, the brook dashes
down a steep incline until the foaming tide comes to rest in a
deep pool. What becomes of the large pebbles which have been
swept down? Do they go on or do they stop? If you go to the
outlet of the pool you will see that the water is coming out with
nothing in its grasp but the fine clay and sand, the gravel and
pebbles having been dropped by the less rapid current of the
pool. This is one of the most important of the brook's lessons,
for anything that tends to check the current makes it drop some
of the sediment that it carries (Fig. 44). Yonder is an old tree
stump with its crooked roots caught fast on the bottom; the mid-

stream current rushes
against it only to be thrown
back in a boiling eddy, and
the waters split in twain and
flow by on either side with
their current somewhat
checked. In the rear of
the stump is a region of
quiet water where the brook
is building up a pile of
gravel. Farther on, the
banks of the brook are low

*Fig. 45. A delta built by a tiny rill flowing
from a steep clay bank.*

and here the waters no
longer remain in the channel, but overflow the low
land, spreading out on either side in a broad sheet. The increased
friction of this larger area reduces the current, and again we see
the brook laying down some of its load. The sand and gravel
deposited here is spread out in a flat plain called a *flood plain*,
because it is built up when the stream is in flood. It is on the
large flood plains of rivers that many of our richest farm lands
occur. These receive, each spring when the stream is in flood,
a fresh coating of soil mixed with fragments of vegetable matter,
and thus grow deeper and richer year by year. The flood plains
of the Mississippi and of the Nile are notable examples of this
important form of stream deposit.

And now let us make one more rainy-day observation before
going back to our warm, dry homes. Just ahead on the other
side of that clump of alders and willows lies the pond into which
the brook flows and where its current is so checked that it gives

up almost all its burden of sediment. Close to the shore it has dropped its heaviest fragments, while the sand and clay have been carried farther out, each to be dropped in its turn, carefully assorted as to size and weight. Here you can see that the stream has partly filled this end of the pond, and it is now sending its divided current out over the deposit which it has made in a series of branching rivulets. This deposit is called a *delta* (Fig. 45), and deltas are another important form of stream deposits. In the lakes and ponds, deltas may grow outward until the lake is filled, when the stream will meander across the level plain without much current and hence without much cutting power (Fig. 46). In the sea, great deltas are being formed in some places, like those at the

Fig. 46. A brook flowing across a pond which has been filled.

mouths of the Mississippi, the Nile, and the Ganges. Large areas of dry land have thus been built. Deltas, like flood plains, afford rich farming lands when they are built high enough to remain above the water.

Here let us end our study of the brook for to-day, and wait until the rain ceases and the water runs clear again ; then we can see the bottom and can also learn by contrast how much more work the brook has been doing to-day than it does when the volume of water is less.

On the road home, however, we can notice how the temporary streams, as well as the everflowing brook, have been cutting and depositing. See where this tiny rill has run down that steep

clay bank until its current was checked at the foot.   Notice how
it has spread out its sediment in a fan-shaped deposit.   This
form of deposit is sometimes made by larger streams, especially
in a mountainous country with plains at the foot of the slopes.
They are called *alluvial fans* or *cone deltas* (Fig. 47), but they are
not as important as flood plains and deltas.

The first dry, sunny morning that comes we visit the brook
again.   It no longer roars, but its clear waters now sing a pleasant
melody as they ripple along the stony bed.   We can see at a
glance that comparatively little work is going on to-day, and yet

*Fig. 47.   A brook building a delta into a lake.   Formerly the brook flowed
straight ahead, but its own delta has caused it to change its direction.*

if we look closely, we shall see glittering particles of sand moving
along the bottom.   The clear water, however, allows us to study
the bottom which before was hidden by the load of mud.

First we see the rounded boulders and pebbles of all sizes
which must have been rolled about for a long time to make them
so smooth.   Some of them are so very hard that we cannot even
scratch them with our knives ; others are soft and easily broken.
What would be the effect of rolling together stones of such varying hardness?   We must think of these stones as the tools with
which the brook cuts and grinds, for water without sediment
can do little more than slightly to dissolve the rock.

Let us go at once to the little waterfall, for we shall be curious to see what lies at the bottom of the whirling eddy that drew our attention yesterday. As we look down into the sunlit pool we see that the eddy is gone, for the volume of water is not great enough to cause it to revolve, but there in the rock on the bottom is a deep basin-like hole. In the bottom of this hole we shall see a number of well-rounded stones, with perhaps some sand and gravel. These stones are the tools which, whirled about by the eddying water, have cut the basin-like holes. Holes of this sort are common in rocky stream beds, especially in the neighborhood of falls or in places where falls have once been ; they are called *pot-holes* and represent another form of stream cutting (Fig. 48).

Fig. 48. A pot-hole cut in the rock of a stream's bed.

Next let us visit the flood plains which we saw forming when the water was high. Now we shall find the brook flowing in its channel with the flood plain deposits left high and dry. If we dig down into the flood plain, we shall see that it is made up of successive layers varying in thickness and in the size of the fragments. Each of these layers represents a period of high water and the size of the fragments in the layer tells us something of the strength of the current, and therefore of the intensity of the flood. Some layers are thicker than others, showing a longer period of flood, or perhaps several floods in which there was little variation. This *stratification*, as it is called, is one of the peculiarities of water deposits and it is due to the assorting power of currents which vary in force. If we were to cut into the delta we should find the same thing to be true, — a regular succession of layers, though sometimes confused by changes in direction of flow.

To-day we shall notice something which escaped our attention when it was held by the rushing torrent — the valley bottom is much wider than the bed of the stream ; if we keep our eyes open we shall see the explanation of this in the abandoned channels, where, owing to some temporary obstructions, the stream has been turned from side to side of the valley, now cutting on one bank and now on the other. In this turning from side to side the cutting area of the stream is increased, and it goes on widening its valley as well as cutting it downward.

And now we have learned some of the most important ways in which the busy brook is toiling ; but there are other points which we might have seen, and in some brooks there are special features to be noted. However, we have learned that the brook is no idler, that its main work is to conduct to the ocean the rain that falls upon the earth's surface, and that in doing this it is wearing down the hills, carrying them away only to build up in other places. The cheerful song of the brook takes on a new meaning as we lie in the shade and watch it hurry by. It is not the song of idleness nor of pleasure, but like the song with which a cheerful and tireless worker seeks to make its task lighter.

INSECT LIFE OF A BROOK.*

BY MARY ROGERS MILLER.

HAT wader, be he boy or water-fowl, has not watched the water-insects? How they dart hither and thither, some skimming the surface, others sturdily rowing about in the clear shallows! The sunlight fastens, for an instant, their grotesque reflections on the smooth bottom, then away — the shadow is lost, except for the picture it left in the memory of the onlooker.

The splashing, dashing wader, with his shout and his all-disturbing stick, stands but a poor chance of making intimate acquaintances among water-folk. Your true brook-lover is a quiet individual except when occasion demands action. The lad who, from the vantage ground of a fallen log or overhanging bank, looks down on the housekeeping affairs of his tiny neighbors has the right spirit. Indeed, I doubt whether these little folk are aware of his presence or curiosity.

Time was when the enjoyment of brook-life was limited to boys. White aprons, dainty slippers and fear of being called "Tom-boy" restrained the natural impulses of the "little women." Happily that day is past, and it no longer looks queer for girls to live in the open air and sunshine, free to chase butterflies and hunt water-bugs with their brothers.

My brooks abound in swift eddies, perfect whirlpools in miniature, and water-falls of assorted sizes. They have also their quiet reaches, where whirligig beetles perform their marvelous gyrations, and bright-eyed polliwogs twirl their tails in early May. On the banks are ferns and mosses; sometimes willows and alders form a fringing border.

The heart-leaved willows along many brooksides are found to

---

* Nature-Study Quarterly, No. 5: Leaflet 18, June, 1900.

bear at the tips of many of their branches, knob-like bodies which look like pine cones. (Fig. 49.) Now everybody knows that wil-lows bear their seeds in catkins. Why, then, should so many brookside willows thrust these cones in our faces? On cutting one of the cones open, we learn the secret. A tiny colorless grub

rolls helplessly out of a cell in the very centre of the cone. It is the young of a small gnat, scarcely larger than a mosquito, and known as a "gall gnat." The cone-shaped body on the willow branch is called a "pine-cone willow-gall." The little gray gnat comes out in the spring. Any one can collect the galls from the willows and keep them in some kind of cage in the house until the gnats come forth.

The pine-cone gall is an enlarged and deformed bud. The twig might have de-veloped into a branch but for the presence of the little larva. The scales of the cone are the parts which under more favorable conditions would have been leaves. The brook-lover cannot afford to miss the pine-cone willow-galls.

Wandering along the brookside in spring or early summer, one is surprised to find so many insect visitors darting about in the air. There are dragon-flies of many shapes, sizes and colors ; dainty damsel-flies perch airily on reeds, their gleaming wings a-flut-ter in the sunshine; sometimes a nervous mud-wasp alights for a moment, and then up and away. The dragon-flies seem in-tent on coming as near to the water as possible without wetting their wings. They pay no heed to other visitors, yet how easily they escape the net of the would be collector ! Let them alone. Their business is important if we would have a new generation of dragon-flies to delight the eye next year. The eggs of these creatures are left in the water and the young ones are aquatic. If you would know more of them, dip down into the stream in some sluggish bay. Dip deep and trail the net among the water plants. Besides dragon-fly nymphs there will be caddice-worm cases like tiny cob-houses, water-boatmen, back-swimmers, and

Fig. 49. Knob-like bodies re-sembling pine cones.

giant water-bugs.* These are insects characteristic of still or sluggish water, and are found in spring and summer.

The insects which skip lightly over the surface of the water where the current is not too strong, are water-striders. (Fig. 50.) Some are short and stout, others slender-bodied; but all have long thin legs. Their color is nearly black. As they scurry about in the sunshine the delighted watcher will sometimes catch a glimpse

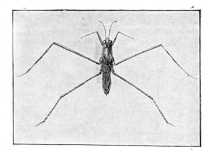

Fig. 50. Water-striders have long, thin legs.

of their reflections on the bottom. Six oval bits of shadow, outlined by rims of light; there is nothing else like it! Be sure you see it.

Let us leave the quiet, restful pools and the sluggish bays, and follow the hurrying water to the rapids. Every stone changes the course of the current and the babble makes glad the heart of the wayfarer. Let us "leave no stone unturned," until we have routed from his favorite haunt that genius of the rapids, the dobson. (Fig. 51.) These creatures bear other common names. They are prized by fishermen in the black bass season. Dirty brown in color and frankly ugly in appearance and disposition, these larvæ, for such they are, have little to fear from the casual visitor at the water's edge. When a stone is lifted, the dobsons beneath it allow themselves to be hurried along for some distance by the current. The danger over, they "catch hold" and await their prey farther down stream. In spite of their vicious looking jaws these insects are not

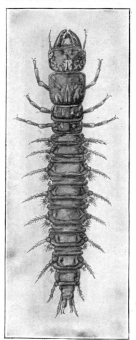

Fig. 51. The dobson makes no pretensions to beauty. (Natural size).

---

* These and other forms found in still or slow flowing water are described and pictured in Leaflet No. XII, Life in an Aquarium.

venomous.   At the very worst they could do no more than pinch the finger of the unwary explorer.

When the dobson is full grown, it is called a hellgrammite fly

or horned corydalis. It has lost none of its ugliness, though it has gained two pairs of thin, brownish-gray wings, and flies about in the evening. It has been known to create some consternation by flying in at an open window. It is harmless and short-lived in the adult stage.

Upturned stones are likely to bring to view other strangers. Lying close against these wet stony surfaces one usually finds young May-flies. (Fig. 52.*) These, like the young dragon-flies, are called *nymphs*.

When they are ready to leave the water they make their way to the shore, and, clinging to some convenient tree trunk or building, they shed their nymph skins. I have seen trees and buildings on the banks of the St. Lawrence river literally covered with these cast skins. In the early morning in June and July one may watch the molting process, the unfolding of the gauzy wings, and the unsheathing of the long filaments. (Fig. 53.)

Fig. 52. May-fly nymph. (Three times natural size).

Do not believe that May-flies are harmful. They are sometimes too numerous for comfort at summer resorts where myriads of them swarm about the lights ; but stories of their stinging and biting are entirely without foundation. They are short-lived in the adult stage. The name of the family to which they belong, *Ephemeridæ*, suggests their ephemeral existence. It is of these that poets have sung.

Stone-fly nymphs, also, cling closely to the flat stones. The cast skins of these are frequently found on the banks of streams.

* Figures 52, 53 and 54 are adapted from Dr. R. Leuckart's Zoological Charts.

They resemble the May-fly nymphs but can be identified by a comparison with these illustrations. (Fig. 54)

Sometimes on the very brink of a cataract one will see what appear like patches of loose black moss. Strangely enough, these are the larvæ of black-flies, related to the terrible black-fly of the north woods. The black-fly larvæ can live only in the

Fig. 53.   The May-fly sheds its nymph skin.   (Twice natural size.)

swiftest water. There they pass through their transformations and succeed in emerging into their aërial stage, in spite of the rushing current.

All these things and many more are seen by those who frequent the water brooks. Observers cannot tell all they see, for some things are too deep for words. They can and do say to one and all, "Come, let us visit the brook together. The

water and all that dwell in it and round about, invite us and
make us welcome."

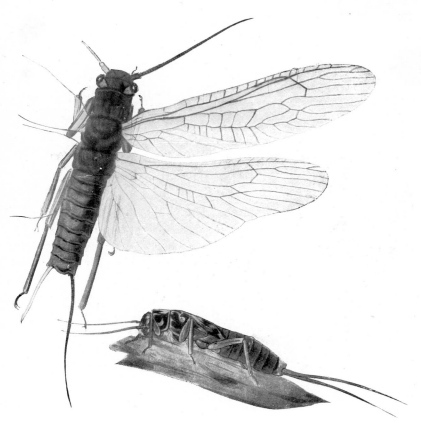

Fig. 54.   Stone-fly, showing one pair of wings.   The lower figure is a nymph.
(Twice natural size.)

LEAFLET XII.

LIFE IN AN AQUARIUM.*

By MARY ROGERS MILLER.

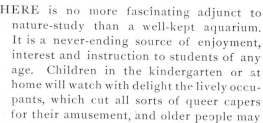

THERE is no more fascinating adjunct to nature-study than a well-kept aquarium. It is a never-ending source of enjoyment, interest and instruction to students of any age. Children in the kindergarten or at home will watch with delight the lively occupants, which cut all sorts of queer capers for their amusement, and older people may read some of nature's choicest secrets through the glassy sides of the little water world. To many, the word aquarium suggests a vision of an elaborately constructed glass box, ornamented with impossible rock-work and strange water plants, or a globe in which discouraged and sickly-looking gold-fish appear and disappear, and take strange, uncanny shapes as they dart hither and thither.

Such forms of aquaria have their place in the world, but they are not suited to the needs of an ordinary school-room. Every school may have some sort of an aquarium if the teacher and pupils are willing to give it some daily thought and care. Without such attention a fine aquarium may become an unsightly and disagreeable object, its inhabitants unhealthy and its beauty and usefulness lost.

The great fundamental principle underlying success in making and maintaining an aquarium is this : *imitate nature.* We all know how much easier it is to formulate a principle, and even to write a book about it, than to put it into practice. Most of us have not had the time and opportunity for the close observation of nature necessary to interpret her methods and to imitate her. It is to those teachers who are anxious to learn what nature has to teach and who wish to lead their pupils to a higher and wider conception of life, that these suggestions are offered.

Four things are important in making and keeping an aquarium :
1. The equilibrium between plant and animal life must be

---

* Teachers' Leaflet No. 11. May, 1898.

secured and maintained. It is probable that an aquarium in an elementary school is mainly used for the study of animal life;

but animals do not thrive in water where no plants are growing. Nature keeps plants and animals in the same pond and we must follow her lead. The plants have three valuable functions in the aquarium. First, they supply food for the herbivorous creatures. Second, they give off a quantity of oxygen which is necessary to the life of the animals. Third, they take up from the water the harmful carbonic acid gas which passes from the bodies of the animals. Just how the plants do this is another story.

Fig. 55. A museum jar aquarium. (More animal life would make a better equilibrium.)

2. The aquarium must be ventilated. Its top should be broad and open. Every little fish, snail and insect wants air, just as every boy and girl wants it. A certain quantity of air is mixed with the water, and the creatures must breathe that or come to the surface for their supply. How does Mother Nature manage the ventilation of her aquaria,—the ponds and streams? The plants furnish part of the air, as we have said. The open pond, whose surface is ruffled by every passing breeze, is constantly being provided with fresh air. A tadpole or a fish can no more live in a long-necked bottle than a boy can live in a chimney.

3. The temperature should be kept between 40° and 50° Fahr. Both nature and experience teach us this. A shady corner is a better place for the aquarium than a sunny window on a warm day.

4. It is well to choose such animals for the aquarium as are adapted to life in still water. Unless one has an arrangement of water pipes to supply a constant flow of water through the aquarium, it is better not to try to keep creatures that we find in swift streams.

Practical experience shows that there are certain dangers to guard against,— dangers which may result in the unnecessary suffering of the innocent. Perhaps the most serious results come from overstocking. It is better to have too few plants or animals than too many of either. A great deal of light, especially bright sunlight, is not good for the aquarium. A pond that is not shaded soon becomes green with a thick growth of slime or algæ. This does not look well in an aquarium and is likely to take up so much of the plant-food that the other plants are " starved out." The plants in the school-room window may provide shade for the aquarium, just as the trees and shrubs on its banks shade the pond. If we

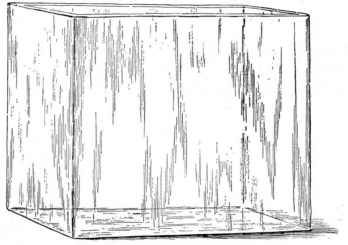

Fig. 56. A rectangular glass aquarium.

find green slime forming on the light side of our miniature pond, we should put it in a darker place, shade it heavily so that the light comes in from the top only, and put in a few more snails. These will make quick work of the green slime, since they are fond of it, if we are not.

Some of the most innocent-looking " water nymphs " may be concealing habits that we can hardly approve. There are some which feed on their smaller and weaker neighbors, and even on the members of their own families. We know that such things go on in nature, but if we wish to have a happy family we must keep the cannibals by themselves.

After an aquarium has been filled with water and the inhabitants well established, it is not necessary to change the water, except in case of accident. The water that is lost by evaporation has to be replaced. It should be poured in gently in order not to disturb the water and destroy its clearness. If a piece of rubber tubing is available, a practical use of the siphon can be shown and the aquarium replenished at the same time. It is a good plan to use rain water, or clear water from a pond, for this purpose.

A piece of thin board or a pane of glass may be used as a cover to keep the dust out of the aquarium. This need not fit tightly or be left on all the time. A wire netting or a cover of thin cotton net would keep the flying insects from escaping, and it might be tied on permanently. Dust may be skimmed off the top of the water or may be removed by laying pieces of blotting paper on the surface for a moment.

If any of the inhabitants do not take kindly to the life in the aquarium, they can be taken out and kept in a jar by themselves — a sort of fresh air and cold water cure. If any chance to die they ought to be removed before they make the water unfit for the others. Bits of charcoal in the water are helpful if a deodorizer or disinfectant is needed.

Fig. 57. A home-made aquarium.

Experience, the dear but thorough teacher, is of more value to every one of us than many rules and precepts. Nothing can rob us of the pleasure that comes of finding things out for ourselves. Much of the fun as well as much of the success in life comes from overcoming its difficulties. One must have a large store of patience and courage and hopefulness to undertake the care of an aquarium. After it is once made it is less trouble to take care of than a canary or a pet rabbit. But most things that are worth doing require patience, courage and hopefulness, and if we can add to our store of any of these by our study of life in an aquarium we are so much the better for it.

Two kinds of aquaria will be found useful in any school. Permanent ones — those which are expected to continue through a season or through a whole year if the school-room is warm enough to prevent freezing ; and temporary ones — those which are for lesson hours or for the study of special forms.

If some one phase in the life of any aquatic animal is to be studied during a short period, it is well to have special temporary aquaria. Also, when a talk on some of the occupants of the larger aquarium is to be given, specimens may be placed in small vessels for the time being and returned later. For such purposes glass tumblers can be used, or small fruit jars, finger bowls, broken goblets set in blocks of wood, ordinary white bowls or dishes, tubs, pails or tanks for large fishes, — in fact any wide-mouthed vessel which is easy to get. Special suggestions will be made in connection with the study of some of the water insects and others.

A permanent aquarium need not be an expensive affair. The rectangular ones are best if large fishes are to be kept, yet they are not essential. Here, again, it is easier to write directions for the construction of a perfect aquarium than it is for the most patient teacher, with the help of the boys who are handy with tools, to put together a box of wood and glass that will not spring a leak some day and spoil everything. But failures do not discourage us ; they make us only more determined. If a rectangular water-tight box is out of the question, what is the next best thing ? One of the busiest laboratories in New York State has plants and animals living in jars of all shapes and sizes, — fruit jars, glass butter jars, candy jars, battery jars, museum jars, and others of like nature. There are rectangular and round aquaria of various sizes kept by all firms who deal in laboratory supplies, and if some money is to be spent, one of these is a good investment. Fig. 56 shows one of these rectangular ones, and Fig. 57 shows a round one of small size which is useful and does not cost much.

A GOOD SCHOOL AQUARIUM.

A cheap, substantial aquarium for general use may be made of glass and "angle" or "valley" tin. Pieces of glass are always handy and the tin can be had at any tin-shop. The tinsmith will know just how to cut, "angle" and solder it.

The following directions for making an aquarium of this kind are supplied us by Professor C. F. Hodge of Clark University. He has made and used them for years with great satisfaction in the university laboratory and in graded schools.

10

The illustration (Fig. 58, 59) shows various sizes. A good all-round size has these dimensions : 12 inches high, 15 inches long and 8 inches wide. One may use spoiled photographic plates for small desk aquaria, in which to watch the development of "wigglers," dragon-fly nymphs or other water insects. Lids of wire screen are shown on some of the aquaria in the picture (1, 2 and 3).

To make the frame.— If the aquarium is to be 10 x 8 x 5 inches, we shall need two pieces of glass for sides 10 x 5 inches, two for ends 8 x 10, and one for bottom 8 x 5 ; and two strips of tin ¾ inch wide, 28 inches long, and four strips 10⅜ inches long. These should be angled by the tinner, and out of them we shall make the frame. The 28-inch strips should be cut with tinner's snips

Figs. 58, 59. Permanent aquarium made of tin and glass.

half way in two at 10⅜, 5⅜, 10⅜ and 5⅜ inches, cutting off the end at the last mark. This keeps the top and the bottom of the frame each in one piece. Next we bend them into shape. When the corners are well squared they should be soldered. The four 10⅜ pieces make the vertical corners and we will solder them in place. An easy way to be sure that each angle is square is to hold it in a mechanic's square while soldering it.

To set the glass.— Lay the aquarium cement (see recipe) on evenly all around the bottom of the frame and press the bottom glass into place. Put in the sides and ends in the same way. Next carefully put a few very limber twigs into the aquarium to hold the glass against the frame till the cement takes hold. Cut off the extra cement with a knife and smooth it nicely. Cover the frame with asphaltum varnish or black lacquer. In a week it will be ready to use.

Double thick glass must be used for large aquaria.

Cement.— Shun all resinous cements that require to be put on hot. The following is a recipe for cement used in successful angle tin aquaria, for both salt and fresh water :

> 10 parts, by measure, fine, dry, white sand,
> 10 parts plaster of Paris,
> 10 parts litharge,
> 1 part powdered resin.

Stir well together and, as wanted, mix to consistency of *stiff* putty with *pure* boiled linseed oil.

The formula given by the U. S. Fish Commission is recommended:

> 8 parts putty,
> 1 part red lead,
> 1 part litharge.

Mix, when wanted, to consistency of *stiff* putty, with raw linseed oil.

After reading all these directions and getting the idea of an aquarium, one should think the whole matter out for himself and make it just as he wants it. Directions are useful as suggestions only. The shallow form is better for raising toads, frogs and insect larvæ ; the deeper aquaria show water plants and fishes to better advantage.

Inhabitants of the Aquarium.

It is now time to begin to think about what shall be kept in the aquarium. At the bottom a layer of sand, the cleaner the better, two or three inches deep will be needed. A few stones, not too large, may be dropped in on top of this first layer, to make it more natural. The water plants come next and will thrive best if planted securely in the sand. The most difficult thing is to get the water in without stirring things up. A good way is to pour the water in a slow stream against the inside of the aquarium. The best way is to use a rubber tube siphon, but even then the water ought not to flow from a very great height. If the aquarium is large, it had better be put in its permanent place before filling.

Fig. 60. Eel-grass.

The aquarium will soon be ready for snails, polliwogs, and what ever else we may wish to put into it. In the course of a few days the plants will be giving up oxygen and asking for carbon dioxid.

Plants that thrive and are useful in aquaria.— Many of the common marsh or pond plants are suitable. The accompanying illustrations show a few of these. Nothing can be prettier than some of these soft, delicate plants in the water. The eel-grass, or tape grass (Fig. 60), is an interesting study in itself, especially at blossoming time when the spiral stems, bearing flowers, appear.

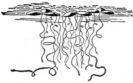

Fig. 61.   Duck-weed.

Any who are especially interested in the life-history of this plant may read in reference books a great deal about what other observers have learned from the plant concerning its methods of growth and development. The best that we learn will be what the plant itself tells us day by day.

Some of the best reference books on both plant and animal life are found in the New York State Teachers' Library and can be obtained by teachers through the school commissioners.

Every boy and girl who likes to taste the fresh, peppery plants which they find growing in cold springs, knows watercress. If the aquarium is not too deep, this plant will grow above the surface

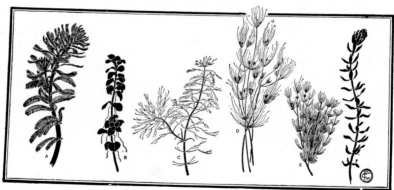

Fig. 62.   Water plants.

and furnish a resting place for some snail which, tired perhaps by its constant activity, enjoys a few minutes in the open air.

Duck-weed or duck's-meat (Fig 61) grows on the surface, dangling its long thread-like roots in the water. A little of it is enough. Too much would keep us from looking down upon our little friends in the water.

The parrot's feather (Fig. 62, A) is an ornamental water plant that can be obtained from a florist; a plant that looks very like it grows in our ponds. It is called water-milfoil.

The water purslane, B, or the common stoneworts, *Nitella* and *Chara*, D, E, the waterweed, F, and the horn-wort, C, appear graceful and pretty in the water. If you do not find any of these, you are sure to find others growing in the ponds in your neighborhood which will answer the purpose just as well.

Animals that may be kept in aquaria.— The snail. The common pond snail with the spiral shell, either flat or conical, can be found clinging to the stems of the cat-tails or flags and to floating rubbish in ponds or swamps. If these are picked off carefully and taken home in a pail of water they will be valuable inhabitants for the aquarium. They are vegetable feeders and unless there is some green slime in the water, cabbage or lettuce leaves may be put where the snails can get them. The eggs of the snail are

Fig. 63. Snail.

excellent food for fishes, and if a few could be secured for special study, their form, habits and development may be made delightful observation and drawing lessons. Snails can be kept out of the water for some time on moist earth. Land snails and slugs should be kept on wet sand and fed with lettuce and cabbage leaves. The common slug of the garden is often injurious to vegetation. It may always be tracked by the trail of slime it leaves behind it. Gardeners often protect plants from those creatures by sprinkling wood-ashes about them.

Minnows. Every boy knows where to find these spry little fellows. They can be collected with a dipper or net and will thrive in an aquarium if fed

Fig. 64. Snail with conical shell.

with earth worms or flies or other insects. If kept in small quarters where food is scarce, they will soon dispatch the other occupants of the jar. They will, however, eat bits of fresh meat. If the aquarium is large enough, it would hardly be complete without minnows.

Cat fish.—It will not be practicable to keep a cat fish in the permanent aquarium. If one is to be studied it can be obtained at any fish market or by angling, the latter a slow method, but one which will appeal to every boy in the class. The cat fish should be kept in a tub, tank, or large pan of water, and if not wanted for laboratory work, they might be fried for lunch, as cat fish are very good eating.

Gold fish are a special delight if kept in large aquaria. These may often be obtained from dealers in the larger cities. Those who wish other fish for study should be able to get information from the New York State Fish Culturist, concerning the species that are suited to life in still water, and how to get and take care of them.

The clam.—If empty clam shells are plenty on the bank of some stream after a freshet, a supply of clams may be obtained by

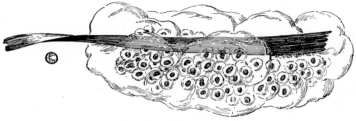

Fig. 65.   "Frog spawn."

raking the mud or sand at the bottom of the stream. They can be kept in a shallow pan, and if the water is warmish and they are left undisturbed for a time, they will move about. If kept in a jar of damp sand they will probably bury themselves. They feed on microscopic plants and might not thrive in the permanent aquarium.

Crawfish or crayfish.—These can be collected with nets from under stones in creeks or ponds. They can live very comfortably out of the water part of the time. There is small chance for the unsuspecting snail or water insect which comes within reach of the hungry jaws of the crawfish, and the temporary aquarium is the safest place for him. Many who live near the ocean can obtain and keep in sea water the lobster, a cousin of the crawfish, and will find that the habits of either will afford much amusement as well as instruction. The school boy generally knows the crawfish as a "crab."

The frog.—The study of the development of the common frog

is accompanied with little or no difficulty. To be sure there are some species which require two or three years to complete their growth and changes, from the egg to the adult, yet most of the changes can be seen in one year. Frogs are not at all shy in the spring, proclaiming their whereabouts in no uncertain tones from every pond in the neigh-

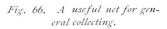

Fig. 66. *A useful net for general collecting.*

borhood. The "frog spawn" can be found clinging to plants or rubbish in masses varying in size from a cluster of two or three eggs to great lumps as large as the two fists. The "spawn" is a transparent jelly in which the eggs are imbedded. Each egg is dark colored, spherical in shape, and about as large as a small pea. The eggs of the small spotted salamander are found in similar masses of jelly and look very much like the frog's eggs. If a small quantity of this jelly-like mass be secured by means of a collecting net or by wading in for it, it may be kept in a flat white dish with just enough clean, cool water to cover it, until the young tadpoles have hatched. As they grow larger a few may be transferred to a permanent aquarium prepared especially for them in a dish with sloping sides, and their changes watched from week to week through the season. The growing polliwog feeds on vegetable diet; what does the full grown frog eat?

Fig. 67. *The predaceous diving-beetle.*

Insects that can be kept in aquaria.— Insects are to many the most satisfactory creatures that can be keep in aquaria. They are plentiful, easy to get, each one of the many kinds seems to have habits peculiar to itself, and each more curious and interesting than the last.

Some insects spend their entire life in the water; others are aquatic during one stage of their existence only. Those described here are a few of the common ones in ponds and sluggish streams, of the central part of the state of New York. If these cannot be found, others just as interesting may be kept instead. One can hardly make a single dip with a net without bringing out of their hiding places many of these "little people."

The predaceous diving-beetle (Fig. 67) is well named. He is a diver by profession and is a skilled one. The young of this beetle are known as "water-tigers" (Fig. 68), and their habits justify the name. Their food consists of the young of other insects ; in fact it is better to keep them by themselves unless we wish to have the aquarium depopulated. When the tiger has reached his full size, his form changes and he rests for a time as a pupa ; then comes forth as a hard, shiny beetle like Fig. 67.

The water-scavenger beetle (Fig. 69), so called because of its appetite for decayed matter, is common in many ponds. It has, like the diving beetle, a hard, shiny back, with a straight line down the middle, but the two can be distinguished when

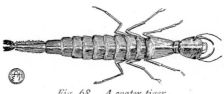

Fig. 68. A water-tiger.

seen together. The young of this beetle look and act something like the water-tigers, but have not such great ugly jaws.

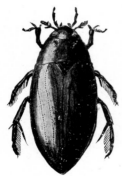

Fig. 69. A water-scavenger beetle.

There are three other swimmers even more delightful to watch than those already mentioned. The water-boatmen (Fig. 70), with their sturdy oar-like legs and business-like way of using them, are droll little fellows. They are not so large as the back-swimmers. Fig. 71 shows a back-swimmer just in the act of pulling a stroke. These creatures swim with their boat-shaped backs down and their six legs up. We must be careful how we handle the back-swimmers, for each one of them carries a sharp bill and may give us a thrust with it which would be painful, perhaps poisonous.

The water-scorpion (Fig. 72) is a queer creature living in a neighborly way with the boatmen and back-swimmers, though not so easy to find. Do not throw away any dirty little twig which you find in the net after a dip among water plants near the bottom of a stream or pond. It may begin to squirm and reveal the fact that it is no twig but a slender-legged insect with a spindle-shaped body. We may handle it without danger, as it is harmless. This

Fig. 70. Water-boatman.

is a water-scorpion, and his way of catching his prey and getting his air supply will be interesting to watch. He is not shy and will

answer questions about himself promptly and cheerfully. Fig. 72 will give an idea of the size and appearance of this insect.

No water insect except the big scavenger beetle can begin to compare in size with the giant water-bug (Fig. 73). We may think at first that he is a beetle, yet the way he

Fig. 71. A back-swimmer.

crosses his wings on his back proves him a true bug. In quiet ponds these giants are common enough, but the boy or girl who "bags" a full-grown one at the first dip of the net may be considered lucky.

The b o a t m e n, back-swimmers and giants all have oars, yet are not entirely dependent on them. They have strong wings, too, and if their old home gets too

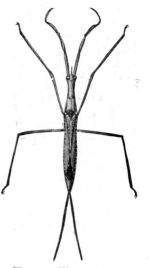

Fig. 72. Water-scorpion.

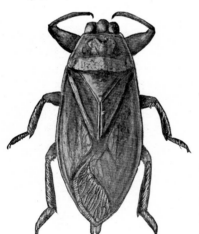

Fig. 73. Giant water-bug.

thickly settled, and the other insects on which they feed are scarce, they fly away to other places. The giant water-bug often migrates at night, and is attracted to any bright light he sees in his journey. This habit has given him the popular name of "electric-light bug."

Among the insects which spend but part of their life in the water, we shall find many surprises. It made us feel queer when we learned that the restless but innocent-looking wiggler of the rain-water barrel was really the young of the too familiar mosquito.

The adult mosquito leaves its eggs in tiny boat-shaped masses on
the surface of stagnant water, where food will be abundant for the
young which soon appear. Some time is spent by the wigglers
in eating and growing before they curl up into pupæ. Insects are
rarely active in the pupa stage. The mosquito is one of the very
few exceptions. From these lively pupæ the full-grown mosquitoes emerge. Fig. 74 shows a small
glass tumbler in which are seen the three
aquatic stages of the mosquito's life
and an adult just leaving the pupa
skin. Nothing is easier than to watch
the entire development of the mosquito,
and the changes must be seen to be
fully enjoyed and appreciated. It would
be interesting to note the differences
between the mosquitoes that come out
of the small aquaria. A supply of
wigglers may be kept in the permanent
aquarium where they serve as food for
the other insects.

Fig. 74. *Temporary aqua-
rium, containing eggs, larvæ and pupæ of mosquito.*

Every child knows the dragon-fly or
darning-needle, and none but the
bravest of them dare venture near one
without covering ears or eyes or mouth,
for fear of being sewed. Many and
wide-spread are the superstitions con-
cerning this insect, and it is often difficult to bring children to
believe that this creature, besides being a thing of beauty, is not
only harmless but actually beneficial. If they knew how many
mosquitos the darning-needle eats in a day they would welcome
instead of fearing the gay creature.

The young of the dragon-fly live a groveling existence, as different as can be from that of their sun-loving parents. Their food
consists of mosquito larvæ, water-fleas and the like, and their
method of catching their prey is as novel as it is effective. Pupils
and teacher can get plenty of good healthy entertainment out of
the behavior of these awkward and voracious little mask-wearers.
The first dip of the net usually brings up a supply of dragon-fly
nymphs and of their more slender cousins, the damsel-fly nymphs.
The latter have expanded plate-like appendages at the hind end
of the body which distinguish them from the dragon-fly nymphs.

The transformation of one of these young insects into an adult is one of the most interesting observation lessons that can be imagined for a warm spring morning. If a dragon-fly nymph should signify its intention of changing its form in my school-room, I should certainly suspend all ordinary work and attend to him alone. Each child should see if possible this wonderful transfiguration.

Floating in the water of a pond or stream one may find a little bundle of grass or weed stems, with perhaps a tiny pebble clinging to the mass. Close examination will prove this to be the "house-boat" of one of our insect neighbors, the caddice-worm. Contrasting strangely with the untidy exterior is the neat interior, with its lining of delicate silk, so smooth that the soft-bodied creature which lives

Fig. 75.   The life history of a dragon-fly as seen in an aquarium.

inside is safe from injury. The commonest of the many forms of houses found here are those illustrated in Figs. 76 and 77. These

Fig. 76.   Case of caddice-worm.

*Fig. 77. An-
other caddice-
worm case.*

Fig. 78.   Caddice-fly.

will find all they wish to eat in a well-stocked aquarium. When full grown they will leave the water as winged creatures, like Fig. 78, and return to its depths no more.

There is surely no lack of material furnished by Mother Nature for the study of aquatic life. Every one who really believes in its usefulness can have an aquarium, and will feel well repaid for the time and effort required when the renewed interest in nature is witnessed which this close contact with living beings brings to every student. Let us take hold with a will, overcome the difficulties in the way, and teacher and pupils become students together.

LEAFLET XIII.

A STUDY OF FISHES.*

By H. D. REED.

HE first forms of animal life which attract the young naturalist's attention are doubtless the birds. These are most interesting to him because of their beautiful colors, their sweet songs, and the grace with which they fly. But who has watched the fishes in a brook or an aquarium and is not able to grant them a place, in beauty, grace and delicate coloration, equal to the birds? To be sure, fishes cannot sing, yet there are so many other interesting facts in connection with their habits and life-histories that it fully makes up for their lack of voice.

THE PARTS OF A FISH.

While observing a living fish and admiring its beauty, it will probably occur to some of us that a fish consists only of a head and tail. Yet this is not all. Between the head and tail is a part that we may call the trunk. It contains the digestive and other organs. There is no indication of a neck in a fish. Any such constriction would destroy the regular outline of the animal's body and thus retard the speed with which it moves through the water. But head, trunk and tail are not all. There are attached to the outer side of the fish's body certain appendages that are called fins.

Before discussing some of the different kinds of fishes and their habits, it will be necessary to learn something about fins, for the fins of all fishes are not alike. When a fish moves through the water, it bends its tail first to one side and then to the other. This undulatory movement, as it is called, pushes the fish's body ahead. One can observe the movements easily upon a specimen kept alive in an aquarium jar. At the extreme end of the tail

---

* Nature-Study Quarterly, No. 8: Leaflet 21. January, 1901.

there is a broad, notched fin which aids the tail in propelling and steering the body. We will call this the *tail* or *caudal* fin (Fig. 79 B). In most of our common fishes there are seven fins — six without the caudal. The first of these six is a large fin situated near the middle of the back. This is the *back* or *dorsal* fin (Fig. 79 A). Sometimes we may find a fish that has two dorsal fins. In this case the one nearest the head is called first dorsal and the next one behind it the second dorsal. Near the head, in a position corresponding to our arms, is a pair of fins which are called the *arm* or *pectoral* fins (Fig. 79 E). Farther back towards the tail, on the under side of the fish, is another pair, correspond-

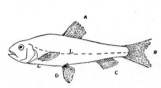

Fig. 79. Diagram of a fish to show : A, dorsal fin ; B, caudal fin ; C, anal fin ; D, pelvic fins ; E, pectoral fins ; L, lateral line.

ing in position to the hind legs of a quadruped. This pair is called the *leg* or *pelvic* fins (Fig. 79 D). Just behind the pelvic fins is a single fin, situated on the middle line of the body. This is the *anal* fin (Fig. 79 C). The pectoral and pelvic fins are called paired fins because they are in pairs. The others which are not in pairs are called median fins, because they are situated on the mid-

dle line of the body. The paired fins serve as delicate balancers to keep the body right side up and to regulate speed. They are also used to propel the body backwards. After naming the different fins of the fish in the schoolroom aquarium, it will be interesting to observe the uses of each.

On the side of the body, extending from the head to the caudal fin, is, in most fishes, a line made up of a series of small tubes which open upon the surface. This is called the *lateral line*, and acts in the capacity of a sense organ (Fig. 79 L). Is the lateral line straight or curved? Does it curve upwards or downwards? Does the curvature differ in different kinds of fishes? Do all the fishes you find possess a lateral line? Is the lateral line complete in all fishes, *i. e.*, does it extend from the head to the caudal fin without a single break?

WHERE FISHES SPEND THE WINTER.

As winter approaches and the leaves fall and the ground becomes frozen, the birds leave us and go farther south into warmer climates where food is more abundant. We are all familiar with this habit of the birds, but how many of us know or have even wondered what the fishes have been doing through the cold winter months while the streams and ponds have been covered with ice? Before the warmth of spring comes to raise the temperature of the streams, let us go to some familiar place in a brook where, during the summer, are to be found scores of minnows. None are to be found now. The brook shows no signs of ever having contained any living creatures. Suppose we go farther up or down the stream until we find a protected pool

Fig. 80. 1. Shiner ; 2, Barred Killifish ; 3, Black-nosed Dace ; 4, Creek Chub ; 5, Young of Large-mouthed Black Bass ; 6, Varying-toothed Minnow.

the bottom of which is covered with sediment and water-soaked leaves. With our net we will dip up some of the leaves and sediment, being sure that we dip from the very bottom. On looking over this mass of muddy material we may find a fish two or three inches long, with very fine scales, a black back, a silvery belly and a blackish or brown band on the side of the body extending from the tip of the nose to the tail. This is the *Black-nosed Dace* (Fig. 80). If specimens of this fish are caught very early in the

spring, one will be able to watch some interesting color changes.
As the spawning time approaches, the dark band on the sides and
the fins change to a bright crimson. Sometimes the whole body
may be of this gaudy color. During the summer the lateral band
becomes orange. As the season goes, the bright colors gradually
fade until finally, in the fall and winter, the little black-nose is
again clothed in his more modest attire. A great many of the
fishes, and especially the larger ones, seek some deep pond or
pool in the stream at the approach of winter, and remain near the
bottom. If the pond or stream is so deep that they do not become
chilled they will remain active, swimming about and taking food

Fig. 81. The Common Catfish or Bullhead.

all winter. But when the stream is very shallow and the fishes
feel the cold, they settle down to the bottom, moving about very
little and taking little or no food. The carp collect in small numbers and pass the winter in excavations that they make in the
muddy bottom. If the débris thrown up by the water across the
marshy end of a lake be raked over during the winter, one will
probably find some of the smaller catfishes spending the season in
a semi-dormant state.

Some interesting experiments may be tried with the fishes in
the aquarium jar. Keep them for a few days where it is cold and
then bring them into a warmer room and note the difference in
their activity.

THE COMMON CATFISH OR BULLHEAD.

This sleepy old fellow differs in many respects from most of our common fishes. He has no scales. About the mouth are eight long whisker-like appendages, called barbels (Fig. 81). Perhaps he is called catfish because he has whiskers about his mouth like a cat. Any one who has ever taken a catfish from the hook probably knows that care is needed in order not to receive a painful prick from the sharp spines in his pectoral and dorsal fins.

There is nothing aristocratic about the catfish. In warm pools and streams where the water is sluggish and the muddy bottom is covered with weeds, he may be found moving lazily about in search of food. His taste is not delicate. Animal substance, whether living or dead, satisfies him. When in search of food he makes good use of his barbels, especially those at the corners of his mouth, which he uses as feelers. The catfish will live longer out of water than most of our other food fishes. They will live and thrive in water which is far too impure for "pumpkin seeds" or bass. They spawn late in the spring. The mother fish cares for her young much as a hen cares for her chickens. When they are old enough to take care of themselves, she weans them.

THE COMMON SUNFISH OR PUMPKIN SEED.

Some evening just at sunset visit a quiet pool in a nearby stream. Drop in your hook baited with an "angle worm" and presently the dancing cork shows that you have a "bite." On "pulling up" you find that you really have a fish. It is a beautiful creature, too — thin flat body shaped something like the seed of a pumpkin. His back is an olive green delicately shaded with blue. His sides are spotted with orange, while his belly is a bright yellow. His cheeks are orange-color streaked with wavy lines of blue. Just behind his eye on his "ear-flap" is a bright scarlet spot. This is the common *Sunfish*

Fig. 82. The common Sunfish or Pumpkin Seed.

or *Pumpkin Seed* (Fig. 82). He is a very beautiful, aristocratic little fellow, "looking like a brilliant coin fresh from the mint."

Keep him alive in an aquarium jar with a shiner. Compare the two fishes, as to the size and shape of their bodies and fins. Feed them different kinds of food, such as worms, insects and crackers, and try to discover which they like best and how they eat.

The sunfishes prefer quiet waters. They lay their eggs in the spring of the year. The male selects a spot near the banks of the stream or pond where the water is very shallow. Here he clears a circular area about a foot in diameter. After making a slight excavation in the gravel or sand, the nest is completed. The eggs are then deposited by the female in the basin-like excavation. He watches his nest and eggs with great diligence, driving away other fishes that chance to come near.

THE BLACK BASSES.

The black basses are not usually found in small streams where it is most pleasant for teachers and pupils to fish. They are fishes that seek the rivers and lakes. There are two kinds of black bass, the *Large-mouthed* and the *Small-mouthed.* As the name indicates, the two may be distinguished by the size of the mouth. In the large-mouthed black bass the upper jaw extends to a point behind the eye, while in the small-mouthed species it extends to a point just below the middle of the eye (Fig. 83).

Fig. 83. Adult Small-mouthed Black Bass.

Both kinds of black bass may be found in the same body of water. The character of the bottoms over which they are found, however, differs. The small-mouthed prefers the stony bars or shoals. The large-mouthed, on the contrary, selects a muddy bottom grown over with reeds. They feed upon crayfish ("crabs"), minnows, frogs, worms, tadpoles and insects. Our black basses are very queer parents. They prepare a nest in which the eggs are deposited. Both male and female are very courageous in the defense of their eggs and young. As soon as the young fishes are able to take care of themselves the parent fishes leave them, and after that time may even feed upon their own children.

THE STICKLEBACK.

The sticklebacks are queer little fellows indeed (Fig. 84). The slender body, extremely narrow tail, and the sharp, free spines in front of the dorsal fin, give them at once the appearance of being both active and pugnacious little creatures. The stickle-

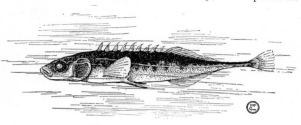

Fig. 84. A Stickleback.

backs are detrimental to the increase of other fishes since they greedily destroy the spawn and young of all fishes that come within their reach. They build nests about two inches in diameter, with a hole in the top. After the eggs are laid the male defends the nest with great bravery. The little five-spined brook stickleback in the Cayuga Lake basin, N. Y., is most commonly found in stagnant pools, shaded by trees, where the water is filled with decaying vegetable matter,— the so-called "green frog-spawn" (spirogyra), and duck weed. If you supply the stickle-backs with plenty of fine vegetable material, you may induce them to built a nest in the aquarium jar, but they must be caught and placed in the jar early in the season before they spawn.

THE JOHNNY DARTERS.

In New York State, every swift stream which has a bed of gravel and flat stones ought to contain some one of the Johnny darters, for there are a great many different kinds (Fig. 85). They are little creatures, delighting in clear water and swift currents where they dart about, hiding under stones and leaves, or resting on the bottom with their heads up-stream. The body of a darter is compact and spindle-shaped, gradually tapering from the short head to a narrow tail. The eyes are situated nearly on top of the head. The color of the darters varies greatly with the different kinds. Some are very plain, the light ground color being broken only by a few brown markings. Others are gorgeous in their colorings, it seeming as if they had attempted to reproduce the rainbow on their sides. Such kinds are indeed very attractive and are ranked with the most beautifully colored of all our common fishes. When a darter swims, he appears bird-like, for he flies through the water much as a bird flies through the air. He does not use his tail alone in swimming, as the catfish, the sunfish, the stickleback, and most of the other fishes do, but flies with his pectoral fins.

You surely must have a Johnny darter in your aquarium jar. The Johnnies are true American fishes. Though small, they face the strong currents and eke out a living where their larger cousin, the yellow perch, would perish. There are many interesting facts

Fig. 85.   A Johnny Darter.

which may be learned from the Johnny darters when kept alive in an aquarium. When not actually moving in the water, do the Johnnies rest on the bottom of the jar or remain suspended in the middle apparently resting on nothing, as the other aquarium fishes do? When a fish remains still in the middle of the jar he does so because he has a well-developed air-bladder to help buoy him up, and when a fish dies it is the air-bladder which causes him to turn over and rise to the top. Now if the Johnnies always rest on the bottom of the jar when not swimming and if one happens to die and does not rise to the top we may know that, if he has an air-bladder at all, it is only a vestigial one. It would be interesting also to find out for ourselves whether a Johnny darter can really "climb trees" (I mean by trees, of course, the water plants in the aquarium jar), or if he can perch upon the branches like a bird.

THE MINNOWS.

All the small fishes of the brooks are called minnows, or more often "minnies," by the boy fisherman. The boy believes that they grow into larger fishes. This is not true. The minnows are a distinct group of fishes and, for the most part, small ones. They do not grow to be bass or pike or sunfishes or anything else but minnows. Some of the minnows, however, are comparatively large. Two of these are the *Creek Chub* (Fig. 80), and the *Shiner* (Fig. 80). The chub is the king of the small brooks, being often the largest and most voracious fish found in such streams. His common diet probably consists of insects and worms, but if very hungry he does not object to eating a smaller fish. During the spawning season, which is springtime, the male chub has sharp, horny tubercles or spines developed upon the snout. We are able to recognize the creek chub by means of a black spot at the front of the base of the dorsal fin.

Fig. 86. A convenient form of aquarium jar supplied with water plants. The bottom is covered with clean sand and flat stones.

The shiner or red-fin has much larger scales than the chub. The back is elevated in front of the dorsal fin, giving him the appearance of a hump-back. His sides are a steel-blue with silvery reflections. While the shiner is not the largest, it is almost everywhere one of the most abundant brook fishes. In spring the lower fins of the male become reddish. Like the chub, he has small horny tubercles developed on the snout.

RANDOM NOTES.

Did you ever see a fish yawn? Watch a shiner in your aquarium. Sometimes you may see him open his mouth widely as though he was very sleepy. Again you may find him resting on the bottom of the jar taking a nap. Fishes cannot close their eyes when they sleep for they have no eyelids.

A convenient way to collect fishes for the schoolroom aquarium is to use a dip net. The ordinary insect net will do, but it is better to replace the cheese-cloth bag by a double thickness of mosquito-bar, thus enabling one to move the net through the water more rapidly. By dipping in the deep pools, among grasses 'and under the banks with such a net one can soon obtain fishes enough to stock an aquarium (Fig. 86). The aquarium jar should never be placed in the sun. It is better to have only three or four fishes in an aquarium at one time. Some flat stones on the bottom of the jar will afford them convenient hiding places.

For further notes on aquaria, consult Leaflet No. XII.

LEAFLET XIV.

THE OPENING OF A COCOON.*

By MARY ROGERS MILLER.

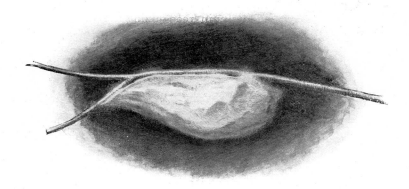

MONG the commonest treasures brought into the schools by children in the fall or winter are the cocoons of our giant silk-worms. If one has a place to put them where the air is not too warm or dry, no special care will be necessary to keep them through the winter. Out-door conditions must be imitated as nearly as possible. If early in the fall one is fortunate enough to meet one of these giants out for a walk, it is the simplest thing in the world to capture him and watch him spin his marvelous winter blanket. Two members of this family of giant insects are quite common in this state, the largest the Cecropia, called sometimes the Emperor, and the Promethea.

Fig. 87. Cocoon of the Cecropia moth. It sometimes hangs from a twig of a fruit tree.

The Cecropia moth often measures five or six inches across — a veritable giant. Its main color is dusty brown, with spots and

---

*Nature-Study Quarterly, No. 4 : Leaflet 17. March, 1900.

bands of cinnamon brown and white. On each wing is a white crescent bordered with red and outlined with a black line. The body is heavy and covered with thick, reddish-brown hairs, crossed near the end with black and white lines. On its small head are two large feathery feelers or antennæ. The Cecropia moth emerges from the cocoon, full grown, in early summer, when out of doors. Those kept in the house often come out as early as March. The eggs are deposited by the adults upon apple, pear, cherry, maple and other shade and fruit trees. Professor Comstock says that the spiny caterpillars which hatch from the eggs in about two weeks, are known to feed upon the leaves of some fifty species of plants. One could therefore hardly make a mistake in offering refreshment to these creatures, since they are anything but epi-

Fig. 88. End of cocoon of Cecropia, inside view, showing where the moth gets out.

cures. The full-grown caterpillar, having spent the summer eating and growing, with now and then a change of clothes, is often three inches long and an inch in diameter. It is a dull bluish green in color. On its back are two rows of wart-like protuber- ances (tubercles), some yellow, some red, some blue. As there is nothing else in na- ture which is just like it, one need have no difficulty in recognizing the Cecropia in its different phases.

The cocoon which this giant silk-worm weaves is shown in Fig. 87. It may be found on a twig of some tree in the dooryard, but sometimes on a fence-post or equally unexpected place. Inside the cocoon the brown pupa, alive but helpless, waits for spring.

After the moth comes out it is interesting to examine the struc- ture of the cocoon, and to discover how the moth managed to free itself without destroying the silken blanket (Fig. 88).

Swinging loosely from last summer's twigs in lilac bushes, and on such trees as wild cherry and ash, one often finds the slender cocoons of the Promethea moth (Fig. 89). We cannot help admir- ing the skill and care displayed by the spinner of this tidy winter overcoat. The giant silk-worm which spun it chose a leaf as a foundation. He took care to secure himself against the danger of falling by fastening the leaf to the twig which bore it by means of shining strands of silk. It is easy to test the strength of this fastening by attempting to pull it loose from the twig.

The moths which come from these cocoons do not always look alike, yet they are all brothers and sisters. The brothers are almost black, while the wings of the sisters are light reddish brown, with a light gray wavy line crossing the middle of both wings. The margins of the wings are clay-colored. On each wing is a dark velvety spot. The adults emerge in spring and are most often seen in the late afternoon. Their flight is more spirited than that of the Cecropia, which moves very sedately, as becomes a giant.

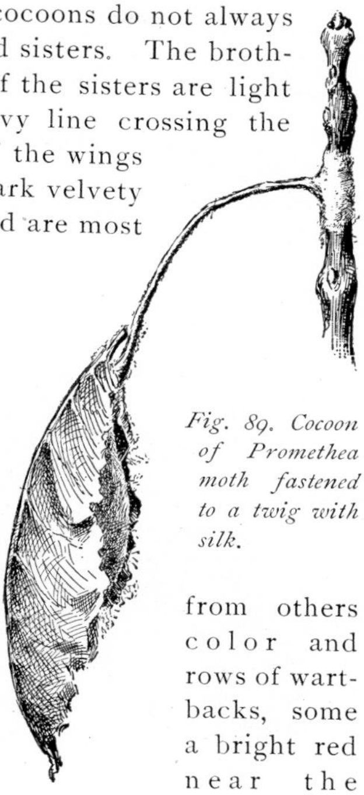

The caterpillars of this species, the young Prometheas, feed during the summer on leaves of wild cherry, ash and other trees. They grow to be about two inches long, and are distinguished by their pale bluish green yellow legs. They also have like elevations on their black and shining, four of and one large and yellow hindmost end.

Fig. 89. Cocoon of Promethea moth fastened to a twig with silk.

from others color and rows of wart-backs, some a bright red near the

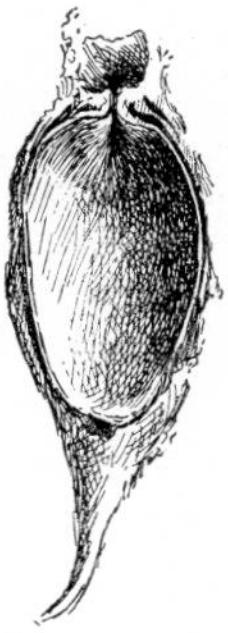

Fig. 90. Cocoon of Promethea, cut open lengthwise to show the valve-like device at upper end through which the adult moth pushes its way out.

*   *   *

The life of these giant insects is divided into four distinct stages : the egg, deposited by the adult moth usually on or near the food plant ; the larva, or caterpillar stage, when most of the eating and all the growing is done ; the pupa, passed inside the cocoon woven by the larva ; and the adult, a winged moth.

The life-cycle or generation is one year, the winter being passed in the pupa stage. The insect lives but a short time in the adult stage and the egg stage is but two or three weeks. Most of the summer is devoted to the caterpillar phase of its life.

These creatures are entirely harmless. They seldom appear in numbers sufficient to make them of economic importance.

LEAFLET XV.

A TALK ABOUT SPIDERS.*

By J. H. COMSTOCK.

 F all our little neighbors of the fields there are none that are more universally shunned and feared than spiders, and few that deserve it less. There is a wide-spread belief that spiders are dangerous, that they are liable to bite, and that their bites are very venomous. Now this may be true of certain large species that live in hot countries ; but the spiders of the Northern United States are practically harmless.

It is true, spiders bite and inject venom sufficient to kill a fly into the wound made by their jaws. But they are exceedingly shy creatures, fearing man more than they are to be feared. If an observer will refrain from picking up a spider there is not the slightest danger of being bitten by one ; and excepting a single uncommon species no spider is known in this part of the country whose bite would seriously affect a human being.

On the other hand, spiders do much to keep in check various insect pests, and hence must be regarded as our friends. It is, however, from a different point of view that we wish to look upon them at this time. It is as illustrations of remarkable development of instinctive powers, and of wonderful correlation of structure and habit, that we would have the reader study these creatures. The teacher of nature-study can find no more available or more fertile field from which to take subjects for interesting children in the world about us. Let us then put aside our fears and go into the fields and see whether we can learn something of the ways of these spinners.

THE FUNNEL-WEB WEAVERS.

Often on summer mornings the grass of the roadsides and fields is seen to be carpeted with little sheets of glistening silk, the webs of the grass-spider. None were observed the day before ; and we

* Nature-Study Quarterly, No. 9 : Leaflet 22. May, 1901.

wonder at the sudden appearance of this host of weavers. Later in the day the webs have vanished! Have the weavers rolled them up and carried them off? We remember that there was an especially fine one near the end of the veranda steps; we examine the place carefully and find that it is still there, but not so conspicuous as it was. The warm sun has dissipated the dew which rendered visible to our dull eyes the tapestry of the fields. Now that our eyes are opened we can find the webs everywhere and are impressed with a suspicion that perhaps ordinarily we see very little of what is around us.

We examine one of the webs carefully and find that it is a closely woven sheet made of threads running in all directions; that it is attached to spears of grass, and supported by numerous guy lines, and that from one side a funnel-like tube extends downwards. If, while we are watching, an insect alights on the sheet, there darts from the tunnel, where she was concealed, the owner of the web, a dark-colored spider; and the insect must be agile if it escapes.

If you attempt to catch the spider it retreats to its tunnel; and when you examine the tunnel the spider is not there. You find that the tube is open below, that there is a back door by which the spider can escape when hard pressed.

We call those spiders that makes webs of this kind *The Funnel-web Weavers*. They are long-legged, brown spiders, which run on the upper surface of their webs; these are usually made on grass, but sometimes they are found in the angles of buildings, and in quite high places.

The Cobweb Weavers.

The webs that we most often find in the corners of rooms are of a different kind and are made by the members of a family known as *The Cobweb Weavers*. In these webs there is not such a definite sheet of silk as in those of the funnel-web weavers, but instead a shapeless maze of threads extending in all directions. Many of the cobweb weavers, however, make their webs in the fields on bushes, and weave in them a flat or curved sheet, under which the spider hangs back downward. The funnel-web weavers run right side up; the cobweb weavers hang inverted. Some of the cobweb weavers do not remain in their webs, but have a nest in a neighboring crack or corner, from which they rush to seize their prey, and sometimes there is a funnel-shaped tube leading to their nest. But these spiders differ from the true funnel-web weavers in running back downwards on the lower side of their webs.

THE ORB WEAVERS.

The spider webs that most often excite admiration are those in which the supporting threads radiate from a center like the spokes of a wheel, and bear a spiral thread. Such webs are known as orb-webs ; and the family of spiders that make them, *The Orb Weavers.*

Few if any of the structures built by lower animals are more wonderful than these webs ; but they are so common that they are often considered hardly worthy of notice. If they occurred only in some remote corner of the earth, every one would read of them with interest.

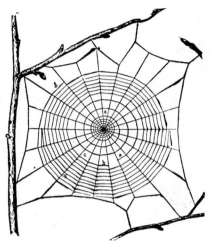

The webs or nets of the different species of orb weavers differ in the details of their structure ; but the general plan is quite similar. There

Fig. 91. Nearly completed orb-web.

is first a framework of supporting lines. The outer part of this framework is irregular, depending upon the position of the objects to which the net is attached ; but the central part is very regular, and consists of a number of lines radiating from the center of the net (Fig. 91). All of these supporting lines are dry and inelastic. Touch them with your pencil and you find that they neither stretch nor adhere to it. Upon these radiating lines there is fastened in a very regular manner a thread which is sticky and elastic. This will adhere to your pencil, and will stretch several times its normal length before breaking. Usually this sticky thread is fastened to the radiating lines so as to form a spiral ; but a few species make nets in which it is looped back and forth. And even in the nets where the greater part of the thread is in a spiral there are in most cases a few loops near the lower margin (Fig. 91). Examine the next orb-web you find and see whether it is true in that case.

Many of the orb weavers strengthen their nets by spinning a

zigzag ribbon across the center. This ribbon is made by spreading apart the spinnerets, the organs from which the silk is spun, and which will be described later. Ordinarily the tips of the spinnerets are held close together so that they form a single thread, but by spreading them apart many threads can be spun at once, thus forming a ribbon.

Some orb weavers are not content with making a simple zigzag band across the center of the net, but weave an elaborate bit of lace in this position. Fig. 92 is from a photograph of the center of the net of one of these spiders, which was found near Ithaca.

In studying the various kinds of orb-webs one should pay particular attention to the center of the web; for this part differs greatly in the webs of the different species. There is usually a *hub* composed entirely of dry and inelastic silk woven in an irregular manner; outside of this there are several turns of a spiral thread which is also dry; this constitutes the *notched zone*, a name suggested by the fact that the spiral line is attached for a short space to each radius it crosses, thus giving the line a notched course. In many cases it is here, on the hub and the notched zone, that the spider waits for its prey; and it is obvious that sticky silk in this place would be objectionable. Between the notched zone and the *spiral zone*, the part furnished with the sticky spiral thread, there is a clear space, the *free zone*, crossed only by the radii. This gives the spider an opportunity to pass from one side of the web to the other without going around the entire web.

Fig. 92. Lace-like hub of an orb-web.

Some orb weavers do not wait upon the hub but have a retreat near one edge of the net, in which they hang back downwards. While resting in these retreats they keep hold of some of the lines leading from the net, so that they can instantly detect any jar caused by an entrapped insect.

When an insect in its flight touches one of the turns of the sticky line the line adheres to it, but it stretches so as to allow the insect to become entangled in other turns of the line. If it were not for this elasticity of the sticky line, most insects could readily tear themselves away before the spider had time to reach them.

In running over its net the spider steps upon the radii, carefully avoiding the sticky line; otherwise it would destroy its own net.

The rapidity with which a spider can cross its net without touching the sticky line is remarkable.

In making its web an orb weaver first spins a number of lines extending irregularly in various directions about the place where its orb is to be ; this is the outer supporting framework. Often the first line spun is a bridge between two quite distant points, as the branches of two separate bushes. How did the spider cross the gulf? It has no wings.

The bridge building can be easily seen on a warm summer evening, the time at which the spiders are most active repairing their old nets and building new ones. The spider lifts the hind end of its body and spins forth a thread ; this is carried off by the wind, until, finally striking some object, it becomes fast to it. The spider then pulls in the slack line, like a sailor, and when the line is taut fastens it to the object on which it is standing, and the bridge is formed.

After making the outward framework, the radiating lines are formed. A line is stretched across the space

Fig. 93. Nearly completed orb-web.

so as to pass through the point which is to be the center of the orb. In doing this the spider may start on one side, and be forced to walk in a very roundabout way on the outer framework to the opposite side. It carefully holds the new line up behind it as it goes along, so that it shall not become entangled with the lines on which it walks ; one or both hind feet serve as hands in these spinning operations ; for, as the spider has eight feet, it can spare one or two for other purposes than locomotion. When the desired point is reached the slack is pulled in and the line fastened. The spider then goes to the point where the center of the orb is to be, and, fastening another line, it walks back to the outer framework, and attaches this line an inch or two from the first. In this way all of the radiating lines are drawn. The next step is to stay these

radii by a spiral line, which is begun near the center, and attached
to each radius as it crosses it. The turns of this spiral are as far
apart as the spider can conveniently reach.

All of the threads spun up to this stage in the construction of
the web are dry and inelastic. The spider now proceeds to stretch
upon this framework a sticky and elastic line, which is the most
important part of the web, the other lines being merely a framework to support it. In spinning the sticky line, the spider begins
at the outer edge of the orb, and passing around it, fastens this
line to each radius as it goes. Thus a second spiral is made. The
turns of this spiral are placed quite close together, and the first
spiral, which is merely a temporary support, is destroyed as the
second spiral progresses. Fig. 93 represents a web in which the

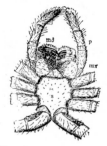

Fig. 94. Wasp, with head,
  thorax and abdomen
  separated.

Fig. 95. Spider, showing
  division of the body into
  cephalothorax and ab-
  domen.

Fig. 96. Lower side of cephalothorax of a spider ;
  md, mandible ; mx,
  maxilla ; p, palpus ; l,
  lower lip ; s, sternum.

second spiral is made over the outer half of the radii. In this
figure, *aa* represents the temporary stayline ; *bb*, the sticky spiral ;
and *cc*, the fragments of the first spiral hanging from the radii.

THE PARTS OF A SPIDER.

Spiders differ much in appearance from the true insects. In the
insects the body is composed of three regions : the head ; the
thorax, to which the legs are attached ; and the abdomen or hind
part of the body (Fig. 94). In the spiders the head and thorax
are grown together, forming a region which is known as the
cephalothorax ; to this the *abdomen* is joined by a short, narrow
stalk (Fig. 95). Spiders differ also from insects in the number of
their legs, spiders having eight legs and insects only six.

Spiders have two pairs of jaws, which, except in the Tarantula family, move sidewise like the jaws of insects. The first pair of jaws are called the *mandibles*. Each mandible consists of two segments, a strong basal one and a claw-shaped terminal one, at the tip of which the poison gland opens (Fig. 96). The second pair of jaws is known as the *maxillæ*. These jaws are situated just behind the mandibles, one on each side of the mouth. Each maxilla bears a large feeler or *palpus*. These palpi vary greatly in form ; frequently, especially in females, they resemble legs ; hence many spiders appear to have five pairs of legs. In the male spiders the last segment of the palpus is more or less enlarged, ending in a complicated, knob-like structure (Fig.

97). It is thus easy to determine the sex of a spider by merely examining the palpi.

The greater number of spiders have four pairs of eyes (Fig. 98), but there may be only one, two, or three pairs ; and certain cave spiders are blind. The eyes appear like little gems set in the front of the cephalothorax. They are most prominent in the jumping

Fig. 97. Maxilla and palpus of male house-spider.

Fig. 98. Head of spider, showing eyes and mandibles.

spiders, which stalk their prey on plants, logs, fences, and the sides of buildings.

The most characteristic feature of spiders is their spinning organs. The silk is secreted in glands within the abdomen, and while in the body it is a fluid. It passes out through the *spin-*

Fig. 99. Spinnerets of a spider.   *Fig. 100. A group of spinning tubes.*   *Fig. 101. Viscid silk from an orb-web.*   *Fig. 102. Spinnerets and cribellum of a curled-thread weaver.*

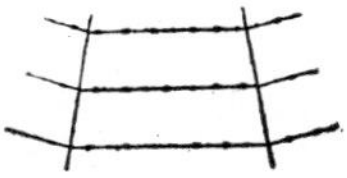

nerets, which are situated near the hind end of the abdomen. There are two or three pairs of spinnerets. These are more or less finger-like in form, and sometimes jointed (Fig. 99). Upon the end of each spinneret there are many small tubes, the *spin-*

ning tubes (Fig. 100), from which the silk is spun. Some spiders have as many as one hundred and fifty or two hundred of these spinning tubes on each spinneret.

Ordinarily the tips of the spinnerets are brought close together, so that all of the minute threads that emerge from the numerous spinning tubes unite to form a single thread. Hence this tiny thread, which is so delicate that we can see it only when the light falls on it in a favorable way, is composed of hundreds of threads. It is not like a rope, composed of separate strands; for all the minute threads fuse together into a single thread. The change in the silk from a fluid to a solid cord, strong enough to support the weight of the spider, must take place quickly after the silk comes in contact with the air on leaving the spinning tubes; the minute size of the threads coming from the spinning tubes doubtless facilitates this change.

Sometimes a spider will spread its spinnerets apart, and thus spin a broad ribbon-like band. We have seen a spider seize a large grasshopper which was entangeled in its web, and rolling it over two or three times, completely envelop it in a sheet of silk spun from its spread-apart spinnerets. We have already described bands spun by orb weavers across the hub of the net in this way.

It is supposed that the two kinds of silk spun by the orb weavers are spun from different spinnerets, and that the viscid silk comes from the front pair. When this silk is first spun, the viscid matter forms a continuous layer of liquid on the outside of it. But very soon this layer breaks up into bead-like masses — in a way similar to that in which the moisture on a clothes line on a foggy day collects into drops (Fig. 101).

There are two families of spiders that have spinning organs differing from those of all other spiders. They have in front of

the usual spinnerets an additional organ, which is named the *cribellum* (Fig. 102, c). This bears spinning tubes like the other spinnerets, but these tubes are much finer. These spiders have also on the next-to-the-last segment of the hind legs one or two rows of curved spines; this organ is the *calamistrum* (Fig. 103). By means of the calamistrum these spiders comb

Fig. 103. Last two segments of hind leg of spider, showing calamistrum.

from the cribellum a band of loose threads which form a part of their webs.

The Curled-Thread Weavers.

The spiders possessing a cribellum and a calamistrum represent two families, one of which makes irregular webs ; the other, those which are of definite form.

An irregular web of a curled-thread weaver is shown in Fig.

Fig. 104. Web of a curled-thread weaver.

104, from a photograph. In this web the framework is of ordinary silk ; and upon this framework is placed a band of curled or tangled threads (Fig. 105). An insect alighting on a net of this kind is likely to get its feet caught in the tangled silk, and to be held fast till the spider can pounce upon it. Nets of this kind are found on bushes and on the sides of buildings.

There are two quite distinct types of regular webs made by
spiders possessing a cribellum and a calamistrum.
One is a round web which resembles at first sight
those of the orb weavers ; but it differs from the
ordinary orb-web in that the spiral thread is made
of curled or hackled silk. These webs are nearly
horizontal, and are usually made between stones or
in low bushes ; they are not common.

Fig. 105. Fragment of a curled-thread weaver's web, enlarged.

The other type is represented by the web of the
triangle spider. This web is most often found stretched
between the twigs of a dead branch of pine or hemlock. At
first sight it appears like a fragment of an orb-web (Fig. 106) ;
but a little study will show that it is complete. The accompany-

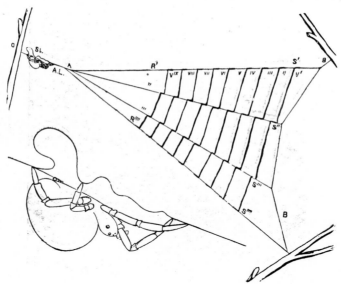

Fig. 106.　Web of the triangle spider.

ing figure, by Dr. B. G. Wilder, who first described the habits of
this spider ("Popular Science Monthly," 1875) illustrates the
form of the web. It consists of four plain lines corresponding
to the radiating lines of an orb-web, and a series of cross lines,
which are spun by the cribellum and calamistrum. Each cross
line is composed of two lines, about 1-500 of an inch apart.
These double lines take the place of the curled threads woven by

other members of the family to which the triangle spider belongs. From the point where the radiating lines meet, a strong line extends to one of the supporting twigs. Near this twig the spider rests, pulling the web tight so that there is some loose line between its legs, as shown in the enlarged figure. When an insect becomes entangled in one of the cross lines, the spider suddenly lets go the loose line so that the whole web springs forward, and the insect is entangled in other cross lines. The spider then draws the web tight and snaps it again. This may be repeated several times before the spider goes out upon the web after its prey.

The triangle spider is a tiny fellow, and so closely resembles the color of the dead branch near which it rests that it is very difficult to find ; its web is more easily seen, though it usually requires careful searching to discover it.

The Motherhood of Spiders.

As a rule young spiders are forced to shift for themselves, and a very hard time they have; but of this we have not space to write. With spiders, the mother's care is devoted chiefly to furnishing protection to her helpless eggs. These are placed in silken sacs, which are often very elaborate in construction and protected with great care.

Fig. 107. Egg-sac of a spider.

The most common egg-sacs are those found in the fields attached to stones and pieces of wood (Fig. 107). They are disk-shaped objects, silvery in color, and about the size of an old-fashioned three-cent piece.

The egg-sacs of the cobweb weavers can be found suspended in their webs ; and those of the orb weavers, in various situations. Fig. 108 represents the large egg-sac of one of the orb weavers. This is made in the autumn, and contains at that season a large number of eggs — five hundred or more. These eggs hatch early in the winter ; but no spiders emerge from the egg-sac until the following spring. If egg-sacs of this kind be opened at different times during the winter, the spiders will be found to increase in size but diminish in numbers as the season advances. In fact, a strange tragedy goes on within these egg-sacs : the stronger spiders calmly devour their weaker brothers, and in the spring those that survive emerge sufficiently nourished to fight their battles in the outside world.

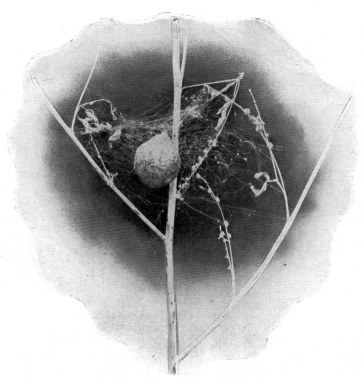

Fig. 108.   Egg-sac of an orb weaver.

The females of the *Running Spiders* not only make a carefully constructed egg-sac, but also care for the young spiders for a time. The running spiders are the large dark-colored, hairy spiders, often found under stones and rubbish;

Fig. 109.   Lycosa and egg-sac.

they are so-called because they capture their prey by running. The females of most of the species (those of the genus *Lycosa*) drag after them their egg-sac, which is attached to the spinnerets (Fig. 109) ; and when the young hatch, they climb on their mother's back, and are carried about for a time.

One of the running spiders (*Dolomedes*) carries her egg-sac with her mandibles until the young are ready to emerge. At this time the mother fastens the egg-sac in a bush, and spins irregular threads about it, among which the young spiders remain for a time (Fig. 110). In the specimen figured, the egg-sac was concealed in the upper part of the web.

The Ballooning Spiders.

In warm autumn days, innumerable threads can be seen streaming from fences, bushes, and the tips of stalks of grass, or floating through the air. These are made by the *Ballooning Spiders*, which are able to travel long distances, hundreds of miles, through the air by means of these silken threads.

The ballooning spider climbs to some elevated point, and then, standing on the tips of its feet, lifts its body as high as it can, and spins out a thread of silk. This thread is carried up and away by a current of air. When the thread is long enough the force of the air current on it is sufficient to bear the spider up. It then lets go its hold with its feet and sails away. That these spiders travel long distances in this manner has been shown by the fact that they have been seen floating through the air at sea far from land.

Fig. 110. Nursery of Dolomedes.

LEAFLET XVI.

LIFE HISTORY OF THE TOAD.*

By S. H. GAGE.†

 N account of its economic importance, and because the marvelous changes passed through in growing from an egg to a toad are so rapid that they may all be seen during a single spring term of school, the common or warty toad has been selected as the subject of a leaflet in nature-study. Toads are found everywhere in New York, and nearly everywhere in the world; it is easy, therefore, to get abundant material for study. This animal is such a good friend to the farmer, the gardener, the fruit-grower, the florist and the stock-raiser that every man and woman, every boy and girl, ought to know something about it.

Furthermore, it is hoped and sincerely believed that the feeling of repugnance and dislike, and the consequent cruelty to toads, will disappear when teachers and children learn something about their wonderful changes in form, structure and habits, and how harmless and helpful they are. Then, who that knows of the chances, the dangers and struggles in the life of the toad, can help a feeling of sympathy; for after all, how like our human life it is. Where sympathy is, cruelty is impossible, and one comes to feel the spirit of these beautiful lines from Coleridge's " Ancient Mariner: "

> " *He prayeth best who loveth best*
> *All things both great and small;*
> *For the dear God who loveth us*
> *He made and loveth all.*"

It was William Harvey, the discoverer of the circulation of the

---

* Teachers' Leaflet, No. 9, May, 1897.

† It was the desire of the author to tell the story of this leaflet in pictures as well as in words, and he wishes to express his appreciation of the enthusiasm and ability with which the illustrations were executed by Mr. C. W. Furlong.

In this edition are added half-tone reproductions of photographs to bring out more completely the life story.

blood, who first clearly stated the fact that every animal comes from an egg. This is as true of a toad as of a chicken.

The toad lives on the land and often a long way from any pond or stream, but the first part of its life is spent in the water ; and so it is in the water that the eggs must be looked for. To find the eggs one should visit the natural or artificial ponds so common along streams. Ponds from springs or even artificial reservoirs or the basins around fountains, also may contain the eggs. The time for finding the eggs depends on the season. The toad observes the season, not the almanac. In ordinary years, the best time is from the middle of April to the first of May.

One is often guided to the right place by noticing the direction from which the song or call of the toad comes. The call of the toad is more or less like that of the tree toads. In general it sounds like whistling, and at the same time pronouncing deep in the throat, bu-rr-r-r-r-. If one watches a toad while it makes its call, one can soon learn to distinguish the sound from others somewhat similar. It will be found that different toads have slightly different voices, and the same one can vary the tone considerably, so that it is not so easy after all to distinguish the many batrachian solos and choruses on a spring or summer evening. It will be noticed that the toad does not open its mouth when it sings, but, instead, the resonator or vocal sac under its mouth and throat is greatly expanded. One must be careful to distinguish the expansion of the mouth in breathing from the expansion of the vocal sac. See the left hand toad in the drawing (Fig. 111) for the vocal sac, and the toad in hibernation (Fig. 121) for the expansion of the mouth in breathing. It is only the males that possess the vocal sac, so that the toad chorus is composed solely of male voices.

The eggs are laid in long strings or ropes which are nearly always tangled and wound round the water plants or sticks on the bottom of the pond. If the pond is large and deep, the eggs are laid near the shore where the water is shallow. If the eggs have been freshly laid in clear water the egg ropes will look like glass tubes containing a string of jet black beads. After a rain the eggs are obscured by the fine mud that settles on the transparent jelly surrounding them, but the jelly is much more evident than in the freshly laid egg strings.

Secure enough of the egg string to include 50 or 100 eggs and place it in a glass fruit dish or a basin with clean water from the

Fig. 111. *The toad in various stages of development from the egg to the adult*

pond where the eggs were found. Let the children look at the
eggs very carefully and note the color and the exact shape. Let
them see whether the color is the same on all sides. If the eggs
are newly laid they will be nearly perfect spheres.

Frogs, salamanders and tree toads lay their eggs in the same
places and at about the same time as the toad we are to study.

Fig. 112. Just hatched toad tadpoles climbing up where the water is better aerated.

Only the toad lays its eggs in strings, so one can be sure he has
the right kind. The others lay their eggs in bunches or singly on
the plants, so they never need be mistaken for the ones sought.

The eggs which are taken to the school house for study should
be kept in a light place ; an east, south or west window is best.

It requires only a short time for the eggs to hatch. In warm weather two to four days are usually sufficient, but in the cool days of April it may require ten days. As the changes are so very rapid, the eggs ought to be carefully looked at two or three times a day to make sure that all the principal changes are seen. If a pocket lens or a reading glass is to be had it will add to the interest, as more of the details can be observed. But good sharp eyes are sufficient if no lens is available.

Hatching.—Watch and see how long it is before the developing embryos commence to move. Note their change in form. As they elongate they move more vigorously till on the second or third day they wriggle out of the jelly surrounding them. This is

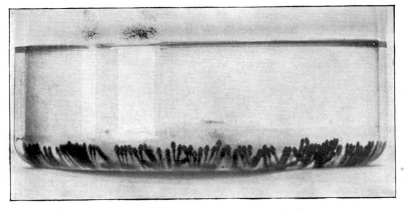

Fig. 113. Older toad tadpoles with their heads up.

hatching, and they are now free in the water and can swim about. It is curious to see them hang themselves up on the old egg string or on the edge of the dish (Fig. 112). They do this by means of a peculiar v-shaped organ on their heads.

How different the little creatures are, which have just hatched, from the grown up toad which laid the eggs! The difference is about as great as that between a caterpillar and a butterfly.

Tadpoles, polliwogs.—We call the young of the frog, the toad and the tree toad, tadpoles or polliwogs. The toad tadpoles are black. As they increase in size they may become greyish. Those raised in the house are usually darker than those growing in nature.

The tadpoles will live for some time in clear water with apparently nothing to eat. This is because in each egg is some food, just as there is a large supply of food within the egg shell to give the chicken a good start in life. But when the food that the mother supplied in the egg is used up, the little tadpoles would die if they could not find some food for themselves. They must grow a a great deal before they can turn into toads ; and just like children and other young animals, to grow they must have plenty of food.

Feeding the tadpoles.— To feed the tadpoles it is necessary to imitate nature as closely as possible. To do this, a visit to the pond where the eggs were found will give the clue. Many plants are present, and the bottom will be seen to slope gradually from the shore. The food of the tadpole is the minute plant life on the stones, the surface of the mud, or on the outside of the larger plants.

One must not attempt to raise too many tadpoles in the artificial pond in the laboratory or school-room or there will not be enough food, and all will be half starved, or some will get the food and the rest will starve to death. While there may be thousands of tad-poles in the natural pond, it will be readily seen that, compared with the amount of water present, there are really rather few.

Probably many more were hatched in the school-house than can be raised in the artificial pond. Return the ones not put in the artificial pond to the natural pond. It would be too bad to throw them out on the ground to die.

Comparing the growth of the tadpoles.— Even when one does his best it is hard to make an artificial pond so good as the natural one for the tadpoles, and the teacher will find it very interesting and stimulating to compare the growth and change in the tad-poles at the school-house with those in the natural pond.

As growth depends on the supply of food and the suitability of the environment, it is easy to judge how nearly the artificial pond equals the natural pond for raising tadpoles. It will be worth while to take a tadpole from the natural pond occasionally and put it in with those at the school-house, so that the differences may be more strikingly shown. There is some danger in making a mis-take here, however, for there may be three or four kinds of tadpoles in the natural pond. Those of the toad are almost jet black when young, while the others are more or less brownish. If one selects only the very black ones they will probably be toad tadpoles.

Every week or oftener, some water plants, and perhaps a small stone covered with the growth of microscopic plants, and some water, should be taken from the pond to the artificial pond. The water will supply the place of that which has evaporated, and the water plants will carry a new supply of food. If the water in the artificial pond in the school-room does not remain clear, it should be carefully dipped out and fresh clear water added. It is better to get the water from the pond where the eggs were laid, although any clear water will answer ; but do not use distilled water.

The growth and changes in form should be looked for every day. Then it is very interesting to see what the tadpoles do, how they eat, and any signs of breathing.

All the changes from an egg to a little toad (Fig. 111), are passed through in one or two months, so that by the first of June the tadpoles will be found to have made great progress. The progress will be not only in size, but in form and action.

One of these actions should be watched with especial care, for it means a great deal. At first the little tadpoles remain under water all the time, and do not seem to know or care that there is a great world above the water. But as they grow larger and larger, they rush up to the surface once in awhile and then dive down again, as if their lives depended on it. The older they grow the oftener do they come to the surface. This is even more marked in the large tadpole of the bullfrog. What is the meaning of this ? Probably most of the pupils can guess correctly ; but it took scientific men a long time to find out just why this was done. The real reason is that the tadpole is getting ready to breathe the free air above the water when it turns into a toad and lives on the land. At first the little tadpoles breathe the air dissolved in the water, just as a fish does. This makes it plain why an artificial pond should have a broad surface exposed to the air. If one should use a narrow and deep vessel, like a fruit jar, only a small amount of air could be taken up by the water and the tadpoles would be half suffocated.

As the tadpoles grow older they go oftener to the surface to get the air directly from the limitless supply above the water, as they will have to do when they live wholly in the air.

Disappearance of the tail.— From the first to the middle of June the tadpoles should be watched with especial care, for wonderful things are happening. Both the fore and hind legs will appear, if they have not already. The head will change in form and so will the body ; the color will become much lighter, and, but for the tail, the tadpole will begin to look something like its mother.

If you keep an especially sharp lookout, do you think you will see the tail drop off ? No, toad nature is too economical for that.

The tail will not drop off, but it will be seen to get shorter and shorter every day ; it is not dropping off, but is being carried into the tadpole. The tail is perfect at every stage ; it simply disappears. How does this happen ? This is another thing that it took scientific men a long time to find out.

It is now known that there are two great methods for removing parts of the body no longer needed. In the first method the living particles in the body which are able to wander all around, as if they were inspectors to see that everything is in order, may go to the part to be removed and take it up piece by piece.

Fig. 114. Transforming tadpole of the green tree toad to show the rapidity of tail absorption. (Change in 24 hours. Natural size.)

HYLA — Natural size. Change in 24 hours ; 28 mm. of tail absorbed in 24 hours ; 1 1-6 mm. per hour. Common toad shortens the tail about 1-5 mm. per hour.

These living particles are known as white blood corpuscles, wandering cells, phagocytes, leucocytes and several other names. In the other method, the blood and the lymph going to the part to be removed dissolve it particle by particle. Apparently the toad tadpole's tail is dissolved by the blood and lymph rather than being eaten up by the phagocytes, although the phagocytes do a part of the work.

Now, when the tadpole is ready to dispense with its tail, the blood and lymph and the phagocytes take it up particle by particle and carry it back into the body where it can be used just as any other good food would be. This taking in of the tail is done so carefully that the skin epithelium or epidermis is never broken, but covers up the outside perfectly all the time. Is not this a better way to get rid of a tail than to cut it off?

If you look at the picture of the disappearance of the tail in the toad tadpole (Fig. 115) and in the tree-toad tadpole (Fig. 114), you will get an idea how rapidly this takes place. It is easier to see the actual shortening if the tadpoles are put in a white dish of clear water without any water plants. The tadpoles do not eat anything while they are changing to toads, so they will not need to be fed.

Beginning of the life on the land. — Now, when the legs are grown out, and the tail is getting shorter, the little tadpole likes to put its nose out of the water into the air; and sometimes it crawls half way out. When the tail gets quite short, often a mere stub, it will crawl out entirely and stay for some time in the air. It now looks really like a toad except that it is nearly smooth instead of being warty, and is only about as large as the end of a child's little finger (Fig. 115).

Finally, the time comes when the tadpole, now transformed into a toad, must leave the water for the land.

What queer feelings the little toad must have when the soft, smooth bottom of the pond and the pretty plants, and the water that supported it so nicely are all to be left behind for the hard, rough, dry land! But the little toad must take the step. It is no longer a tadpole, or half tadpole and half toad. It cannot again dive into the cool, soft water when the air and the sunshine dry and scorch it. As countless generations of little toads have done before, it pushes boldly out over the land and away from the water.

If one visits the natural pond at about this season (last half of June, first of July), he is likely to see many of the little fellows hopping away from the water. And so vigorously do they hop along that in a few days they may be as far as a mile from the pond where they were hatched. After a warm shower they are particularly active, and are then most commonly seen. Many think they rained down. "They were not seen before the rain, so they must have rained down." Is that good reasoning?

The little toad is careful and during the hot and sunny part of the day stays in the shade of the grass or leaves or in some other moist and shady place. If it staid out in the sun too long it would be liable to dry up.

13

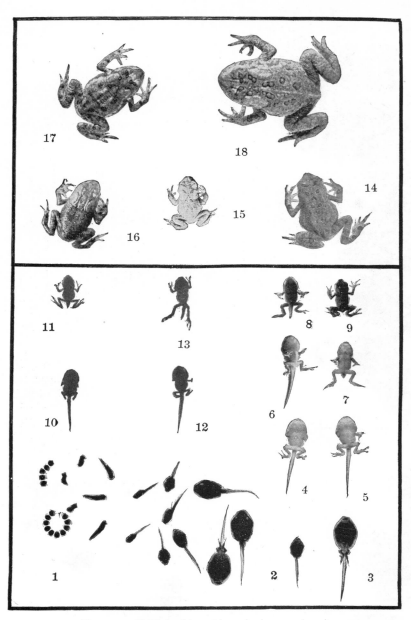

Fig. 115.   Toad development in a single season (1903).

1–18.   Changes and growth, April to November.   1–13.   Development in 25 to 60 days.
15–18.   Different sizes, October 21, 1903.   9, 14.   Different sizes, July 30, 1903.
10, 11.   The same tadpole,—11, 47 hours older than 10.
12, 13.   The same tadpole,—13, 47 hours older than 12.

194

FOOD ON THE LAND.

In the water the tadpole eats vegetable matter; but when it becomes a toad and gets on the land it will touch nothing but animal food, and that must be so fresh that it is alive and moving. This food consists of every creeping, crawling or flying thing that is small enough to be swallowed. While it will not touch a piece of fresh meat lying on the ground, woe to moving snail, insect or worm that comes within its reach!

It is by the destruction of insects and worms that the toad helps men so greatly. The insects and worms eat the grain, the fruits and the flowers. They bite and sting the animals and give men no end of trouble. The toad is not partial, but takes any live thing that gets near it, whether it is caterpillar, fly, spider, centipede or thousand-legged worm; and it does not stop even there, but will gobble up a hornet or a yellow jacket without the least hesitation.

It is astonishing to see the certainty with which a toad can catch these flying or crawling things. The way the toad does this may be observed by watching one out of doors some summer evening or after a shower; but it is more satisfactory to have a nearer view. Put a large toad into a box, or better, into a glass dish with some moist sand on the bottom. In a little while, if one is gentle, the toad will become tame, and then if flies and other insects are caught with a sweep net and put into the dish and the top covered with mosquito netting one can watch the process of capture.

Fig. 116. Toad catching a winged insect, and illustrating how the tongue is extended and brought in contact with the insect. Several other creatures that the toad might eat are shown in various parts of the picture.

It is very quickly accomplished, and one must look sharply. As shown in the little picture (Fig. 116), the toad's tongue is fastened at the front part of its mouth, not back in the throat as with men, dogs, cats and most animals. It is so nicely arranged that it can be extended for quite a distance. On it is a sticky secretion, and when, quick as a flash, the tongue is thrown out or extended, if it touches the insect, the insect is caught as if by sticky fly paper, and is taken into the mouth.

Think how many insects and worms a toad could destroy in a

Fig. 117. Toad making a meal of an angle worm.

single summer. Practically every insect and worm destroyed adds to the produce of the garden and the farm, or takes away one cause of discomfort to men and animals. One observer reports that a single toad disposed of twenty-four caterpillars in ten minutes, and another ate thirty-five celery worms within three hours. He estimates that a good-sized toad will destroy nearly 10,000 insects and worms in a single summer.

Fig. 118. Two newts feasting on tadpoles.

ENEMIES — THE SHADOW SIDE OF LIFE.

So far nothing has been said about the troubles and dangers of the toad's life. Fig. 111 is meant to show the main phases in the life-history. If one looks at it perhaps he may wonder what becomes of all the tadpoles that first hatch, as only two

toads are shown at the top. Is not this something like the other
life-histories? How many little robins or chickens die and never
become full-grown birds! Well, the dangers to the toad begin at
once. Suppose the eggs are laid in a pond that dries up before the
little toads can get ready to live on the
land ; in that case they all die. The
mother toads sometimes do make the
mistake of laying the eggs in ponds that
dry up in a little while. You will not
let the artificial pond at the school-
house dry up, will you? Then sometimes there is an especially dry summer, and only those that transform very
early from tadpoles to toads are saved.

In the little picture (Fig. 118) is
shown another source of danger and
cause for the diminution in numbers.
The newts and salamanders find young
tadpoles very good eating and they
make way with hundreds of them.
Some die from what are called natural
causes, that is, diseases, or possibly they
eat something that does not agree with
them. So that while there were multitudes of eggs (1,000 or more from each
toad), and of just hatched tadpoles, the
number has become sadly lessened by
the time the brood is ready to leave the
water.

Then when they set foot on land,
their dangers are not passed. They
may be parched by summer's heat or
crushed under the feet of men or cattle.
Birds and snakes like them for food.

Fig. 119. In danger from a
crow.

Figs. 119 and 120 show some of these dangers. Is it a wonder,
then, that of all the multitudes of tadpoles so few grow up to be
large toads?

We have so few helpers to keep the noxious insects in check, it
is not believed that any boy or girl who knows this wonderful
story of a toad's life will join the crows, the snakes and the salamanders in worrying or destroying their good friends.

MOULTING AND HIBERNATION.

There are two very interesting things that happen in the life of many of the lower animals; they happen to the toad also. These are moulting, or change of skin, and hibernation, or winter sleep. Every boy and girl ought to know about these, and then, if on the lookout, some or all of the things will be seen.

Moulting.— Probably everybody who lives in the country has seen a snake's skin without any snake in it. It is often very perfect. When the outside skin or cuticle of a snake or a toad gets old and dry or too tight for it, a new covering grows underneath, and the old one is shed. This is a very interesting performance, but the toad usually sheds it in a retired place, so the process is not often seen. Those who have seen it say that a long crack or tear appears along the back and in front. The toad keeps

Fig. 120. Snakes frequently swallow toads hind legs foremost, as shown in the picture. This is especially true of the garter snake, which is a great enemy of the toad.

moving and wriggling to loosen the old cuticle. This peels the cuticle off the sides. Now, to get it off the legs and feet, the toad puts its leg under its arm, or front leg, and in that way pulls off the old skin as if it were a stocking. But when the front legs are to be stripped the mouth is used as is sometimes done by people in pulling off their gloves. Do you think it uses its teeth for this purpose? You might look in a toad's mouth sometime, and then you would know.

It is said that when the skin is finally pulled off the toad swallows it. This is true in some cases; at least it is worth while keeping watch for. It is certain that the toad sometimes swallows the cast skin; it is also certain that in some cases the cast skin is not swallowed. After a toad has shed his old skin, he looks a great deal brighter and cleaner than before, as if he had just got a new suit of clothes. If you see one with a particularly bright skin, you will now know what it means.

Hibernation.— The toad is a cold-blooded animal. This means that the temperature of its blood is nearly like that of the surrounding air. Men, horses, cows, dogs, are said to be warm-blooded, for their blood is warm and of about the some temperature whether the surrounding air is cold or hot.

When the air is too cool, the toad becomes stupid and inactive. In September or October a few toads may be seen on warm days or evenings, but the number seen becomes smaller and smaller ; and finally, as the cold November weather comes on, none are seen. Where are they ? The toad seems to know that winter is coming, that the insects and worms will disappear, so that no food can be found. It must go into a kind of death-like sleep, in which it

Fig. 121. Toad in the winter sleep. (Natural size).

hardly moves or breathes. This winter sleep or hibernation must be passed in some safe and protected place. If the toad were to freeze and thaw with every change in the weather it would not wake up in the spring.

The wonderful foresight which instinct gives it, makes the toad select some comparatively soft earth in a protected place where it can bury itself. The earth chosen is moist, but not wet. If it were dry the toad would dry up before spring. It is not uncommon for farmers and gardeners to plough them up late in the fall or early in the spring. Also in digging cellars at about these times they are found occasionally.

In burying itself the toad digs with its hind legs and body, and pushes itself backward into the hole with the front legs. The earth caves in as the animal backs into the ground, so that no sign is left on the outside. Once in far enough to escape the freezing and thawing of winter, the toad moves around till there is a little chamber slightly larger than its body ; then it draws its legs up close, shuts its eyes, puts its head down between or on its hands, and goes to sleep and sleeps for five months or more.

When the warm days of spring come it wakes up, crawls out of bed and begins to take interest in life again. It looks around for insects and worms, and acts as if it had had only a comfortable nap.

The little toad that you saw hatch from an egg into a tadpole and then turn to a toad, would hibernate for two or three winters,

Fig. 122. The same toad awake in the spring. (Natural size).

and by that time it would be quite a large toad. After it had grown up and had awakened from its winter sleep some spring, it would have a strong impulse to get back to the pond where it began life as an egg years before. Once there it would lay a great number of eggs, perhaps as many as a thousand or two, for a new generation of toads. And this would complete its life cycle.

While the toad completes its life cycle when it returns to the water and lays eggs for a new generation, it may live many years afterward and lay eggs many times, perhaps every year.

Many insects, some fish and other animals, die after laying their eggs. For such animals the completion of the life cycle ends the life-history also. But unless the toad meets with some accident it goes back to its land home after laying the eggs, and may live in the same garden or dooryard for many years, as many as eight years, and perhaps longer. (See Bulletin No. 46, Hatch Experiment Station of the Massachusetts Agricultural College, Amherst, Mass.)

ERRONEOUS NOTIONS ABOUT THE TOAD.

If one reads in old books and listens to the fairy tales and other stories common everywhere, he will hear many wonderful things about the toad, but most of the things are wholly untrue.

One of the erroneous notions is that the toad is deadly poison. Another is that it is possessed of marvelous healing virtues, and still another, that hidden away in the heads of some of the oldest ones are the priceless toad-stones, jewels of inestimable value.

Giving warts.— Probably every boy and girl living in the country has heard that if one takes a toad in his hands, or if a toad touches him anywhere he will " catch the warts." This is not so at all, as has been proved over and over again. If a toad is handled gently and petted a little it soon learns not to be afraid, and seems to enjoy the kindness and attention. If a toad is hurt or roughly handled a whitish, acrid substance is poured out of the largest warts. This might smart a little if it got into the mouth, as dogs find out when they try biting a toad. It cannot be very bad, however, or the hawks, owls, crows and snakes that eat the toad would give up the practice. The toad is really one of the most harmless creatures in the world, and has never been known to hurt a man or a child.

A boy might possibly have some warts on his hands after handling a toad ; so might he after handling a jack-knife or looking at a steam engine ; but the toad does not give the warts any more than the knife or the engine.

Cows giving bloody milk.— It is a common belief in the country that if one kills a toad his cows will give bloody milk. Cows will give bloody milk if the udder is injured in any way, whether a toad is killed or not. There is no connection whatever between the bloody milk and a killed toad.

Living without air and food.— Occasionally one reads or hears a story about a toad found in a cavity in a solid rock. When the rock is broken open it is said that the toad wakes up and hops

around as if it had been asleep only half an hour. Just think for
a moment what it would mean to find a live toad within a cavity
in a solid rock. It must have been there for thousands, if not for
millions of years, without food or air. The toad does not like a
long fast, but can stand it for a year or so without food if it is in
a moist place and supplied with air. It regularly sleeps four or
five months every winter, but never in a place devoid of air. If
the air were cut off the toad would soon die. Some careful experiments were made by French scientific men, and the stories told
about toads living indefinitely without air or food were utterly
disproved.

It is not difficult to see that one working in a quarry might hon-
estly think that he had found a toad in a rock. Toads are not
very uncommon in quarries. If a stone were broken open and a
cavity found in it, and then a toad were seen hopping away, one
might jump at the conclusion that the toad came out of the cavity
in the rock. Is not this something like the belief that the little
toads rain down from the clouds because they are most commonly
seen after a shower ?

SURVEYS AND MAPS.

In considering the suggestions made in this leaflet, we thought
of the hundreds of schools throughout the state and wondered
whether there might not be some difficulty in finding the ponds
where the toads lay their eggs, and in finding some of the things
described in the other leaflets.

The teachers and students in Cornell University found this
difficulty in 1868 when the University opened. The great Louis
Agassiz came to the University at the beginning to give a course
of lectures on natural history. The inspiration of his presence
and advice, and of those lectures, lasts to this day.

Agassiz, and the University teachers, who had many of them
been his pupils, saw at once that the region around Ithaca must
be full of interesting things ; but they did not know exactly
where to find them. Agassiz himself made some explorations, and
the professors and students took hold of the work with the greatest
enthusiasm. They explored the beautiful lake, the streams, hills,
valleys, gorges, ponds and marshes. Careful notes were kept of
the exact locality where every interesting thing was found and
simple maps were made to aid in finding the places again.
Finally, after several years, knowledge enough was gained to construct an accurate map for the use of all. A part of this map,

showing only the most important features, is put into this leaflet
to serve as a guide (Fig. 123).

It will be seen that the University is made the starting point.
With a few hints it is believed that every school can make a
good beginning this year on a natural history survey of the
region near its school-house, and in the preparation of a map
to go with the survey.

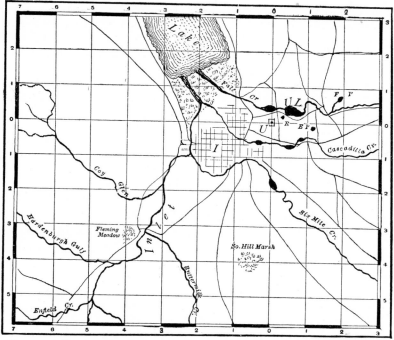

Fig. 123. Simple map showing the position of Cornell University, the city of
Ithaca, Cayuga Lake, and the roads and streams and ponds near the University.
From W. R. Dudley's map in "The Cayuga Flora." Scale, 1 centimeter to the
kilometer.

U. Cornell University.
U. L. University Lake in Fall Creek.
R. Reservoir supplied from University Lake, and supplying the campus.
E. P. East Pond where the eggs of the toad, tree toad, frogs and salamanders are found.
F. P. Forest Home Pond. A very favorable place for eggs, tadpoles, etc.
Inlet. The inlet of the lake. The lampreys are abundant near Fleming's meadow.

Preparation of the map.— It is well to have the map of good size.
A half sheet of bristol board will answer, but a whole sheet is
better. About the first thing to decide is the scale to which the

map is to be drawn. It is better to have the scale large. Twelve inches to the mile would be convenient. Divide the map into squares, making the lines quite heavy. If so large a scale were used it would be advantageous for locating places to have the large squares divided into square inches, but much lighter lines should be used so that there will be no confusion with the lines representing the miles.

Locating objects on the map.— The corner of the school-house containing the corner stone should be taken as the starting point. If there is no corner stone, select the most convenient corner. Put the school-house on the map anywhere you wish ; probably the center of the map would be the best place. In the sample map the University is not in the center, as it was desired to show more of the country to the south and west than to the north and east.

The map should of course be made like other maps, so it will be necessary to know the four cardinal points of the compass before locating anything on it. Perhaps the school-house has been placed facing exactly north and south or east and west, that is, arranged with the cardinal points of the compass ; if so, it will be the best guide. If you are not sure, determine with a compass. With it the points can be determined very accurately. Having determined the points of compass, commence to locate objects in the landscape on the map as follows : Get their direction from the starting point at the corner of the school-house, then measure the distance accurately by running a bicycle on which is a cyclometer, straight between the starting point and the object. The cyclometer will record the distance accurately and it can be read off easily. If no bicycle with a cyclometer is available, one can use a long measuring stick, a tape measure or even a measured string ; but the bicycle and cyclometer are more convenient and accurate, especially when the distances are considerable.

Suppose the distance is found to be one-sixth of a mile due west. It should be located two inches west of the corner taken as the starting point. If the direction were south-west, then the two inches would be measured on the map in that direction and located accordingly. Proceed in this way for locating any pond or marsh, forest or glen. Now, when the places are located on the map, you can see how easy it would be for any one to find the places themselves. While the exact position should be determined if possible and located, one does not often take a bee-line in visiting them, but goes in roads, often a long distance around.

In locating the objects on the map, every effort should be made to get them accurately placed, and this can be done most easily by knowing the distances in a straight line.

It is hoped that every school in the state will begin this year making a natural history survey and a map of the region around its school-house. The map will show but few locations, perhaps, but it can be added to from year to year, just as the University map has been added to ; and finally each school will have a map and notes showing exactly where the toads lay their eggs, where fish and birds are ; and where the newts and salamanders, the different trees and flowers, rocks and fossils may be found.

If the dates are kept accurately for the different years, one can also see how much variation there is. Indeed, such nature-study will give a sure foundation for appreciating and comprehending the larger questions in natural science, and it will make an almost perfect preparation for taking part in or for appreciating the great surveys of a state or a country. It is believed that if accurate information were collected and careful maps made by the different schools, the Empire State could soon have a natural history survey and map better than any now in existence in any state or country.

To the Teacher :

It is the firm belief of those who advocate nature-study that it is not only valuable in itself, but that it will help to give enjoyment in other studies and meaning to them. Every pupil who follows out the work of this leaflet will see the need of a map of the region around the school-house. This will help in the appreciation of map work generally.

So many of the beautiful and inspiring things in literature are concerning some phase of nature, that nature-study must increase the appreciation of the literature ; and the noble thoughts in the literature will help the pupils to look for and appreciate the finer things in nature.

It is suggested that as many of the following selections as possible be read in connection with the leaflet :

" The Fiftieth Birthday of Agassiz," by Longfellow.

The " Prayer of Agassiz," by Whittier. Professor Wilder, who was present, assures the author that this describes an actual occurrence.

This " Silent Prayer" is also mentioned in an inspiring paragraph by Henry Ward Beecher in the Christian Union, 1873.

The first part of Bryant's " Thanatopsis," Coleridge's " Ancient

Mariner," Burns' "On Scaring Some Water Fowl in Loch-Turit," and " To a Mouse."

Cowper's "The Task," a selection from book vi., beginning with line 560. This gives a very just view of the rights of the lower animals.

In connection with the disappearance of the tail, read Lowell's " Festina Lente," in the Biglow Papers. For older pupils, Shakespeare's picture of the seven ages in the human life cycle might be read. " As You Like It," Act II, Scene II, near the end, commencing, " All the world's a stage," etc.

Kipling's Jungle Books, and the works of Ernest Thompson-Seton and William J. Long will help one to see how the world might look from the standpoint of the animals.

One of the most satisfactory books to use in connection with nature-study is Animal Life, by President David Starr Jordan and Professor Kellogg. This gives the facts that every teacher ought to know in connection with the processes of reproduction.

Attention is also called to A. H. Kirkland's Bulletin No. 46 of the Hatch Experiment Station of the Massachusetts Agricultural College, and to the Nature-Study Leaflet on the Toad, by Dr. C. F. Hodge, of Clark University, Worcester, Mass.

Fig. 124.   From egg back to toad.

LEAFLET XVII.

LIFE IN A TERRARIUM.*

By ALICE I. KENT.

And Nature, the old nurse, took
The child upon her knee,
Saying: "Here is a story-book
Thy Father has written for thee."
— *Longfellow to Agassiz.*

FORTUNATE are the children and the teachers who are so placed that Nature's story book is close at hand. But city children and their teachers need not despair, for Nature, the old nurse, is loving and bountiful and will rewrite, in living characters, many a page from the wondrous book, for those who care to read. One such a page may be a terrarium — a confined plot of

Fig. 125. Life in the terrarium.

earth on which things may live and grow (from *terra*, "earth," as aquarium is from *aqua*, "water"). Within its narrow confines, the

---

* Nature-Study Quarterly No. 8: Leaflet 21, January, 1901.

whole drama of the beautiful life of many a tiny creature may be rewritten.

Here is a fragment of the drama, as written in one terrarium.

This terrarium was made from an old berry crate (Figs. 125, 126). When the children saw it first, last fall, this is what it looked like : a large rectangular box, grass-green in color, thirty-nine inches long, eighteen inches wide, and fifteen inches high. The long sides were of glass, the short sides and top of green wire netting. The top could be removed like the lid of a box. It stood upon a pedestal-table provided with castors. In the bottom of the terrarium were three inches of rich soil, covered with the delicate green of sprouting grass-seed. In one corner was a mossy nook, and in another a mass of thistles and clover.

Fig. 126. Butterfly-time in the terrarium world.

At one end, a small cabbage was planted and at the other lay several sprays of glossy pin-oak. Suspended from the top, was a large spray of purple thistles.

Among the thistles in the corner, ten pendants of vivid green, bright with golden points, could be seen. They were the chrysalids of the monarch, or milkweed, butterfly. Among the cabbage leaves, were many of the pale green eggs and several of the caterpillars of the cabbage butterfly. Among the sprays of oak in the corner, several oak caterpillars were feeding.

Before many days had passed, the drama of life began. One by one, the chrysalids of the milkweed butterfly paled in color and, becoming transparent, showed through their whitened walls the orange-colored wings of the developing butterflies within·

They then burst, freeing their gorgeous tenants. This happened until there were seven butterflies in the terrarium. As two of these proved discontented with their new home, they were set free. The five others spent the little round of their aërial life seemingly happy and satisfied. They lived from three to six weeks and showed some individuality in their tastes and habits. Sometimes they chose the mossy corner for their resting place. On other occasions they preferred the netting at the ends and top of the terrarium. In fact, the netting at the ends of the terrarium was a source of pleasure to these butterflies, as it served as a secure resting place and an agreeable and convenient pathway to the top. One of them spent nearly all its life on the thistles suspended from the top. These thistles were kept fresh a long time by placing their stems in a large sponge which was frequently drenched with water.

The butterflies showed some individuality in their eating also. Thistle, clover, golden-rod, nasturtiums, and honey-suckle were offered to them The thistle and the golden-rod were most frequently visited, and next to these the nasturtiums were most favored. Another fact noted was that most of the butterflies continued to visit the flower first chosen. When, however, a thick syrup of sugar and water was offered to them, the flowers were much neglected, only one butterfly persisting in flower-visiting. Golden-rod was its choice. If the syrup was fresh-made every morning and was placed in a convenient spot, the butterflies never failed to sip it. They generally slept clinging to the wire-netting at the ends or top of the terrarium.

In the meantime, the cabbage began to attract the watchful eyes of the wondering children. As it had industriously sent out many tiny roots, it proved a safe and satisfactory home for its hidden occupants. Soon, one by one, the caterpillars began to appear at the edges of the uppermost leaves. They began small tours in the vicinage of the cabbage, and, finally, as with the butterflies, the end wire nettings proved to be an easy pathway to the top of the terrarium. Here several found good resting places, and slowly changed to chrysalids.

One day a cabbage butterfly obligingly flew in at the open window. It was caught and placed in the terrarium. It, too, proved to be very fond of sugar syrup. One morning the syrup was accidentally spilled on the wooden ridge at the bottom of the terra-

14

rium outside of the netting. The butterfly was so hungry that it could not wait for food more conveniently placed ; so it stretched its tongue out, full length, through the netting, and in that way obtained it. The children were surprised to find its tongue somewhat longer than its body.

At this time, the cabbage was removed so that the eggs and the remaining young caterpillars could be observed. The protecting coloring of the eggs and caterpillars was first noticed. One little boy at first announced that the caterpillars were green because they were not ripe, a good example surely of the danger of reasoning from analogy !

Very soon the inhabitants of this terrarium world began to increase. A father and two mother grasshoppers and a young one, with his "armor on," came to live there ; also a "woolly bear," several other species of caterpillars, several species of beetles, a big horse-fly, some lady-bugs, and a cicada. About this time too, some very unwelcome immigrants appeared. These were the ichneumon flies. So numerous did they become in a very short time, that they threatened desolation to this prosperous community. Nature's methods were then scrutinized and the services of two tree-toads were sought. Their response was immediate and cordial. Soon not an ichneumon fly could be found.

The grasshoppers were partial to celery, over-ripe bananas, and moisture. Three days after they became inhabitants of this

miniature world, the mother grasshopper dug a hole in the ground and laid eggs. The observing children then had before them living illustrations of the three stages of grasshopper life.

The tree-toads were both amusing and accommodating. They, too, liked the wire netting at the ends of

Fig. 127. Hand over hand. the terrarium, and delighted the children by climbing up foot over foot, or hand over hand, like odd four-handed sailor boys (Fig. 127.) This brought into plain view the tiny suckers on their feet.

After the ichneumon flies had disappeared, a new difficulty arose. The ground became mouldy, and the grass died down. The terrarium was then placed by an open window and left there several hours for a number of days until it was thoroughly dried out. Then bird-seed was planted and the ground was watered thereafter with a small plant syringe. This gave sufficient, but not excessive moisture, and it was one of the pleasures of the children to imitate a rainy day in the terrarium world. And it was a pleasing experience, for there were splashes of water on the glass sides and many shining drops on the netting and verdure, which soon grew several inches tall ; there was the same delightful odor of rich fresh earth that one enjoys during summer rains, and the sunshine touched with brilliancy the gay fall flowers and the gorgeous outspread wings of the butterflies.

At this time the terrarium had an annex in the shape of a wooden box, a foot square, with a gauze top. Here lived two mother spiders with their egg-balls carefully hung on the cobweb beams of their homes. One day a beautiful yellow silk egg-ball was found out of doors, and when it was carefully opened to show the eggs with which it was filled, the gratifying discovery was made that these eggs were hatching. They were very tiny and very numerous. They were inclosed in a silken pouch and were the exact color of its lining. When resting the little spiders seemed to hold their legs under the body, and they were so small and so like the egg in general appearance that if they had not run about when disturbed they would never have been discovered. As soon as the egg ball was opened they exploited their one talent, for they ran out on the fingers of the person who held the ball and then suspended themselves by almost invisible threads from all parts of the fingers. When they were to be returned to the egg-ball they were gently pushed up. They then obligingly ran back into their silken home, which was carefully closed as before. These little ones were kept a week or ten days and were then allowed to escape and establish homes for themselves. The life history of the spider was thus seen, although, unfortunately, our adult spiders did not belong to the same species as the young ones.

To return to the terrarium : It was now early in November and each day found one or more of the terrarium inhabitants missing. One of the caterpillars disappeared and a cocoon made of its own hair was found in its place ; several chrysalids were found on the top of the terrarium ; the butterflies and the grasshoppers, one by one, went into that sleep from which there is no awakening ; and a number of the other creatures disappeared. The children finally concluded that the latter had gone to sleep in the ground. The grasshoppers and the tree-toads were the last to take their rest, but just before they answered Mother Nature's call to slumber, a large garden toad came to bear them company.

He was a very interesting toad for he bore signs of having lived through what must have been almost a tragedy. He had lost the lower half of one front leg and had the scar of a long gash on his throat. These disfigurements seemed not to cause him the least unhappiness, for he had a very bright wide-awake expression and was as plump and complacent as a toad should be. The loss of his leg caused him a little inconvenience, for he sometimes lost his balance when hopping and fell on his back. He occasionally found it difficult to right himself at once, but a few vigorous kicks and jumps generally placed him right side up. Three days after he became a member of the terrarium community, he, too, heard Mother Nature's call to bed, and partially buried himself. Each day he covered himself more completely, until finally only the top of his head and two sleepy eyes were to be seen. One day, about a week afterward, he disappeared entirely. He proved to be a very restless sleeper, and frequently showed himself during the sunniest parts of nearly every day all winter, occasionally coming entirely out of his earthy covering. He served as a sort of barometer all winter, appearing in bright and disappearing in gloomy weather. He never, however, left the spot he had chosen for his bed.

"Winter is the night of the year," and the little terrarium world indoors exemplifies it as truly as the great fields of Nature's domain out of doors. The soil is dry and hard in this miniature world and the verdure has dried down to palest green and brown. In its earthy bed, the caterpillars, beetles, and other creatures lie cosily asleep, and with the masses of tiny eggs, await the vivifying touch of spring.

LEAFLET XVIII.

DIRECTIONS FOR COLLECTING AND PRESERVING INSECTS.*

BY ANNA BOTSFORD COMSTOCK.

IT is the purpose of this leaflet to give a few suggestions to aid those pupils of the secondary schools who desire to make collections of insects.

There are several good reasons why children should be encouraged to make collections of flowers' birds and insects ; and the least of these reasons is the possession of such a collection on the part of the child. Making a collection of natural history specimens should only be the means to an end, *i. e.*, training the child to observe. When eyes are opened to the wonders of nature, every roadside, brook and woodland is fraught with interest which is undreamed of by those who are nature-blind. It is sad to think of the hosts of people who go through this beautiful world having eyes but seeing not, having ears but hearing not. The eyes must be unsealed in youth, when the mind is alert and receptive if the man or woman is to find in later life that Nature is not only a resource and recreation but an ever faithful friend holding out comforting arms to those who are weary in soul and body.

Not only does the study of nature open the child's eyes, but it also teaches him the value of accuracy. The young naturalist soon understands that an observation is worth nothing unless it is truthful. On the other hand, nature-study cultivates the imagination. The wonders in the lives of insects, plants, and birds are so illimitable that almost anything *seems* possible. Few indeed are the studies wherein the fire kindled by imaginative *seeming* is guarded and checked by the facts of actual *seeing*.

There are a few points in favor of beginning with insects when the child first attempts making a collection of natural objects. Insects are to be found everywhere and are easily caught ; it requires no technical skill to preserve them, as is the case with

* Teachers' Leaflet No. 7, June, 1897.

birds ; they retain their natural forms and colors better than do flowers. To secure the desired results for the pupil when he is making his collection of insects, the teacher should take care that he makes his observations incidentally, thus subserving the true methods of nature-study, which is to teach the child while he remains unconscious of the fact that he is being taught. The teacher, therefore, should ask the young collector, " Where did you catch this butterfly ? " " Where did you find this beetle ? " " Upon what plant or flower did you find this bug ? " " Did you hear this cricket chirp ? If so, how did he do it ? " etc., etc. ; thus making him tell orally or in a written language lesson the things he has seen while collecting. The differences in the appearance and structure of the insects caught should also be brought out by questions. These questions may be adapted to pupils of any age, and the success of this part of the work must ever depend upon the interest and genius of the teacher.

The objection is sometimes raised that collecting and killing insects and birds incite the child to cruelty and wanton destruction of life. This seems good *a priori* reasoning, but experience does not confirm it. We have always found that those who collect and take an interest in insect life are much more careful about killing or hurting insects than are other people ; the entomologist of all men takes the greatest pains to avoid stepping upon the caterpillar or cricket in his path ; also the young ornithologists who have come under our observation show the greatest devotion to the rights and interests of birds. Our experience is that as soon as the child begins to take an interest in insects he begins to see matters from their point of view, and this insures a proper regard for their right to life. It will be well, however, for the teacher to impress upon the pupil that he should kill no insect that is not desired for his collection.

The articles necessary for collecting insects are few and inexpensive. One net and one killing bottle may do service for a grade or an entire country school, thus reducing the expense to a minimum.

INSECT NET. FIG. 128.

Materials required.

1. A handle about three feet long ; an old broom handle will do.

2. A piece of tin three inches wide, long enough to reach around the handle.

3. A piece of No. 3 galvanized wire 3 feet 6 inches long.

4. One-sixth of a yard of heavy sheeting.

5. Three-quarters of a yard of cheese cloth.

Bend the wire into a ring about a foot in diameter and bend back about 3 inches of each end of the wire so they may be inserted into a hole drilled into the end of the handle. The piece of tin should be fastened around the end of the handle where the wire is inserted to hold it securely in place. If practicable, a tinsmith should be called upon to help in bending the wire and fastening it to the handle. After this is done, take the sheeting and fold it over the wire double, using only enough to fit around the wire without gathering; the object of this heavy cloth is to prevent the net from wearing out quickly. Make the cheese cloth into a bag with rounded bottom and just wide enough to fit the facing of sheeting, to which it should be sewed securely, and the net is finished.

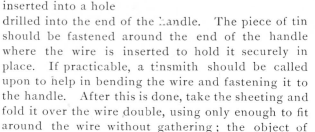

Fig. 128. Insect net.

How to Use the Net.

To be successful, the net must be swung swiftly. Insects have many eyes and are very wide awake and have no desire to be caught; therefore, the collector must be very active if he gets anything. One method of using the net is called "sweeping;" to do this take the handle about a foot and a half above the ring and pass the net quickly back and forth striking it against the grass in front of you as you walk through open fields; the net must be turned at each stroke and kept in rapid motion or the insects will escape. After a time the net should be examined and the insects put in the killing bottle.

Another method of using the net is called "beating." This method is used in collecting insects from bushes, and consists of lifting the net, mouth upward, and striking it sharply against the branches or leaves, thus jarring the insects into it.

To use the net in water, sweep the water plants as quickly as possible. In running streams, overturn stones, holding the net just below them with the mouth up stream. An old dipper made into a sieve by perforating the bottom with an awl is a good utensil for collecting water insects.

THE KILLING BOTTLE. FIG. 129.

It is desirable to kill the insects in a humane way, so that they will not suffer by the process; it is also desirable that they should not revive after they are pinned, both for their own sakes as well as for the sake of the feelings of the collector. The best way to secure painless and sure death for the insects is by the means of a " cyanide bottle."

Materials needed for a killing bottle.

1. A bottle with a wide mouth ; a morphine bottle or a small olive or pickle bottle will do. Even a glass fruit-can holding a pint will answer very well, although taking off and putting on the cover consumes more time than is desirable.

2. A cork that will fit the bottle tightly and is long enough to handle easily.

Fig. 129. Killing bottle.

3. Two cents' worth of cyanide of potassium.

4. One cent's worth of plaster of Paris.

These latter materials may be procured from any drug store.

Place the lump of cyanide of potassium in the bottle and pour in enough water to cover it. Add immediately enough plaster of Paris to soak up all the water ; leave the bottle open in a shady place for an hour and then wipe the dry plaster of Paris from its sides, put in the cork, and it is ready for use. The plaster of Paris forms a porous cement, which, while it holds the cyanide fast in the bottom, also allows the fumes of the poison to escape and fill the bottle. It should be labelled " poison," for cyanide of potassium is very poisonous. If kept corked when not in use, a killing bottle made like this will last a whole season.

The first rule in using the killing bottle is this : do not kill any more insects than you need for your collection. The second rule is : do not breathe the fumes of the bottle, for they smell badly and are not good for you. When you uncork the bottle to put an insect in it, hold it away from your face and cork it up again as quickly as possible.

Some insects may be caught from flowers, etc., directly into the bottle by holding it uncorked beneath them for a moment ; the fumes of the poison soon overcome them and they drop into the bottle. In taking insects from the net, hold the bottle in the right hand and the cork in the left ; insert the bottle into the net and place the mouth of it over an insect crawling on the inside of the net, then put the cork on the outside of the net into the mouth of the bottle, net and all, for a moment until the insect falls into the bottom of the bottle ; then remove the cork and take the rest of the imprisoned insects in the same way. Insects should be left in the bottle at least an hour, and may be left in there over night without injury to the specimens.

INSECT PINS. FIG. 130.

After the insects are caught they should be pinned so that they may be arranged in the collection in an orderly manner. Common pins are not good for pinning insects ; they are too thick and they corrode very soon, covering the specimens with verdigris. Regular insect pins are desirable as they are very slender and do not corrode so quickly. These may be obtained of any dealer in entomological supplies at a cost of fifteen cents per hundred.

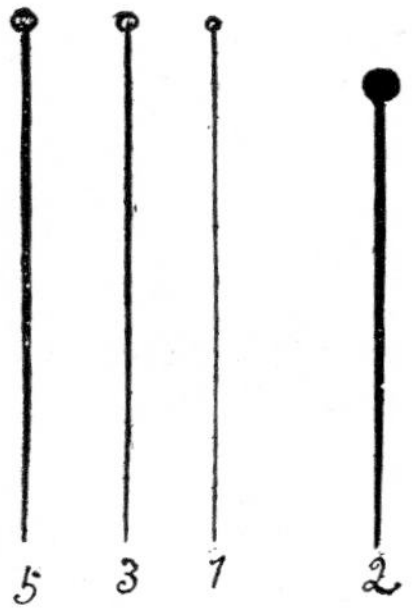

Fig. 130. Insect pins, 1, 3, 5, are German insect pins. 2 is a steel mourning pin.

Ask for the German insect pins Nos. 1, 3 and 5. If these pins are too expensive you can use the black steel mourning pins. These come in shallow boxes one by two inches square and have round glass heads and the boxes are labelled " Germany ; " these may be procured from any dry goods store. However, insects pinned with any beside regular insect pins cannot be sold or exchanged.

All insects except beetles should be pinned through that part of the body just back of the head, as shown in Figs. 137, 139, 140, 141. Beetles should be pinned through the right wing-cover, as shown in Fig. 138. About one-fourth of the pin should project above the back of the insect. Very small insects may be gummed to a narrow strip of card board and the pin put through the card board.

LABELLING SPECIMENS.

Specimens should be labelled with the date of capture and the locality. Thus the butterfly, Fig. 141, would be labelled thus :

Ithaca, N. Y.

Aug. 12, 1896.

The paper on which this label is written should be slipped upon the pin with which the butterfly is pinned and placed just below the insect. Labels should be as small as possible and be neatly cut.

INSECT BOXES.

For the beginner nothing is more convenient than an empty cigar box, which may be obtained at any store where cigars are sold. (Fig. 131.) The bottom of the box should be covered with some soft, firm material into which pins may be pushed without bending them. There are many such materials. Sheet cork or pressed peat may be obtained of dealers in entomological supplies. Some ingenious boys use regular bottle corks, cut into cross sections about ¼ inch thick. Others take the pith of dried cornstalks divided in half lengthwise. The cheapest and most easily

Fig. 131. A convenient box for the use of the young collector.

procurable of the purchasable materials is cork linoleum. This is for sale in most carpet stores. Get the quality that is about ¼ inch thick, which costs about $1 per yard ; put it into the box cork-side up. Any of these materials can be fastened to the bottom of the box with glue or with tacks. In all cases they should be covered neatly with white paper, for the insects appear better against a white background.

For permanent collections, wooden boxes with glass tops are much safer ; and as the insects may be seen through the glass these boxes are more practical for school collections. This kind of a box is shown in Fig. 132. Its sides are 18 by 16 inches and its height is three inches outside measure. The upper edge of the sides of the bottom part of the box is made with a tongue which fits into a groove made in the lower edge of the sides of the cover. This is done so that the top and bottom parts of the box shall fit very closely together in order that museum pests cannot get in and destroy the specimens.

Fig. 132. Insect box made of wood, with glass top.

In Fig. 133 is a cross section through one side of the box, showing how it should be made and giving measurements. In the drawing the glass is fitted into a groove in the inner side of the cover. This glass might be puttied in like a window pane if it is found difficult to make the groove. The corners of the box may be mitred and dove-tailed, or mitred and nailed; the latter is more easily done. Any carpenter or cabinet maker can make this box. Great care must be taken to use only thoroughly seasoned wood in its construction ; otherwise the bottom will be sure to warp and shrink and leave cracks through which the museum pests will enter.

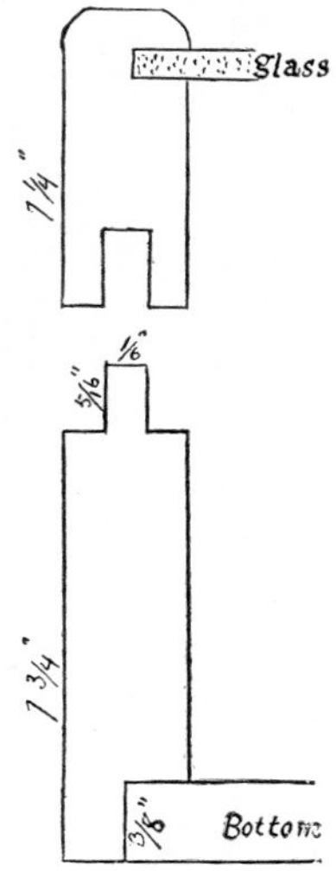

The cost of such a box will vary from $0.75 to $1. Basswood should be used for its construction ; pine is not at all suitable on account of the resin in it. Screw eyes may be put into these boxes and they may be hung on the walls of the schoolroom like pictures.

MUSEUM PESTS.

These are small beetles which find their way through the narrowest crevice into the insect boxes and lay their eggs on the pinned insects.

The larvæ when they hatch work within the specimens at first but after a time destroy the bodies entirely. The presence of these little rascals may be detected by dust on the bottom of the box just below the infested

Fig. 133. A cross-section of the side of insect box Fig. 132, showing method of construction and giving measurements.

insect. As soon as this dust is observed, pour into one corner of the box a tablespoonful of carbon bisulfide, or benzine, and close the box quickly. The teacher or parent should put the substances into the boxes, as the first is a poison and both are very inflammable. As a method of preventing the beetles from attacking the collection it is well to fasten a "moth ball" into one corner of the box. These may be obtained at a drug store.

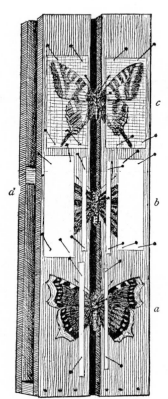

Fig. 134. A spreading-board.

Spreading-Board. Fig. 134.

Butterflies and moths look much better in a collection when their wings are extended at right angles to the length of the body. To arrange them thus we have to use what is termed a spreading-board.

Materials needed for a medium sized spreading-board.

1. Two strips of pine or other soft wood 18 inches long, 1½ inches wide and ½ inch thick.
2. One strip of wood 18 inches long, 3¼ inches wide and ½ inch thick.
3. Two cleats 3¼ inches wide, ¾ inch high and ½ inch thick; and two cleats 1 inch wide and as high and thick as the others.
4. A strip of cork or linoleum 17 inches long and a little less than an inch wide.

To construct the spreading-board, take the two narrow strips of wood, place them one-fourth inch apart and on the under side fasten them across the ends of the longer cleats. Then on the same side as the cleats tack the piece of cork or linoleum over the space between the strips of board, and as the cleats are one-half inch wide the linoleum should cover all the space left. Then midway the boards fasten the two smaller cleats. Fig. 135 shows a cross-section of the spreading-board just in front of these two middle cleats. Now it is ready for the bottom board which will fit exactly if directions are followed, and this completes it. The space b e t w e e n the two upper boards is wide enough to take in the body of the moth or butterfly. The cork or linoleum below the space will hold firmly the pin on which the butterfly is impaled. The cleats hold the top and b o t t o m boards

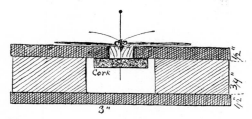

Fig. 135. A cross-section of spreading-board in front of the cleat "d" in Fig. 134.

apart and so protect the points of the pins. Spreading-boards may be made much smaller or much larger to suit moths of different sizes ; the space between the top boards must always be large enough to admit the body of the insect.

To use the spreading-board : Insert the pin with the butterfly on it into the linoleum just far enough so that the body of the insect will be in the space between the boards up to the wings, Fig. 135. Place the wings out flat on the board and fasten them there with narrow strips of paper pinned across them, Fig. 134, a. While held down by these strips of paper arrange them so that the hind margins of the front wings shall cover the front margins of the hind wings and shall be in a line at right angles to the body ; then pin larger pieces of paper over the rest of the wings, Fig. 134, b. Sometimes isinglass is used instead of paper to hold the wings down, Fig. 134, c. The insects should be left on the spreading-board at least three days ; and when the board has insects on it, it should be kept in a box where the museum pests and mice cannot get at it.

Sometimes when the moths are not spread soon after being killed, they become so stiff that the wings cannot be moved without breaking them. In such cases the insects should be put on paper in a jar which has some wet sand in the bottom and which can be covered tightly. The air in such a can is so moist that in two or three days the insect will become limber and may be spread with ease.

WHERE TO COLLECT INSECTS.

The border of a piece of woods where many shrubs and weeds are growing is an especially good place for collecting many kinds of insects.   Any place where there is a great variety of plants and flowers will give a variety of insects.   Banks of streams and underneath stones in the fields are good places for collecting.

When to Collect Insects.

The best time of the year is during the summer months.   The best time of day is in the forenoon after eight o'clock, and in the twilight at evening.

At night many moths may be caught by making a paste of sugar and water (unrefined sugar is best) and painting it upon tree trunks with a brush after sunset.   The paste should cover a space two inches wide and several inches long.   After dark seek these places cautiously with a lantern and moths will be found sucking the paste ; these may be caught with the killing bottle if you move carefully so as not to frighten them ; they do not seem to mind the light of the lantern.

Electric street-lights attract many insects which may be caught in the net.   A lamp set in an open window is also a very good lure on warm nights in the spring and summer.

Arranging the Insects in Boxes.

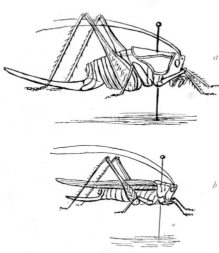

Fig. 136. a, Cricket. b, Grasshopper.

After collecting insects comes the desire to arrange them properly, putting together in neat rows those that resemble each other. To classify insects correctly requires much study.   The scope of this leaflet admits of only a few suggestions about the most common insects.

Dragon Flies. — There are many kinds of these, but they all have four wings, finely netted and transparent, the hind wings being as large or larger than the front wings. These are perfectly harmless insects.

Grasshoppers, Crickets and Katydids.—These are known to all,

Fig. 136. There are two families of grasshoppers: those with long horns or antennæ and those with short antennæ. Katydids, crickets, cockroaches and walking-sticks are near relatives to the grasshoppers.

Bugs.— These insects have the

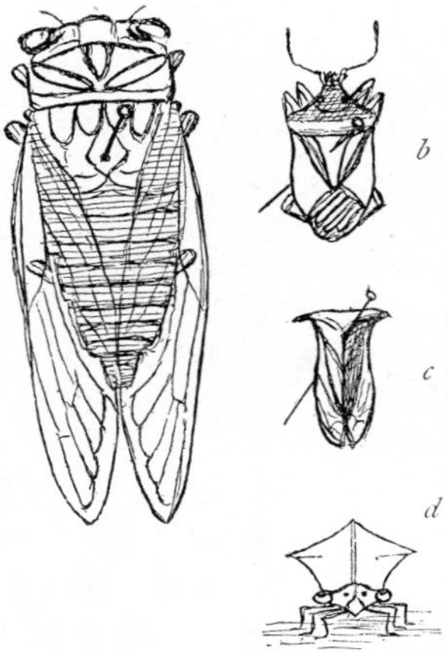

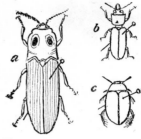

Fig. 137. *a, Cicada. b, Stink-bug. c, Leaf-hopper. d, Leaf-hopper — front view.*

Fig. 138. Beetles — showing the pin through the right wing cover. *a, Snappping beetle. b, Wood-boring beetle. c, Water beetle.*

front pair of wings thick and heavy at the base and thin and transparent at the tips, Fig. 137, *b.* The squash-bug, the chinch-bug, and the electric-light bug are examples of these. Some bugs have the front wings entirely thin and transparent and sloping like a steep roof over the back of the insect, like the cicada, Fig. 137, *a* ; and the Brownie bug, Fig. 137, *c, d.*

Beetles. — These have hard wing-covers which meet in a straight line down the

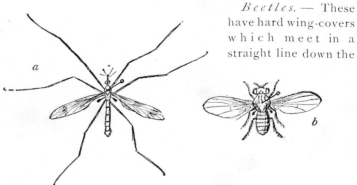

Fig. 139. *Flies — showing the knobs just below the wings. Note that flies have only two wings. a, Crane fly. b, Pomace fly — enlarged.*

back and have a pair of thin wings folded under them, Fig. 138. The " June bug " or " May beetle " and the potato beetle are good examples of beetles.

Flies.— These have only two wings, usually transparent. Behind

Fig. 141.   The Red Admiral butterfly.   Note the knobbed antennæ.

Fig. 140. a, Wasp. b, Bee. Note these have four wings.

each of these wings a short thread with a knob on it extends out on each side of the body instead of hind wings, Fig. 139. House-flies, horse-flies and mosquitoes are examples of flies.

Bees, Wasps and Ants.— Bees, wasps and the winged form of ants have four transparent wings, Fig. 140. Some flies resemble bees and wasps, but if examined it will be found that they have only two wings instead of four.

Fig. 142.   The Cabbage butterfly.

Fig. 143.   The Bass-wood leaf-roller moth.

Butterflies and Moths.— Butterflies and moths may be told apart by the following character : The antennæ or horns of the butter-flies are always threadlike and knobbed at the tip, Figs. 141, 142, while the antennæ of moths are in various shapes, but never bear knobs at the tips, Figs. 143, 144, 145, 146.

Fig. 144. The Imperial moth. A common night-flying moth.

Fig. 145. An under-wing moth.

15

Fig. 146.   The Luna moth.   A common night-flying species.

DEALERS IN ENTOMOLOGICAL SUPPLIES.

The following is a list of the dealers in entomological supplies that have advertisements in the current American entomological journals :

A. Smith & Sons, 269 Pearl Street, New York, N. Y.

John Akhurst, 78 Ashland Place, Brooklyn, N. Y.

M. Abbott Frazar, 93 Sudbury Street, Boston, Mass.

Entomological Society of Ontario, Victoria Hall, London, Ont.

Queen & Co., 1010 Chestnut Street, Philadelphia, Pa.

The Bausch & Lomb Optical Company, 515–543 N. St. Paul Street, Rochester, N. Y.

LEAFLET XIX.

SOME TENT-MAKERS.*

By ANNA BOTSFORD COMSTOCK.

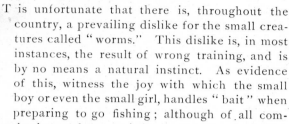

I T is unfortunate that there is, throughout the country, a prevailing dislike for the small creatures called "worms." This dislike is, in most instances, the result of wrong training, and is by no means a natural instinct. As evidence of this, witness the joy with which the small boy or even the small girl, handles " bait " when preparing to go fishing; although of all common " worms " surely the angle-worm is least attractive from any point of view. A still more striking example is the hardihood with which young fishermen catch the dobson to use as a lure for bass — for the dobson is not only very ugly in appearance but is also vicious, often pinching severely the careless fingers of its captors. Thus the dislike for insects being the result of the point of view, it should be the first duty of the teacher to remove this repulsion. In the lesson which follows there is no occasion for teacher or pupils to touch the insects unless they choose to do so; but an attempt is made to arouse an interest in the habits and ways of insect life. If we can succeed in arousing the child's interest in the actions of a caterpillar, he will soon forget his dislike for the " little brothers " which live upon foliage and which experience miraculous changes of form during their short lives.

In selecting the Apple-tree Tent Caterpillar for this lesson we have been guided by the following facts : First, it is to be found in early spring; second, its life-history from egg to cocoon is accomplished within the limits of the spring term of our schools ; third, it is common everywhere ; fourth, it is an important insect from an economic point of view, and the children may be taught how to keep it out of the orchards, thus making the lesson of practical use.

In this lesson the teacher is encouraged to use her own methods and originate new ones to make the work interesting. The Leaflet

---

* Teachers' Leaflet No. 5, June, 1897.

is meant for the exclusive use of the teacher and the text should not be shown to the pupils. The pictures on page 235 are to be shown to the pupils at the teacher's discretion. When answers are herein given to the questions asked, they are meant to aid the teacher in drawing out the correct replies from the children.

MATERIALS NEEDED.

1. A pocket lens or a tripod lens is desirable, but not a necessity. These lenses may be bought from or ordered through any jeweler or bookseller. They cost from twenty-five cents to one dollar each. It is worth while for any teacher to possess one of these magnifiers as a means of interesting her pupils in many things.

2. A bottle, a broad-bottomed one being preferable so that it will not tip over easily. This bottle is to be filled with water in which a small branch of the apple tree may be placed to keep it fresh. A common ink bottle will do to begin with. Fig. 147.

3. A wooden or pasteboard box, twelve or fourteen inches square,— a soap box or hat box will do. In place of a cover, nail or paste mosquito netting or cheese cloth over the top ; remove the bottom so that the box may be placed over the bottle and the branch of apple in it. This is called a "breeding-cage," and its use is to keep the insects from straying about the schoolroom.

Fig. 147. The bottle with the twigs bearing the egg-masses. The tent is being woven below.

4. A twig bearing the egg-mass of the tent caterpillar. These are easily found before the leaves appear on the apple tree or the wild cherry tree.

METHODS OF USING THE LEAFLET.

The teacher should give the pupils a preliminary talk on tents. Speak of the tents used by Indians, by armies, by circuses, by campers, and describe them each in turn. The teacher should use all the facts at her disposal, and all her ingenuity to get the children interested in this subject. Spend a little time for two or three days in discussing tents, and get the pupils to tell orally or in essays all they know about tents. When sufficient interest is thus aroused, tell them this : "The reason we have talked about tents is that we are going to study some little folks who make tents and live in them. Their tents are not made of bark like the Indian's or of canvas like the soldier's, but are made of the finest silk, which is spun and woven by the tenters themselves. These silken tents are not pitched upon the ground and fastened down by ropes and pegs, for these folk, like the Swiss Family Robinson, live in trees. Many people live in one of these tree tents, and they are all brothers and sisters. Now, just where these tents are made, and how they are made, and what sort of little people make them are things which we shall find out if we watch carefully and patiently."

Lesson I.— The Eggs. Fig. 149, *a*.

The teacher, having found the egg-mass, should show it to the pupils and let them, during play hours, collect some for themselves. Say that they are eggs, but explain no further. Get the children to examine the egg-masses ; ask the following questions :

On what part of the trees are these egg-masses found ?

What is the shape of the egg-mass ? (Bring out the fact that they look like a portion of the twig swollen or budded.)

What is the color of the egg-mass ?

Is there much difference in color between the egg-mass and the branch ?

Has this similarity in color any use ? (Develop the idea that the shape and the color of the egg-mass make it resemble the twig so closely as to hide it from birds or any animal that would be likely to eat the eggs.)

Does the egg-mass shine ?

Why does it shine ? *Answer.* Because there is a coat of varnish around the eggs.

Why was varnish put around the eggs ? (Get the answer by asking why varnish is put on wood. Varnish is put around the eggs to preserve them and to keep them dry during the rains and snows of autumn and winter.)

If the eggs are near the hatching period the varnish will have scaled off, revealing the tiny white eggs ; if not, let the teacher remove the varnish with a knife or pin, thus exposing the eggs. If the teacher has a lens the children should view the eggs through it. Exhibit the picture Fig. 149, b, which represents the eggs greatly enlarged showing the net-work of cement which holds them in place. Ask the children to compare the shape of these eggs with that of bird's eggs, and bring out the fact that these are

thimble-shaped.   Then ask the pupils to guess what sort of
mother laid these eggs, cemented them fast with a network, and
then covered them with a coat of waterproof varnish.   After sufficient interest is aroused on this point, explain to them : "One
day last July a little moth or miller was flitting about the tree
from which these twigs were taken.   If we could have been there
and caught her we should have found her a pretty little creature
with four wings covered with down and a soft fuzzy body.   In
color she was a pale rosy-brown, and had two bands of pale yellow
across each front wing."   (Call attention to the picture of the
moth, Fig. 149, e.*)

"This is the little mother which laid her eggs in a ring around
the twig and covered them with a waterproof coat to keep them
safe and sound until this spring, when they will hatch."

What will come out of these eggs when they hatch?   The
teacher should not answer this question, but let the pupils watch
the eggs and discover the answer for themselves.

Place the twig with the egg-mass upon it in the bottle of water
(Fig. 147).   It will be best if this twig is a part of a forked branch,
so that the caterpillars may make their web upon it (Fig. 148).
As soon as the eggs hatch ask the following questions :

What sort of young ones hatch out of the eggs ?

Are they like their mother ?

What color are they ?

Why are their heads so large ?   *Answer.*   So that they can gnaw
the lid off the egg and thus get out.

Why should the young ones of a pretty moth be little black
caterpillars ?

(Leave this answer for future investigation.)

After the caterpillars hatch it will be necessary to bring in each
day fresh apple twigs with buds and leaves on them so as to feed
the little prisoners.   It is very desirable that they be kept alive
until they have begun their web and have molted at least twice.
If they show a disposition to wander off, put the breeding cage
over the bottle and branch and so keep them confined with their
food.

To supplement the study of the imprisoned caterpillars, study
should be made at the same time of the insects out of doors and

---

*If a specimen of the moth could be obtained, it would be much more
interesting to the children than the picture. The teacher can collect or
breed the moths in July to use the next spring to illustrate the lesson.

under natural conditions. If none appear upon an apple or wild cherry tree near the school-house, the teacher should transfer a colony to such a tree (Fig. 148). This may be done by fastening a twig with an egg-mass upon it to a branch of the tree. If too late to get the unhatched eggs, get a nest with the small worms in it and tie that to the convenient branch instead. This study of the insects out of doors is very necessary in discovering their normal habits.

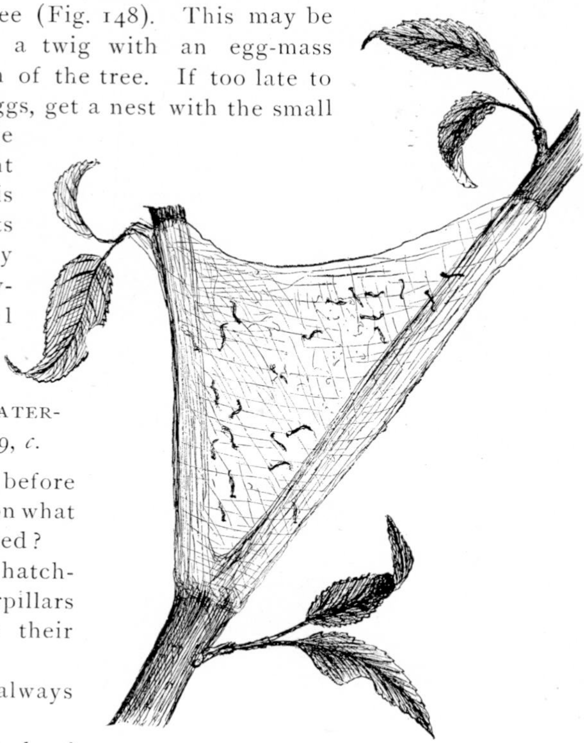

LESSON II. THE CATER-PILLARS. FIG. 149, c.

If the eggs hatch before the leaves appear, upon what do the caterpillars feed?

How long is it after hatching before the caterpillars commence to make their tent?

Where is the tent always formed?

Answer. In the fork of the branches.

Why is this so?

Fig. 148. A young colony of tent-makers on a cherry tree.

Answer. The forking branches offer a convenient support upon which to stretch the tent: and when, as in the case out of doors, the tent is spread in a fork of the larger limbs, these limbs afford two branching roads for the caterpillars to follow in searching for food.

Let the pupils make drawings of the tent as soon as it is large enough to be seen well.

What is the color of the caterpillars when they are a week old?

Upon what do they feed?

At what time of day do they feed?

When on a tree, how far from their tent do they go for food?

Are the paths over which the caterpillars travel when searching for food marked in any way?

Answer. This caterpillar spins a silken thread wherever it goes and therefore leaves a trail of silk behind it.

Of what is the tent made?

Compare the tent with a spider's web and note the differences.

Where does the silk come from, of which the tent is made?

Answer. The silk glands of the caterpillar are situated near the mouth, while those of the spider are on the rear end of the body.

Lesson III.   How the Insects Grow.

The caterpillars shed their skins about five times. The first molt occurs about three days after they hatch; the second molt about four days later; and the third molt about six days after the second. After each molt, the color and markings of the caterpillars are somewhat changed. During some of the molts the pupils should watch a caterpillar change his skin. After the class has seen this operation the teacher may give the following lesson:

Where is your skeleton?

What is it made of?

What is it for? Bring out the fact that the skeleton is a support for the muscles and organs of the body.

Where is an insect's skeleton? Get as many answers to this question as possible, then explain:

The insect's skeleton is on the outside of its body instead of a skin, and the flesh and muscles are supported by it on the inside instead of on the outside like our own. As this skeleton is hard it cannot stretch; as the insect grows and gets too large the shell bursts open and the insect walks out of it. Now underneath this old hard skeleton a new one is formed, which is soft and flexible at first, and so stretches to accommodate the growing insect. After a little time this new skeleton also hardens and has to be shed when it is too small to suit its owner.

Notes should be made by the pupil upon the change of color and markings after the different molts, and the process of molting should be described.

Lesson IV.   The Pupa.   Fig. 149, *d.*

In ordinary seasons, about the middle of May, the caterpillars get their growth. If those in the breeding cage have died or have not thrived, bring in a few full-grown caterpillars from the orchard and put them on some branches in the breeding cage. Give them fresh food each day as long as they will eat; also place some sticks and chips on the bottom of the breeding cage for the worms to "spin up" on. Then have the children observe the following things :

How do the caterpillars begin their cocoons?
Where are the cocoons made?
How are they made?
Draw a picture of a cocoon.

About a week after a cocoon is made, open it carefully with a pair of scissors so as not to hurt the inmate, and let the pupil see the change that has come over the caterpillar.

Have the pupils describe the pupa.
Let the pupils make drawings of the pupa.

The moths will hardly emerge from the cocoons until after the close of the school term. The children should be encouraged to gather the cocoons from the fences around the orchards and from the sticks and the branches on the ground and to carry them home. The cocoons may be placed in pasteboard boxes and kept until the moths emerge, about the middle of July.

LESSON V. DESTROYING THE CATERPILLARS.

After the caterpillars are fully grown and all the processes of growth have been observed by the pupils, the teacher should give a lesson upon the injury which they do to trees and the necessity of keeping the orchards free from these pests. This lesson should be given guardedly so as not to encourage the children to cruelty in killing insects. The teacher should always try to inculcate in the child reverence for life, that wonderful force, which we can so easily take from a creature but which we can never give back. It is better to appeal to the child's sense of justice in giving this lesson. The teacher may vary it to suit her own ideas, but in substance it might be given somewhat as follows :

"All life is sacred ; the smallest worm has as good a right to live in the sight of God as you or any child has. Life should never be taken except when necessary. However, no one has the right to interfere with the rights of another. Neither the child nor the worm has any right to trespass upon the property of any one else."

"Let us see whether these caterpillars are trespassers or not. The farmer works hard to earn the money to buy the land upon which the orchard is planted ; he works hard to earn the money with which to buy the young trees ; he works hard to set out the trees and cultivate the orchard ; therefore the orchard and the fruit of it are his property, and he has a right to drive away all thieves. If men or children steal the fruit, he has a right to appeal to the law and have them fined or imprisoned. If worms come and injure the tree by eating up the foliage, he has a right to keep them out if he can. The leaves are necessary to the tree, for if they are destroyed the tree cannot get the air it needs to keep it vigorous and enable it to mature its fruit. We have seen that these caterpillars destroy the leaves, and thus do great injury to the apple crop. We therefore have a right to destroy these little robbers, as that is the only way we can keep them out of our orchards."

How can the caterpillars be destroyed?

The egg-masses can be collected in winter and early spring from young orchards, and burned.

Tie bits of suet or fresh fat pork to the branches of the trees and thus induce chickadees, nuthatches, and woodpeckers to visit the orchard in winter. These birds will destroy eggs and cocoons of the tent caterpillar, and of other insect pests also.

In large, old trees, we must wait until later. Ask the pupils the following questions :

At what times did we find the worms in their tents ? *Answer.* Early morning ; late afternoons ; and during cold, dark days.

If we should destroy the tents in the middle of a warm, sunny day, what would happen ? *Answer.* The caterpillars, being out feeding on the leaves, would not be hurt, and as soon as they came back would make another tent.

If the tent is destroyed in the early morning or late afternoon or on a cold, dark day, what would happen ? *Answer.* The caterpillars, all being in the tent, would be destroyed.

How may the tents be destroyed ? *Answer.* By wiping them out with a long pole on one end of which is wound a rag saturated with kerosene. Or by burning them out with a torch.

Is it best to destroy the caterpillars early in the season, while they are still small, or to wait until they are large and are about ready to pupate.

If the trees were sprayed with Paris green in the early spring, what would happen ? *Answer.* The caterpillars would be killed as soon as they began to eat, when they were first hatched.

When these caterpillars feed on the leaves of wild cherry they are doing no damage to an orchard. Therefore, when the tents appear on wild cherry trees have we any right to destroy them ? *Answer.* The wise and careful farmer does not allow wild cherry

trees to grow along his fences if they will become breeding places
for insect enemies which will next year attack his orchards.

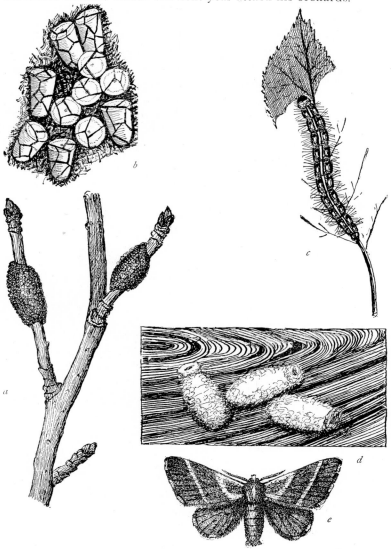

Fig 149   The Curious History of a Tent Caterpillar.
a, The masses of eggs on the twigs of an apple tree. b, The eggs enlarged. c, A full
grown caterpillar. d, Cocoons. e, The moth, or adult insect.

LEAFLET XX.

MOSQUITOES.*

By MARY ROGERS MILLER.

"Nature-Study is learning those things in nature that are best worth knowing, to the end of doing those things that make life most worth living."
— PROFESSOR HODGE in *Nature-Study and Life*.

SPITE of all the efforts of scientists and nature-students to popularize the mosquito, its reputation as a public nuisance is as well sustained as ever, and it seems destined to remain as unpopular as were its ancestors. There is no doubt that these creatures "abound" and that "they are great annoyances to both man and animals," as Dr. Howard tells us in "The Insect Book;" but he has laid a new and even more deadly sin at their door in stating, as he does in no uncertain terms, that "they are active agents in the transfer of disease."

There seems to be no escape from the attention of these persistent "imps o' evil." Though we travel to far Alaska or to icy Greenland we cannot be free. Since we are doomed to existence in the same world with the mosquito it behooves us to discover, if possible, some way to turn the creature to account for our entertainment or instruction. Forget for the moment that you despise mosquitoes, and let us study their ways. By making its life history the subject of some of our lessons we may at least learn how the mosquito lives and develops ; and later we can turn this knowledge to practical account. Since for many generations these creatures have made the human race the subject of insistent study, it is no more than fair that the tables should be turned !

You are not good nature-students until you have recognized and overcome your prejudices. You read the life history of the rabbit and you think you hate its enemies. You watch a family of foxes with their cunning ways, and the mother's care for her

---

* Home Nature-Study Course, Vol. IV, No. 23, May. 1902.

young and you cannot help sympathizing with them in their
struggle for existence.   Every creature in its turn becomes interesting to you when you find yourself wondering about how it
makes its home, rears its young, and gets its food.   As you get
nearer to nature you will cease to feel any pride in the fact that
you " hate " snakes, mosquitoes, and all such " varmints."   Indeed
that hatred, born of ignorance, will have given place to sympathy
and interest.   You have a new point of view.

One of the first questions asked of the returning animals in
early spring is, " How have you spent the winter ? "   The bluebird
and the robin show no signs of weariness after their long flight
from the South.   The " woolly bear " caterpillars look just as they
did in October.   The early butterflies are a trifle worn and shabby
after their hibernation.   But who has thought to inquire where

Fig. 150.   Mosquito's wing.

and how the mosquito has spent the
cold season ?   " Who cares," one may
say, " so long as they don't stay around
where we are as they did last summer?"
Suppose we make it our business

from now on to care about such things, and to inquire into the
ways our plant and animal neighbors have of living and of getting a living.   Are you quite sure that the mosquitoes have not
spent their winter under your protection ?   If in April you had

had occasion to frequent
either   garret   or   cellar
there   you   might   h a v e
found them.   By dozens
and   scores   they   w e r e
waiting for the return of
warm   weather   to   free

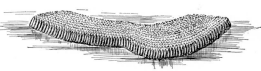
Fig. 151.   Raft of eggs, greatly enlarged.

them.   Many of them winter not as eggs, larvæ, or pupæ, but as
winged adults, as *mosquitoes*.   This rather interferes with the pre-
valent notion that mosquitoes live but for a day.   Would that this
were true, and might that day be short !

THE LIFE HISTORY OF THE MOSQUITO.

The life history of a mosquito is in four chapters, some of
which are exceedingly short, others long.   The length of each
may be varied by the weather and the season.   Moisture and
warmth are particularly advantageous to the rapid development
of these creatures.   Ten days in hot weather may be sufficient

time for the growth of a generation of them, from egg to adult. There are many generations in a year.

The larvæ of mosquitoes are aquatic. They live in stagnant water everywhere, in ponds, swamps, ditches, puddles, rain-water barrels, and horse-troughs. In early spring the female mosquito that has wintered in your garret will probably go to the nearest rain-water barrel or water-tank. She finds her way by instinct, before the sun is up. When you go to replenish your pitcher you will find a little flat cluster of eggs like a tiny raft floating on the surface (Fig. 151). It is dark-colored and the chances are you will not see it unless it gets into your pitcher. By two o'clock in the afternoon there may be from two to four hundred lively little wigglers in the water. Possibly they will wait until the following day. They all hatched from the eggs of

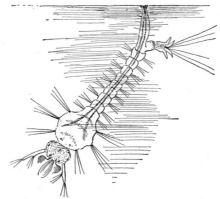

Fig. 152. The larva or wiggler.

one mosquito. They hitch and twitch about in the water, coming often to the surface and hanging there for a moment (Fig. 152). You call them "wigglers." But did you ever wonder why they wiggle, why they come so often to the surface, and why they thrust up the little tube which projects from near the end of the body? Did you ever ask what they find to eat in the water, and how they eat it?

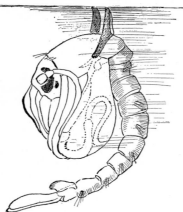

Fig. 153. The active pupa.

The larval stage lasts about ten days in hot summer weather, but longer when the days are cool. Then comes a change in form into the pupa (Fig. 153). The creature is still active and aquatic, though no food is taken. It does not stay long away from the surface while in this stage. Finally, after two or more days as a pupa, the full-grown mosquito emerges and takes wing, leaving its pupa case floating on the top of the water like a forlorn little derelict.

ENEMIES OF THE MOSQUITO.

Besides man, the mosquito has many natural enemies. In the water especially they fall easy victims to the thousand-and-one insect ogres. The nymphs of dragon-flies are especially fond of wigglers, and there has been much said and written about raising dragon-flies as a safeguard against mosquitoes. Most of the predaceous insects which live in still water feed on young mosquitoes, while the adults often fall prey to their more swiftly flying insect neighbors.

HOW TO STUDY THE MOSQUITO.

Over and around the tumbler place a piece of close-woven mosquito netting to confine the adult insects. A glass tumbler two-thirds full of rain-water, a little cluster of eggs, or a half dozen wigglers, a keen observer, and you have a nature-study opportunity not to be surpassed in the finest laboratory. If you have already seen a part of the life history, do not be satisfied until you have completed your chain of observations. Get the eggs ; watch the hatching, the molting, the transformations. See every stage. Learn something new every time you look at the wiggler or the mature mosquito. It is not at all necessary that you let these insects escape into the school-room and cause trouble.

Those who wish more minute description, with many illustrations of mosquitoes of different kinds, should obtain from the Division of Publications, Department of Agriculture, the published results of Dr. L. O. Howard's studies of mosquitoes. In this pamphlet, from which the drawings in this lesson are copied, the subject of the transfer of disease germs by mosquitoes is very thoroughly discussed, with pictures which distinguish between the common mosquito and those which transfer malaria and other diseases.

Those scientists who had to do with the naming of the many species of mosquitoes had certainly a sense of humor. One would think they named the creatures according to the mildness or malignity of their bite. A few of the names are as follows :

Culex excitans	Culex stimulans
Culex pungens	Culex perturbans
Culex irritans	Culex excrucians

THE CRUSADE AGAINST MOSQUITOES.

By M. V. SLINGERLAND.

There is now a world-wide crusade against mosquitoes, extending from the wilds of Africa through the noted malarial districts of Italy to America. In America a National Mosquito Extermination Society has been formed. This extensive crusade is due to the practical demonstration that some kinds of mosquitoes may transmit malaria, yellow fever and probably other diseases of human beings.

All mosquitoes must have water in which to develop, and the warfare against them consists largely in destroying their watery breeding grounds. This is being done on a large scale, either by draining or by filling in marshes, pools, and similar places which often swarm with the "wigglers." Large areas of such mosquito-breeding waste lands in New Jersey and on Long Island are thus being reclaimed and the mosquito nuisance largely abated.

Aquaria, rain barrels, tanks, small ponds and similar places can be kept free from the "wigglers" by introducing small fish, as gold fish or silver fish, sunfish, "killies," roaches or minnows. An interesting and instructive object lesson could be given by putting a few minnows from a near-by brook into the school aquarium or into a specially prepared glass dish well stocked with the "wigglers."

One can easily prevent mosquitoes from breeding in rain barrels or tanks by covering them with mosquito netting.

Another practicable and successful method is to pour or sprinkle kerosene oil every two or three weeks in a thin film over the surface of cesspools, rain barrels, tanks, ponds or any other body of sluggish water where the "wigglers" are found. This oil film kills the "wigglers" (both larvæ and pupæ) by preventing them from getting to the surface to breathe, and it also prevents the mother mosquito from laying her eggs on the water. There are patent preparations or oils which penetrate all through the water, killing the "wigglers" but spoiling the water for general use, so that such oils are usually applied only to infested cesspools, sewer basins, or manure pits.

By a little concerted effort of local officials, individuals, or by the school children in applying whichever of the above methods is most practicable, much interesting and valuable work could be accomplished and the pestiferous mosquito largely eliminated in many localities.

LEAFLET XXI.

THE WAYS OF THE ANT.*

By ANNA BOTSFORD COMSTOCK.

FOR many years ants have been recognized as among the most interesting of the little animals that people our fields. However, not until recently have we begun to understand, even in a small measure, their economic importance and the part they play in maintaining the balance in insect life. Therefore, we shall give a few studies of ants and their ways, and as a knowledge of their habits is necessary to begin with, we will take up the ant-nest first.

An Ant-Nest.

Two panes of glass laid flat one on the other with a space between of one-eighth of an inch or less, these panes covered with a piece of dark paper or wood to keep out the light and then placed on something that will allow them to be surrounded by water ; a bit of blotting paper two inches square, dampened and placed at one end of the glass chamber — these are all the materials and the art necessary for the construction of a perfectly equipped ant-nest.

Once we wished to make an ant-nest hurriedly, and this is the way we did it : we chose an agate wash basin (Fig. 154), as this would not rust, and filled it half-full of water ; in this we made an island, by placing in it a three-pint agate basin turned bottom side up. We took two discarded negatives, size 4x5 inches, and cleaned off the films ; then we placed one of the pieces of glass on the basin-island, took the stumps of four burnt matches and placed one on each side of this glass near its edge ; then we placed the other piece of glass on top, letting it rest on the matches to make a chamber just high enough for the ants to live in comfortably.

---

* Home Nature-Study Course, Vol. V, No. 1. October, 1903.

This done, we took the cover of a cigar-box and cut it down to the size of the negatives, put a screw-eye in the center to lift it by and placed it on top of the upper glass to make the chamber below quite dark. Then we took a trowel and fruit-can and went after some inhabitants for our island. We went to an open pasture and turned over stones until we found beneath one a heap of yellowish grain-like pupæ and little translucent whitish bodies, which we knew were larvæ, all being cared for by swarms of worker-ants. One of us pushed the trowel beneath, taking up dirt and all, while the other held the can open, into which the trowel was emptied. We hastened back and as gently as possible, taking care to hurt none of our little captives, placed the contents of the can on the top of the nest.

As the first thought of an ant is never for its own safety, but for the safety of its infant sisters, the little workers began to hunt

Fig. 154. An improvised ant-nest.

for a safe and dark place in which to stow away their charges. In running about they soon discovered the space between the two pieces of glass and in a few hours the young ones were moved into the new quarters. Then we cleaned away the earth on top of the nest, and by lifting the cover we were able to see all that was going on within. The water in the wash-basin prevented any of our uneasy captives from escaping, as these little people, so clever in most things, have never yet mastered the art of swimming.

I have an ant-nest on my table as I write, shown in Fig. 156. Instead of matches to keep the two pieces of glass apart I have a narrow strip of canton flannel glued around the edge of the glass floor except for two little doors at the opposite corners; there is also a narrow strip of cloth partitioning the chamber into two rooms with a door at one end. One room I left empty and in the other I placed a bit of blotting paper which I keep damp by occasionally adding a few drops of water. The nest is placed upon a piece of plank 18 inches square. Around the plank near the edge is a groove about an inch deep made with a chisel and kept full of water, so that my ants have a castle with a moat. It was necessary to paint this bit of plank thoroughly, above and below, to keep it from warping.

The ants in my nest I found on a hillside beneath a stone; they are brownish with yellow legs and a little less than a quarter of an inch in length. They were stupid at first and would not discover the chamber prepared for them, but persisted in hiding

Fig. 155. Ant-nest, on a piece of plank, which has a moat near its edge to confine the insects.

their young under bits of earth which were brought in with them. So I made a scoop of a sheet of writing paper and with it placed a heap of the young, with a few of the nurses, in the empty chamber, then put on the glass ceiling and cover and left them. In a few hours the whole colony had moved into this chamber, but evidently it was not humid enough for the health of the young, and by the next morning the pupæ and larvæ and eggs were all in the other chamber arranged around the edges of the blotting paper.

What I have seen of interest in this nest on my table would fill a small volume, if written out in detail. Just now a worker approached a pupa, that appears through the lens like a little bag

of meal tied at one end with a black string ; she examined it carefully with her antennæ and concluded it needed to be moved, and,
though it is as large as she, picked it up in her jaws and carried
it to a position which she regarded as more favorable.   Then she
approached a larva which looks like a little crook-neck squash,
inquired as to its needs with her antennæ and then cleaned it
with her tongue, as a cat licks a kitten, and fed it.   Her next
duty was to pick up a whole bunch of little white oblong eggs
and scurry off with them to get them out of the light.   Then she
stopped to help another worker to straighten out the soft legs and
antennæ of a pale, new sister that was just emerging from the
pupa skin.   By the time I had seen as much as this I felt it my
duty to replace the cover, as the light greatly disturbs the little
captives.   It is said that if a yellow glass be used for the upper
piece, the ants feel that they are in darkness, and their actions
may be watched constantly without disturbing them.

For a permanent nest, it is necessary to secure a queen, which
lays all the eggs for the colony.   She may be recognized by her
larger size and may sometimes be found in a nest under the
stones.   However, it is so difficult to obtain a queen that I more
often bring in the young and the workers; the latter will be content as long as they have the babies to feed and bring up; when
finally this is accomplished, I usually take my colony back to its
nest in the field, where it is made most welcome.   This may seem
sentimental, but after you have watched these little people working so hard and taking such devoted care of their baby sisters
and doing so many wise things in their home, you will be loth to
let the tiny creatures die of discouragement because they have
nothing else to do, and you will be still more loth to let them
loose to scatter, bewildered and helpless, over a strange earth.
However, I have to be very careful and mark the nest to which
they belong, for if I should put them near another colony, my
poor captives would soon die inglorious deaths.

Food which we provide for the ants in captivity should be
varied and should be put on the island, rather than in the nest as
we may thus be able to better clean away the refuse.   Crackers
or bread soaked in sweetened water, sponge cake, berry-jam,
sugar, bits of raw meat, yolks of hard boiled eggs crushed, freshly
killed insects or earth-worms, all may prove acceptable to our
little friends.   Their food may be soft but should not be in a fluid
state.

Questions About Ants.

*If you have not made an ant-nest and observed the ant as indicated,
make some field observations. These may be made with the naked eye,
or with a tripod lens. Such a lens costs about thirty-five cents.*

1. Have you ever seen an ant-hill? If so, describe it.
2. Do all ants build mound nests?
3. In what situations have you found ant-nests?
4. How many kinds of ants do you know?
5. Have you ever seen winged ants? If so, describe the
experience.
6. What is the reason for a winged form of ants?
7. Have you observed ants meet and "converse" with each
other? If so, how did they do it?
8. Have you seen the ants carrying their young? If so, how do
they do it?
9. If you have made an ant-nest, tell what you have seen going
on within it.
10. Tell any experiences you have had with ants, that show their
courage, energy or cleverness.

*Fig. 156. Uncovered ant-nest, viewed from above, looking
through the glass ceiling.*

*The white pieces around the edges and at the center are strips of canton flannel, forming
walls and partition to the nest. Note the doors at the lower left and upper right hand
corners and at lower end of the partition. The piece of blotting paper in the chamber at the
left chanced to have a picture of an eagle upon it. The small white objects are pupæ,
assorted in heaps.*

ANTS AND THEIR HERDS.*

Very soon after the green leaves come, one may notice that the ants seem to be greatly interested in getting to the tops of trees, bushes and vines. If one watches for only a short time, he may see them hastening up and down with that important ant-air which says plainly, "There now, don't hinder me, I haven't a moment to waste." If we should follow with our eyes one of these hurried six-footed Marthas on her way up a tree, we would find that her business was that of milk-maid. Her cows are there pasturing on the leaves overhead, and she hastens to them coaxing for the milk,

Fig. 157. Rose infested with aphids or plant-lice.

which is a clear drop of sweet honeydew. For many years entomologists repeated the statement that the honeydew secreted by aphids or plant-lice for the use of the ants came from the two little tubes on the back of the insect. It is easy to see how this mistake came about; the tubes were there, and so was the honeydew; the tubes suggested a cow's udder, and as the ants use the honeydew the natural inference was that it came from the t u b e s. This interesting error has been printed in so many honorable books, that it has become a classic. As a matter of fact, the caterpillars of our little, blue butterflies do have glands on the abdomen which secrete honeydew for the use of the ants; but the honeydew of the plant-lice, like honey itself, is manufactured in the alimentary canal, and issues from it. Observations have shown that each individual plant-louse may produce from five to seven drops of honeydew in twenty-four hours. If our cows could produce as much in proportion, then a good Holstein would give something like six thousand pounds of milk per day, and would be a highly profitable animal to have in the

---

* Home Nature-Study Course, Vol. V, No. 8, May, 1904.

dairy. Although the honeydew does not come from the little tubes on the back of the plant-louse, yet those tubes have their uses. I once observed a young spider approaching an aphid, which was facing its enemy. As the spider approached, the aphid lifted its abdomen, and thrust one of these tubes over directly in the spider's face, and on this tube there suddenly appeared a little ball of yellow wax. The whole act was so like a pugilist thrusting his fist in his enemy's face that I laughed. The spider retreated and the aphid let its abdomen fall back in its natural position, but the little wax ball remained for some time on the tip of the tube. A German scientist, Mr. Busgen, of the University of Jena, dis-

Fig. 158. A stable made by ants for plant-lice.

covered that a plant-louse smeared the eyes and jaws of his enemy, the aphis-lion, with this wax which dried as soon as applied. In action it was something like throwing a basin of paste at the head of an attacking party. Mr. Busgen discovered that the aphis-lion thus treated was obliged to stop and clean himself before he could go on with his hunt, and meantime the aphid walked off in safety.

The honeydew is excreted in such quantities that often the pavement beneath trees may be seen to be spattered by the drops of this sweet rain. It seems to be excreted solely for attracting the ants. In return for this, the ants give care and protection to their herds. They sometimes take them into their nests and care for them.   In one case, at least, one species of ant builds for one species of aphid (which lives upon dogwood) a little mud stable which protects the aphids from all enemies.   This stable is neatly placed at the fork of the twigs and has a little circular door by which the ants may enter (Fig. 158).   The lady-bug larvæ and the ant-lions both feed voraciously on the aphids ; an ant will attack single-handed one of these depredators, although it be much larger than herself, and will drive it away or perish in the attempt.

Some so-called practical people say, " Let us study only those things in Nature that affect our pocketbook, and not waste our time studying irrelevant things."   If this spirit had animated scientists from the first, many of the most important economic discoveries would never have been made.   This relation of ants to aphids is an example to the point.   For a hundred years has the fact been known that ants use the aphids for their cows, and the practical men said, " This is a very pretty story, but what we want is some method of killing the aphids."   It remained for Professor Forbes, of Illinois, to show the practical application of this " pretty story " in the life history of the corn-root plant-louse, which did great damage to the corn crop of the West.   These plant-lice winter in the ground wherever they chance to be left by the dying roots of the last year's crop, and with their soft bodies could never work their way in the hard earth and to the roots of the newly-planted corn in the spring.   Professor Forbes discovered that the ants in these infested fields make mines along the principal roots of the new corn ; and that they then go out and collect the plant-lice, and place them in these burrows, and there watch over them and protect them.

Observation Lesson on the Relation of Ants to Plant-Lice.

A reading-glass or lens may be used to advantage in making these observations.

Find some plant near at hand that is infested by aphids in order to note from time to time the relation of ants to these little creatures. Some aphids on the petiole and leaves of the Virginia Creeper on our piazza once afforded me a convenient field for daily observation.

1. How does the ant approach the aphid and ask for honeydew?
2. Does she wait long if there is no response ?
3. Does the ant step on the aphids as she runs about among them ?

4. What are the colors of the aphids you have observed?

5. On what plants were they feeding?

6. What sort of mouth parts have the aphids?

7. What part of the plant is their food, and how do they get it?

8. Why does not Paris green applied to the leaves on which aphids are feeding kill them?

9. Have you seen the lady-bird larvæ or the ant-lions destroying aphids? Explain.

10. Have you ever seen the little wax balls on the tubes of the plant-lice? If so, did you note when and why they were produced?

11. Have you ever seen an ant attacking the enemies of plant-lice? Describe.

12. How do you think this relation of ants to aphids affects agriculture?

13. Study what the ants do for the aphids which infest your rose bushes. Do you infer from this that it is well to exterminate the ant colonies in your flower garden?

14. Do you know how to clear your plants of plant-lice? If so, how? If not send to Cornell or some other experiment station for a spray bulletin.

LEAFLET XXII.

THE BIRDS AND I.*

By L. H. BAILEY.

THE springtime belongs to the birds and me. We own it. We know when the Mayflowers and the buttercups bloom. We know when the first frogs peep. We watch the awakening of the woods. We are wet by the warm April showers. We go where we will, and we are companions. Every tree and brook and blade of grass is ours ; and our hearts are full of song.

There are boys who kill the birds, and girls who want to catch them and put them in cages ; and there are others who steal their eggs. The birds are not partners with them ; they are only servants. Birds, like people, sing for their friends, not for their masters. I am sure that one cannot think much of the springtime and the flowers if his heart is always set upon killing or catching something. We are happy when we are free ; and so are the birds.

The birds and I get acquainted all over again every spring. They have seen strange lands in the winter, and all the brooks and woods have been covered with snow. So we run and romp together, and find all the nooks and crannies which we had half forgotten since October. The birds remember the old places. The wrens pull the sticks from the old hollow rail and seem to be wild with joy to see the place again. They must be the same wrens that were here last year and the year before, for strangers could not make so much fuss over an old rail. The bluebirds and wrens look into every crack and corner for a place in which to build, and the robins and chipping-sparrows explore every tree in the old orchard.

If the birds want to live with us, we should encourage them. The first thing to do is to let them alone. Let them be as free from danger and fear as you or I. Take the hammer off the old

---

* Teachers' Leaflet No. 10, May, 1898.

gun, give pussy so much to eat that she will not care to hunt for birds, and keep away the boys who steal eggs and who carry sling-shots and throw stones. Plant trees and bushes about the borders of the place, and let some of them, at least, grow into tangles ; then, even in the back yard, the wary cat-bird may make its home.

For some kinds of birds we can build houses. Some of the many forms which can be used are shown in the pictures at the end of this Leaflet. Any ingenious boy can suggest a dozen other patterns. Although birds may not appreciate architecture, it is well to make the houses neat and tasty by taking pains to have the proportions correct. The floor space in each compartment should be not less than five by six inches, and six by six or six by eight may be better. By cutting the boards in multiples of these numbers, one can easily make a house with several compartments ; for there are some birds, as martins, tree swallows, and pigeons that like to live in families or colonies. The size of the doorway is important. It should be just large enough to admit the bird. A larger opening not only looks bad, but it exposes the inhabit- ants to dangers of cats and other enemies. Birds which build in houses, aside from doves and pigeons, are bluebirds, wrens, tree- swallows, martins, and sometimes the chickadees. For the wren and the chickadee the opening should be an inch augur hole, and for the others it should be about one-and-a-half inches. Only one opening should be provided for each house or compartment. A perch or door-step should be provided just below each door. It is here that the birds often stop to arrange their toilets ; and when the mistress is busy with domestic affairs indoors the male-bird often sits outside and entertains her with the latest neighborhood gossip. These houses should be placed on poles or on buildings in somewhat secluded places. Martins and tree-swallows like to build their nests twenty-five feet or more above the ground, but the other birds usually prefer an elevation less than twelve feet. Newly made houses, and particularly newly painted ones, do not often attract the birds.

But if the birds and I are companions I must know them more intimately. Merely building houses for them is not enough. I want to know live and happy birds, not dead ones. We are not to know them, then, by catching them, or stuffing them, or collecting their eggs. Persons who make a business of studying birds may shoot birds now and then, and collect their eggs. But these persons are scientists and they are grown-up people. They are trying to add to the sum of human knowledge, while we want to know birds just because we want to. But even scientists do not take specimens recklessly. They do not rob nests. They do not kill brooding birds. They do not make collections merely for the sake of making them; and even their collections are less valuable than a knowledge of the bird as it lives and flies and sings.

Boys and girls should not make collections of eggs, for these collections are mere curiosities, as collections of spools and marbles are. They may afford some entertainment, to be sure, but one can find amusement in harmless ways. Some persons think that the securing of collections makes one a naturalist, but it does not. The naturalist cares more for things as they really are in their own homes than for museum specimens. One does not love the birds when he steals their eggs and breaks up their homes; and he is depriving the farmer of one of his best friends, for birds keep insects in check.

Stuffed birds do not sing and empty eggs do not hatch. Then let us go to the fields and watch the birds. Sit down on the soft grass and try to make out what the robin is doing on yonder fence or why the wren is bursting with song in the thicket. An opera-glass or spy-glass will bring them close to you. Try to find out not only what the colors and shapes and sizes are, but what their habits are. What does the bird eat? How much does it eat? Where is its nest? How many eggs does it lay? What color are they? How long does the mother bird sit? Does the father bird care for her when she is sitting? How long do the young birds remain in the nest? Who feeds them? What are they fed? Is there more than one brood in a season? Where do the birds go after breeding? Do they change their plumage? Are the mother birds and father birds unlike in size or color? How many kinds of birds do you know?

These are some of the things that every boy or girl wants to know; and we can find out by watching the birds! There is no harm in visiting the nests, if one does it in the right way. I have visited hundreds of them and have kept many records of the number of eggs and the dates when they were laid, how long before they hatched, and when the birds flew away; and the birds took no offense at my inquisitiveness. These are some of the cautions to be observed: Watch only those nests which can be seen without climbing, for if you have to climb the tree the birds will resent it. Make the visit when the birds are absent, if possible ; at least, never scare the bird from the nest. Do not touch the eggs or the nest. Make your visit very short. Make up your mind just what you want to see, then look in quickly and pass on. Do not go too often ; once or twice a day will be sufficient. Do not take the other children with you, for you are then likely to stay too long and to offend the birds.

Now let us see how intimately you can become acquainted with some bird this summer.

Fig. 159.

Fig. 162.

Fig. 160.

Fig. 161.

Fig. 163.

Suggestions for home-made bird houses.

17

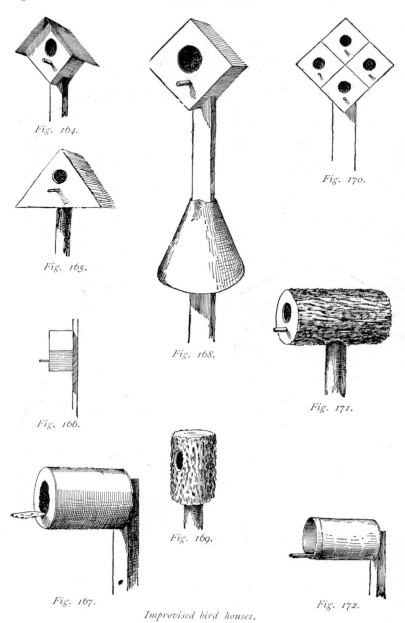

Fig. 164.

Fig. 165.

Fig. 166.

Fig. 167.

Fig. 168.

Fig. 169.

Fig. 170.

Fig. 171.

Fig. 172.

Improvised bird houses.

Fig. 173.

Fig. 176.

Fig. 174.

Fig. 175.

Fig. 177.

Suggestions for home-made bird houses.

LEAFLET XXIII.

THE EARLY BIRDS.*

By L. A. FUERTES.

FTER a long winter, many of us are too impatient for spring to wait for the swelling of the buds, the opening of the early flowers, and the springing of the grass. Several weeks lie between the end of winter and the truly genial spring days, and during this interval we look for something to herald the settled spring season. And the thing which gives us that for which we are unconsciously looking, more than all other signs, is the arrival of the birds. Who has not warmed to the quavering call of the first blue-bird, or been suddenly thrilled some early spring day with the sunny notes of the song-sparrow !

In the southern part of this State, notably in the lower Hudson Valley, the winter is spent by several birds which elsewhere we are accustomed to see only after the winter has passed. Among these are the blue-bird, robin, song-sparrow, white-throated-sparrow, meadow-lark, and possibly the purple-finch. But in most of the State we must wait until the first or second week in March before we can be sure of seeing any of them. It is a question which of the earlier birds will first make its appearance, as these early migrants are much less regular in their movements than those that come late in April and in May, after the weather has become settled. Many a robin and blue-bird arrives during some early warm "spell," to find himself suddenly surrounded by flying snow and blown about by cold winds. But these and a few other hardy ones seem able to stand such rebuffs with great equanimity, and the momentary shining of a fickle March sun will often evoke some pent-up song-sparrow's notes from the shelter of a hedge or thicket. Robins, blue-birds, song-sparrows, cowbirds, meadow-larks, phœbes, bronzed grackles, kingfishers, and doves may be looked upon as the vanguards of the hosts of migrating birds that come to us each year, and the first four or five may be

---

* Nature-Study Quarterly, No. 4: Leaflet 17, March, 1900.

expected almost any time after the first week in March. If the winter has been late, these may not appear until the middle or even the latter part of the month, in which case one is busy keeping track of the arrivals, as the other birds have caught up then, and all come nearly at the same time.

It is unnecessary to give detailed descriptions of robins, blue-birds, and song-sparrows, as nearly everyone is familiar with them ; but some of the other early comers may be more easily recognized if some field impressions of them be given.

*   *   *

Almost any warm day in early March we may hear a thin, clear " tsssss " in a high piping key, and on looking up see from one to five black birds, about the size of orioles, flying in a strange undulating manner — some up and some down, with the wings

held close to their sides during the " drop " in their flight. They are cowbirds. The flock may swirl into the top of a tree and sit close together. (Fig. 178.) If this happens within eyeshot, stop and watch them for a moment. One or two of the males are almost certain to utter the ridiculous song of the species, which, like that of their relatives, the grackles, is accompanied by the most grotesque of actions. The bird spreads its wings to their utmost, spreads and elevates the tail, stretches its neck upwards and forwards, and then, quivering and tottering, nearly falls forward off the perch. The only sound which accompanies this absurd action is a faint chuckling " clk-sfs'k," which is scarcely to be heard a hundred feet away.

Fig. 178. Cowbirds.

*   *   *

With the cowbirds we may expect the arrival of the bronzed grackles, which resemble them much in flight, but are larger and come in far larger flocks — sometimes ten, sometimes a hundred or more. Their arrival is known by the vigorous calls they utter while flying, a loud bass " jook." When seen squabbling in the spruce trees or in the bare branches of the willows fringing the streams, the males are likely to be giving their " song." It is scarcely more of a note than the cowbird's, a rusty squeak, and it is accompanied by a contortion in the same manner. It is not such a pronounced effort, however, and is often only a slight shudder and shrug of the shoulders. They feed, like cowbirds, mostly on the ground, and walk about most sedately in the grass like small crows. In tall grass, however, they waddle too much to be graceful. When taking flight they spread their long pointed tails in a very peculiar and characteristic manner — not out in a horizontal plane, like most birds, but up at the sides in the shape of a gardener's trowel, which gives them an extra-ordinary appearance.

* * *

The redwings begin to come into the marshes soon after the grackles, and are at that time in full feather and song. Their rich, deliberate " clonk-ka lrrrrrrr," interlarded with the clear pip-ing whistles of some of the flock, makes a concert of bird-notes very dear to all who are familiar with it. In their scarlet and black velvet dress these birds are impossible to mistake, whether seen chasing over the marshes, singing from an elm-top, or bal-ancing with spread tail upon some tall reed stalk.

* * *

There is a bird-note so often and so justly mistaken for that of the phœbe that the error certainly merits correction. The spring song of the chick-a-dee (which may be heard on almost any warm day all winter, and is very easy to call forth by even a poorly whistled imitation) is a clear, pure " $\overline{eee}$ —" or " — __ — " which really says " Phœbe " much more plainly than the true phœbe note, this latter being much lower in tone, and only to be heard after March is well on, and almost always in the vicinity of running streams and brooklets ; while the gay little chick-a-dee whistles at any time or place that suits his versatile fancy.

Fig. 179. Meadow larks.

* * *

The mellow flute notes of the meadow larks (Fig. 179) float to us from the middle of some large, open field, and are among the most beautiful bits of bird music we ever hear. They are not to be represented by notes, and can only be most inadequately described. There is great variation in the sequence of notes, but all are beautifully clear and ringing, and have a decided tinge of what would be sadness if it were not so sweet. The bird flies in a very char-

acteristic manner, never raising the wings above the plane of the
back, and when seen below the horizon line always shows the
white feathers in the tail.   His saffron breast and black breast-
mark seldom show on the living birds, and the mottled brown
back is a wonderful safeguard against his many overhead
enemies.

*   *   *

Two or more doves may be seen winging their headlong flight
through the air. These are among the swiftest of birds, and
are generally out of eyeshot almost before you
have seen them. (That is one way of knowing what they are.) In flight, they look like
small pigeons with very long graduated tails,
and when, in some old orchard or open wood,
you see one rise from the ground into a tree,
the white lateral feathers in the tail make
an easily recognizable mark. (Fig. 180.)
Their cooing notes are well known — a high-
pitched "overtone," followed by several long
bell-toned " ͡ooooo,— ͡ooooo," notes.

*Fig. 180. Mourning
doves.*

*   *   *

About April 1 to 10, you may hear a scratching in the dead
leaves among the underbrush in any thickly grown tangle, and
upon cautiously coming up you may discover the authors — not
big grouse as you may have supposed, but a flock of fine, vigorous
fox-sparrows on their way to their northern breeding grounds.
They are bright bay fellows, with boldly blotched brown and
white breasts, diligently scattering the leaves for their food of
seeds, spiders, ants, and various insects. If you have been
fortunate enough not to have been seen you may hear their song,
which is one of the finest of our sparrow songs, readily recognizable as such, though not resembling any of its fellows — a
clear, vigorous carol, often ending abruptly with a rather unmusi-
cal " clip."   If, however, they have seen you, you will be treated
to a sharp " tseep !" and a rear view of a flock of rapidly
retreating birds, for they are not sociable (with us, at least),
and generally take a hint to move on before you know of their
presence. They do not stay long with us on their migration,
and seeing them one day is no indication that you can find
them the next.

*   *   *

Although the white-throated sparrows spend the winter in our southern counties, they do not start their northward journey as early as we might expect, and it is not until the first part of April that we may be sure of finding them. I have one list, indeed that shows their first appearance on May first!

They are to be found in places similar to those which the fox-sparrows choose, and are very similar to them in habits, but the boldly striped head and gray breast are very distinctive marks. Almost all of our native sparrows have a call note, the "tsweep" note, which is hard to distinguish in the different species without much patient listening — and I doubt if any person is infallible in this distinction. The white-throat has this note, as well as the song-sparrow, tree-sparrow (a winter-bird), fox-sparrow, white-crown, chippy, field-sparrow, grass-finch, in fact all our brown-backed sparrows. But the song of the white-throat is his own, and may be heard frequently during his very leisurely journey through our state. His Canadian name, "Peabody bird" is descriptive of his notes, "— ‒‒ -,‒‒ -,‒‒ -."

Fig. 181. White-throated sparrow.

When a number get together and whistle, as if they were singing a round, it makes a very sweet concert.

* * *

One of the foremost birds in the spring movement is the grass-finch (vesper-sparrow or bay-winged bunting). It is to be found in open fields and along roadside fences, in company with meadow larks, and its sweet song may be heard almost any warm evening after the middle of April. Unlike most of our birds, this sparrow sings at its best late in the afternoon and during twilight, which perhaps makes its song seem the sweeter. It is rather a gentle song, though to be heard at some distance, carrying quite as far as that of the song-sparrow. Although the quality of voice is somewhat similar in these two birds, the grass-finch lacks the merry abandon that characterizes the song-sparrow's song, but has instead a deeper chord, which is called by some people sadness. The bird may be easily recognized in the fields by the white tail-feathers, which always show in flight. It is about the size and general color of the song-sparrow.

* * *

By the time the foregoing birds are comparatively common,

and the maple buds are bursting and the lilacs swelling, the gay purple finch appears. He is not purple at all, but has a crimson head, which fades on the lower breast through rosy pink into pure white. He is fond of spruces and larches, feeding greedily on the tender buds as well as on the ants and scale insects that infest them. His song is a fine one, and in addition to the charm of being poured forth in full flight, is so long and intricate that one finds himself holding his breath as the burst of melody continues, as if to help the little fellow catch up with his music.

* * *

Along the banks of some lake or stream, sitting idly on a telegraph pole or wire, rising and settling, elevating and depressing his long parted top-knot, a patriarchal old kingfisher may be

Fig. 182.   Kingfisher.

seen silently awaiting the gleam of a shiner in the water below (Fig. 182). Or perhaps you may first see him flying like a big woodpecker, screaming his chattering cry high in the air, or scaling close to the water under the fringing hemlock branches that overhang the stream. His large size, slate-blue back, loud notes, and characteristic flight make him a hard bird to mistake in any case.

* * *

There are many other birds which pass us on their way north, but they herald rather the summer than the breaking of spring. The following list of spring migrations is taken from Mr. Chapman's " Handbook of the Birds of Eastern North America," and was compiled for use about New York City. The dates nearly coincide with those I have found about the central part of the State, and are, in the main, only a few days in advance of those for the northern counties. The latter dates in the column are about what may be taken for the middle tier of counties.

It is the earnest hope of the writer that these few very brief sketches may be of use to those interested in entering the delightful field of the study of birds ; your experience may and probably will be different from that which I have cited, which only goes to show that everyone must really see for himself, and not only that, but by so doing may make new observations and get new ideas on practically all of even our best known birds. Birds are not, as a rule, hard to watch, and the patience it requires to sit still and "be a stump" long enough for birds to cease noticing you is soon and amply repaid by the new insight into an unknown realm which is sure to follow.

LIST OF BIRDS COMPRISING THE SPRING MIGRATION.

(Until April 20 — Approximate.)

(Taken from Chapman's Handbook of Birds of Eastern North America.)

Date of arrival.		Date of arrival.	
Feb. 15–Mar. 10.	Purple Grackle.	April 1–10	Vesper-sparrow.
	Rusty Grackle.		Savanna-sparrow.
	Red-winged Black-bird.		Chipping-sparrow.
			Tree Swallow.
	Robin.		Myrtle Warbler.
	Bluebird.		American Pipit.
Mar. 10–20	Woodcock.		Hermit Thrush.
	Phœbe.	April 10–20	Yellow-bellied
	Meadow Lark.		Woodpecker.
	Cowbird.		Barn Swallow.
	Fox-sparrow.		Yellow Palm War-
Mar. 20–31	Wilson's Snipe.		bler.
	Kingfisher.		Pine Warbler.
	Mourning Dove.		Louisiana Water
	Swamp-sparrow.		Thrush.
	Field-sparrow.		Ruby-crowned
April 1–10	Great Blue Heron.		Kinglet.
	Purple Finch.		

LEAFLET XXIV.

THE WOODPECKERS.*

By ANNA BOTSFORD COMSTOCK.

IT is best to follow some definite line of bird study for an entire year. All of the observations that could be made in a single month on any bird would give but an inadequate idea of its habits. To know the life of a bird, one must study it month by month for at least one year.

The woodpeckers seem a most attractive group for our study. They are not only very interesting, but of great importance to the farmer, orchadist and forester. There are five common species in New York State that we all may learn to know, and then make observations of our own on their habits. These species are the downy, the hairy, the sapsucker, the flicker and the redhead. The way to begin our observations in winter is to tie a piece of suet to the branch of some tree easily observed from our windows. Such a bird feast as this is on a branch of a chestnut oak in front of my office window, and though I never have time to watch more than momentarily the birds that come there to eat, yet each glance tells me something of their ways, and my own day's work is much brighter and happier therefor. The "downy" (Fig. 183), as he is universally called, comes with his mate every day and they eat greedily of the suet; when they first arrive they are so absorbed in working this food mine that I sometimes stand directly beneath and watch them without frightening them. Perhaps they know that I am the friend who invited them to breakfast. Anyway, as soon as they leave the suet they hunt industriously over my tree, finding there all of the hidden insects, and thus they keep my oak clean and pay for their breakfast. Occasionally the hairy woodpecker comes, a self-invited guest to the suet banquet. To the untrained eye he looks very like an over-grown downy, as he is by two or three inches the longer; but his outer tail feathers are

* Home Nature-Study Course, Vol. IV, No. 30, March, 1903.

entirely white, while the downy's are barred with black ; usually the red cap of the hairy is divided by a black stripe. The hairy is said to be a shy bird, but I have seen him several times this winter at a suet party near dwellings.

In April there is likely to appear in any region of New York State a bird which is often mistaken for the downy or hairy, although it is very different in both coloring and habits. This is the sapsucker, the only woodpecker of bad repute (Fig. 184). However, I am sure its deeds are not nearly so black as they are painted. The male sapsucker has a bright red crown and chin and throat, his breast is yellow, and he is also yellowish on the

Fig. 183. Downy woodpecker.   Fig. 184. Sapsucker.

back ; while the males of the downy and hairy are red-capped and black and white with no yellow.

QUESTIONS ON WOODPECKERS TO BE ANSWERED IN MARCH.

1. What is the difference in appearance between the male and female downy ?

2. How does the downy travel down a tree ; does it go head-first ? What food have you seen it eat ?

3. How does the downy use its tail in going up and down the tree trunk ?

4. Have you approached a woodpecker closely enough to see how its toes are arranged? If so, describe them.

5. How does it manage its head to make its blows forceful?

6. Are you able to discriminate between the hairy and the downy when you see them? How?

7. Do you know the difference in the notes of the hairy and downy? Explain.

DOWNY, SAPSUCKER AND RED-HEAD.*

This morning I was awakened by the beating of a drum over in the woods. My ear was not yet sufficiently trained so that I knew whether my drummer was Mr. Downy or Mr. Hairy, yet I strongly suspected the former. The tattoo of the Sapsucker (which does not nest here) James Whitcomb Riley has aptly characterized as "Weeding out the lonesomeness." This is exactly what the drumming of woodpeckers in the early spring means. The male selects some dried limb of hard wood and there beats out his well-known signal which advertises far and near, "Wanted, a wife." And after he wins her he keeps on drumming to cheer her, while she is busy with her family cares. The woodpecker has no voice for singing, like the robin or thrush, and realizing his deficiency, he does not insist on singing like the peacock, whether he can or no. He chooses rather to devote his voice to terse and business-like conversation, and when he is musically inclined he turns drummer. He is rather particular about his instrument, and, having found one that pleases him in tone, returns to it day after day.

In case the drumming I heard this morning was an advertisement for a wife, I am interested to know what has become of Mrs. Downy, who has been true to her mate all winter. Does, perhaps, the springtime bring divorce as well as marriage? Mr. Burroughs tells of a downy that was absolutely brutal in his treatment of his mate in winter, not allowing her to live in his neighborhood. Be this as it may, the downy and the hairy woodpeckers that have feasted upon my suet this winter have invariably come in pairs, and while only one at a time sits at meat, and the lord and master is somewhat "bossy," yet they seem to get along as well as most married pairs.

The sapsucker is a woodpecker that has strayed from the paths

---

*Home Nature-Study Course, Vol. IV, No. 31, April, 1903.

of virtue; he has fallen into temptation by the wayside, and instead of drilling a hole for the sake of the grub at the end of it he drills it for its own sake. He is a tippler and sap is his beverage. He is especially fond of the sap of the mountain ash, apple, thorn apple, canoe birch, red maple, red oak and white ash. He drills his holes in beautiful rows, and sometimes girdles a limb or tree, and for this he is pronounced a rascal by men who have themselves ruthlessly cut from our land millions of trees that should now be standing. However, the sapsucker does not live solely on sap and the soft cambium layer of the tree; he also feeds on insects wherever he finds them. When feeding their young, sapsuckers are true flycatchers, getting the insects while on the wing. If you find a sapsucker girdling a tree in your orchard or a birch on your lawn, just protect the trees with a wire netting, and let the sapsucker catch mosquitoes for you instead, and remember that he belongs to a good family and is entitled to some consideration, even if he has taken to drink.

The red-head (Fig. 185) is well named, for his helmet and visor show a vivid, glowing crimson that stirs the sensibilities of the color lover. He is readily distinguished from all other woodpeckers because his entire head and the bib under his chin are red. For the rest, he is a beautiful dark metallic blue and white. He is a most adept drummer, and his roll is a long one. One that I observed last spring selected a dead limb at the top of an oak tree and there he drummed merrily every morning. He is an adaptable fellow and has been known to drum on tin roofs and lightning rods, thus braving the dangers of civilization for the sake of better music. Though he can rattle so well when he is musically inclined, he is not, after all, much of a woodpecker, for he lives mostly on insects which he catches while they are crawling or on the wing, and he also likes nuts. He is especially fond of beech nuts, and, being a thrifty fellow as well as musical, in time of plenty he stores up food against time of need. He places his nuts in crevices and forks of branches, in holes in trees, and other hiding places. Lets us watch him this spring and see whether we can discover what he eats.

Fig. 185. The Red-headed Woodpecker.

QUESTIONS ABOUT WOODPECKERS TO BE ANSWERED IN APRIL
AND MAY.

1. Have you observed any species of woodpecker drumming?
2. Have you been able to see the drum? If so, describe it.
3. Are you able to distinguish between the tapping of the wood-pecker when searching for food, and his drumming when he is making music?

18

4. If you have made any observations on the sapsucker, please give them.

5. Have you seen the sapsucker at work? If so, did the holes girdle the tree? Were the holes round or square?

6. Have you seen the red-head this spring?

7. Describe the way the woodpecker uses its tail when climbing a tree.

8. Send for Builetin No. 7, of the United States Department of Agriculture, Division of Ornothology, called "Food of Wood-peckers." Read this Bulletin and answer these questions: Does the sapsucker do more harm than good? What special benefit to us is the red-head? Which is the most useful of our woodpeckers?

THE FLICKER OR YELLOW HAMMER.*

The first time I ever saw a flicker I said, "What a wonderful meadow lark, and what is it doing on that ant hill?" But another glance revealed to me a red spot on the back of the bird's neck, and as soon as I was sure that this was not a bloody gash I knew it belonged to no meadow lark. The golden brown plumage dotted with black, the under wings of luminous yellow, the white spot above the tail, the ashen gray back, and, above all, the oriental ornaments of crescents, — one brilliant red across the back of the neck, one black across the breast, — all conduce to make the flicker one of our most showy and beautiful birds. The flicker has many names, such as golden-winged woodpecker, yellow hammer, highhole, and yarup or wake-up, and many others. It earned the name of highhole because of its way of excavating its nest high up in trees, usually between ten and twenty-five feet from the ground. It especially loves an old apple tree as a site for a nest, and most of our large, old orchards of New York State may boast of a pair of these handsome birds during the nesting season of May and June. However, the flicker is not above renting any house he finds vacant which was made by other birds last year. The flicker earned his name of "yarup" or "wake-up" from his spring song, which is a rollicking jolly "wick-a-wick-a-wick." As a business bird the flicker shines in the rather extraordinary line of eating ants. It has a tongue equipped almost exactly like the tongue of the animal called the ant eater, and it often may be seen using it with great effectiveness in catching the little communal laborers.

* Home Nature-Study Course, Vol. IV, No. 32, May, 1903.

Fig. 186.   Young Flickers.

Those who have observed the flicker during the courting season declare him to be the most silly and vain of all the bird wooers. Mr. Baskett says, "When he wishes to charm his sweetheart he mounts a very small twig near her, and lifts his wings, spreads his tail, and begins to nod right and left as he exhibits his mustache to his charmer, and sets his jet locket first on one side of the twig and then the other. He may even go so far as to turn his head half around to show her the pretty spot on his 'back hair.' In doing all this he performs the most ludicrous antics, and has the silliest of expressions of face and voice as if in losing his heart, as some one phrases it, he had lost his head also."

SUMMARY OF THE STUDY OF WOODPECKERS.

We have now studied our five species of woodpeckers common in New York State, and I trust that you know them all by sight. When you are teaching the children about the woodpecker, there are many interesting stories to tell about the way that his form is adapted to his life. Some of these stories are as follows : First. The woodpecker's bill, which is a drill and chisel, and how he uses it for getting at the grub or the borer in the wood, and for making the hole for the nest, and for drumming when he feels musical. Second. The tongue, which is a barbed spear, and has a wonderful spring attachment of bones which allows it to be thrust far out. This tongue is fitted in each case to get the kind of food which sustains its owner. Third. The feet have a special arrangement of toes which allows the bird to cling tenaciously to a tree trunk. Study the way the fourth toe, which may be compared to our little finger, has been moved around backward so that it acts as another thumb. Fourth. Study how the tail made of stiff feathers is particularly adapted to act as a brace, helping the bird to climb a tree. In studying all these things I would especially recommend you to a little book called, "The Woodpeckers" by Fannie Hardy Eckstrom, published by Houghton, Mifflin & Co., price $1.00.

QUESTIONS ON THE FLICKER.

1. Have you ever seen a flicker?
2. Do you know its song?
3. Has the flicker a straight bill like the downy's?
4. What are the differences between the male and female flicker?

5. Have you ever seen a flicker catching ants? Describe.

6. Do you think the flicker is a beneficial bird? If so, why?

7. Have you ever seen a flicker's nest? Describe.

8. Do you know how the flicker feeds its young? Explain.

9. Describe the difference in color between the male and female of the (a) downy, (b) the hairy, (c) the redhead, (d) the sapsucker, (e) and the flicker.

10. How can you tell the difference between a flicker and a meadow lark during flight?

Downy's long tongue.

LEAFLET XXV.

THE CHICKADEE.*

BY ANNA BOTSFORD COMSTOCK.

He is the hero of the woods ; there are courage and good nature enough in that compact little body, which you may hide in your fist, to supply a whole groveful of May songsters. He has the Spartan virtue of an eagle, the cheerfulness of a thrush, the nimbleness of Cock Sparrow, the endurance of the seabirds condensed into his tiny frame, and there have been added a pertness and ingenuity all his own. His curiosity is immense, and his audacity equal to it ; I have even had one alight upon the barrel of the gun over my shoulder as I sat quietly under his tree.— ERNEST INGERSOLL.

HOWEVER careless we may be of our friends when we are in the midst of the luxurious life of summer, even the most careless among us give pleased attention to the birds that bravely endure with us the rigors of winter. And when this winged companion of winter proves to be the most fascinating little ball of feathers ever created, constantly overflowing with cheerful song, our pleased attention changes to active delight. Thus it is that in all the lands of snowy winters the chickadee is a loved comrade of the country wayfarer ; that happy song, "chick-a-dee-dee-dee," finds its way to the dullest consciousness and the most callous heart.

One day in February we were, with much enjoyment, wading through a drifted highway that skirted a forest, the least twig of which bore a burden of soft snow. Over all hung that silence of winter which is the most "silent silence" that rests upon the earth anywhere outside the desert. No breeze swayed a creaking branch or shook from it the snow in soft thud to the white carpet below. Even the song of the brook was smothered beneath coverlets of ice and pillows of drift. We stood fast, awed by the stillness, when suddenly it was broken by the thrilling notes of

---

* Home Nature-Study Course, Vol. V, No. 3, December, 1903.

the chickadees. We could hardly credit our senses, for it seemed as if the woods was a hopeless place for any living creature that morning. But there before our eyes was a flock of these courageous birds hunting for food on the leeward sides of boles and branches left bare and black in the recent storm. Their tiny weights sent the snow in showers from the terminal twigs, which phenomenon was greeted with triumphant song while the cheerful midgets hunted the relieved branches topside and bottomside for any lurking tidbit. As we watched them, Emerson's poem came to mind :

> " Piped a tiny voice near by,
> Gay and polite, a cheerful cry—
> Chick-chickadeedee ! saucy note
> Out of sound heart and merry throat,
> As if it said, ' Good-day, good Sir !
> Fine afternoon, old passenger !
> Happy to meet you in these places
> Where January brings few faces.' "

Fig. 187. A chickadee at the entrance to its nest.

No wonder that the great American philosopher was attracted by this other American philosopher who sings when he is cold and hungry.

Besides its usual song the chickadee has a song that says " phœbe " much more distinctly than does the song of the phœbe itself. Few people recognize this, and often in February or early March it is announced in the local newspaper, " The phœbe-birds were heard to-day " though it may be weeks yet before these birds arrive. The two songs may be easily distinguished by even the ear untrained to music. In the phœbe song of the chickadee, the last syllable is at least one note lower than the first and has a falling inflection ; while the last syllable of the phœbe bird's song is at least a half note higher than the first and has a rising inflection.

Not long since I visited the deserted nest of a devoted pair of chickadees. It was cuddled down in the bottom of a hole that opened on the very top of a fence post, and, one would imagine, must have been wet more than once while inhabited. However, a large family was raised there during the past season and much enjoyment was derived from watching the many fubsy birdlings that found home and comfort in that unattractive retreat. I looked upon them with special interest, for I was sure they would visit the suet on my trees this winter and thus become friendly neighbors.

As soon as the trees are bare, nail or tie bits of suet to branches which may be observed from your windows. I know of no invest-ment which pays such enormous dividends both to pleasure and pocket as do suet restaurants in orchards patronized by chicka-dees. Every child, at home or school, will be attracted by this experiment.

QUESTIONS ON THE CHICKADEE.

1. Describe the colors of the chickadee above ; below ; wings ; tail ; throat and head.

2. Describe the differences in coloring between the chickadee and the nuthatch.

3. What is the shape of the chickadee's beak and for what is it adapted ?

4. Does it frequent the trunks of trees, or the twigs ?

5. Describe its actions when hunting for food on a twig.

6. What is the chief food of the chickadee ?

7. Why is it of special value to the farmer ?

8. What are the differences in the winter and summer habits of the chickadee ?

9. Do you know the "phœbe" note of the chickadee ?

10. Where do these birds build their nests and of what material ?

11. What are the colors and markings on the eggs ?

12. When is the nesting season ?

THE WHITE–BREASTED NUTHATCH.*

By ANNA BOTSFORD COMSTOCK.

The busy nuthatch climbs his tree,
Around the great bole spirally,
Peeping into wrinkles gray,
Under ruffled lichens gay,
Lazily piping one sharp note
From his silver mailèd throat.
— MAURICE THOMPSON.

" *With more artless inquisitiveness than fear, this lively little acrobat stops his hammering or hatching at your approach, and stretching himself out from the tree until it would seem he must fall off, he peers down at you, head downward, straight into your upturned opera-glass. If there is too much snow on the upper side of a branch watch how he runs along underneath it like a fly, busily tapping the bark, or adroitly breaking the decayed bits with his bill, as he stretches for the spider's eggs, larvæ, etc., hidden there ; yet somehow, between mouthfuls, managing to call out his cherry quank ! quank ! hank ! hank !*"
— NELTJE BLANCHAN.

A VOICE outside is calling at me ; I cannot describe it accurately, but it is making delightful woodsy remarks that make me long to throw aside the pen and go out and wander where the snow is making still softer the carpet of dead leaves on the forest floor. It is not a musical note but it is most enticing and translates into sound the picture of bare-branched trees and the feeling of enchantment that permeates the forest in winter. Neltje Blanchan says the voice reiterates "quank, quank," others say it is "nay, nay"— but no nasal sound of the human voice, and no spelling of the English language adequately represent this call of the white-breasted nuthatch.

On the tree in front of the window I can see the owner of this

---

*Home Nature-Study Course, Vol. V, No. 4, January, 1904.

sylvan voice.　He is a little bird blue-gray above with black head and black and white V-trimmings on the back of his suit, and with soft, white breast.　He is flitting blithely from tree to tree enjoying the snow storm and coming often to the suet feast which I have spread for him and for his little feathered kin.

We have been having exciting times at the suet banquet this morning.　The building in which my office is, stands on a high knoll near the forest-covered brink of a deep gorge.　Thus my window is opposite the tops of the trees. One of our nature-study staff, a brave and gallant knight, who loves birds and knows that I love to watch them, climbed two of these trees at imminent risk of breaking his neck in order to place this suet just opposite my window.　The whole chickadee family and four nuthatches, and Sir Downy and Madam Hairy had been reveling in the feast all the morning when suddenly

Fig. 188.　The nuthatch, one of the winter birds.

one after another three crows appeared upon the scene.　My heart sank as I saw them eying the suet with interest. Nearer and nearer they hopped from branch to branch.　I pounded on the widow and called out, "Go away" in both the crow and the English language, all in vain.　One crow braver or hungrier than the others with one defiant eye on me flapped confidently down and sought to carry the suet off in his beak ; to his surprise it was tied on.　That seemed suspicious and when we raised the window and leaning far out explained matters he lifted slowly with a jeering "caw" that said plainly "I'll call sometime when you are not at home" and with that he and his companions disappeared up the gorge.　The invited guests at the suet table were less disturbed than was I, and I suppose it is rather inconsistent to feed the chickadees and let the ravens go hungry.　But this suet will last the little birds a month while it would hardly furnish a breakfast for three crows ; and in philanthropic enterprises one is obliged to draw the line somewhere even at the cost of consistency.

　　I will return to my nuthatch, who, by the way, has just hammered off a piece of suet and thrust it into a crevice of the bark on the tree bole. Why does he do that : is it for convenience in eating or is it an attempt to store up some of his dinner for future need? Anyway it is bad manners, like carrying off fruit from *table d' hote*. But he is polite enough in another respect ; every time after eating the suet he wipes his beak on his branch napkin with great assiduity, first one side and then the other, almost as if he were sharpening it. The woodpeckers are similarly fastidious in cleaning suet off their beaks.

The loud note of the nuthatch, seeming to be out of proportion to the size of the bird is, by no means, its only note. Yesterday we observed a pair hunting over the branches of an elm over our heads, and they were talking to each other in sweet confidential syllables " wit, wit, wit," entirely different from the loud note that is meant for the world at large.

The nuthatches and chickadees hunt together all winter. This is no business partnership, but one of congeniality based upon similar tastes. Thus it is that the two birds are often confused. There is, however, a very noticeable character that distinguishes them at the first glance. Strange to say the nuthatch has also been confused with the sapsucker and has gained unjust obloquy thereby. How any one with eyes could confuse these two birds is a mystery, for they resemble each other in no particular nor in general appearance.

While the nuthatch finds much of its food on trees, yet Mr. Torrey tells of seeing one awkwardly turning over the fallen leaves for hidden cocoons and other things quite worth his while ; and Mr. Baskett tells of having seem them catch flies in the air and becoming quite out of breath at this unusual exercise.

Audobon made some most interesting observations on the nuthatch. He says they may sleep hanging head downward. He also says of their nesting habits that " both birds work together, all the time congratulating each other in the tenderest manner. The male, ever conspicuous on such occasions, works some, and carries off the slender chips chiseled by the female. He struts around her, peeps into the hole, cherups at intervals, or hovers about her on the wing. While she is sitting on her eggs, he seldom absents himself many moments ; now with a full bill he feeds her, now returns to be assured that her time is pleasantly spent."

The red-breasted nuthatch is sometimes associated with its white-breasted cousin ; it is a smaller bird and is essentially a northern species. The nuthatches get their name from their habit of wedging nuts and acorns into bark and then hatching them open. From every standpoint the nuthatches are most desirable acquaintances, and we cannot spend our time to better advantage than in getting familiar with their interesting habits.

QUESTIONS ON THE WHITE-BREASTED NUTHATCH.

1. Describe from your own observations the colors of the nuthatch above and below.

2. (a) What is the most noticeable character that distinguishes the nuthatch from the chickadee? (b) Does the nuthatch usually frequent the bole or the twigs of a tree? (c) Is there any difference in this respect between the habits of the nuthatch and the chickadee?

3. Does the nuthatch alight with its head down or up?

4. Does it travel down or up? Does it always go in a spiral?

5. What is its food?

6. Does it open nuts for the meat or the grubs within?

7. Does it use its tail as a brace in climbing trees as does the woodpecker?

8. Where does it build its nest?

9. What is the color of the eggs?

10. Why does it seem less common in summer than in winter?

11. How does it use its feet when resting on a tree trunk?

12. Has it any special development of the feet to help it in traveling on tree trunks?

13. Do you know the note of the nuthatch? Describe.

14. How would you spell its note?

15. How does the nuthatch help the farmer and fruit grower?

LEAFLET XXVII.

ABOUT CROWS.*

By MARY ROGERS MILLER.

 THOUSANDS and thousands of crows fast asleep amongst the branches of a grove of pines! The trees themselves look dark and sombre against the snowy hillside, but when the assemblage of dusky birds has gathered there, the shadows thicken and the darkness settles like a pall. Soon all is hushed and silent.

Would you not go miles to see such a sight?

Yet maybe you have lived for years within easy walking distance of a great crow " dormitory " without even suspecting its existence. You may have watched the crows flying overhead every morning and then again every afternoon, without noticing that they came from the same direction each morning and returned at nightfall. This was just my experience until I began to care about crows and their ways. Now I know that there is a sleeping roost a mile or so up one of our wooded valleys and the oldest inhabitant tells me that he remembers seeing "more'n a million " crows up there in winters when he was a boy. Undoubtedly generation after generation of crows return to these sleeping places ; certain localities have probably been so used for centuries.

Although we have crows here all winter they may not be the same individuals that spent the summer here. The center of crow population in the eastern United States from November till February is the neighborhood of Chesapeake Bay. There the food supply is more abundant than where the ground is snow-covered in winter, and thither the crows migrate in innumerable armies. Dormitories from ten to thirty acres in extent and accommodating from ten thousand to three hundred thousand crows each have been found in that region.

Why crows gather thus in companies either small or large is undoubtedly due to their natural sociability. The opportunities

*Home Nature-Study Course, Vol. IV, No. 27, December, 1902.

for exhibition of conversational powers offered by such a custom seems to be greatly appreciated by every crow. Such a babel as they raise when in early morning their watchman rouses them from sleep! They appear to be reviling him for his untimely interruption. For several minutes the woods fairly ring with their loud, coarse shouts. Then, as if resigned to their fate, they take flight towards the feeding grounds. By sunset they all congregate again and after recounting their adventures, settle down early to sleep.

In open winters crows fare well enough. Seeds and berries are easy to get and considerable grain may be found in harvested fields. But like barnyard fowls, crows are omniverous. After the grasshoppers disappear, a supply of animal food is hard to get. The silken egg-sacs of spiders are often found torn open and rifled, while suspiciously near by are the tracks of crows. Undoubtedly rabbits and field mice would unite with the spiders in declaring the crow to be their deadly enemy.

That crows eat corn is undeniable. The farmers know it to their sorrow, the bird's champions reluctantly admit it, the crow himself goes openly into the field, both in winter and summer, with no intent to conceal his intentions. And yet this universally acknowledged habit will bear investigation. Upon the real or supposed injury done to sprouting corn and to roasting-ears, the farmer and his sons base their animosity toward crows and rejoice at the wholesale or retail slaughter of these birds. Carefully prepared estimates show conclusively that the crow is the farmer's friend. Only *three per cent* of the total food of the crow consists of corn in any form, while *twenty-six per cent* consists of insects such as grasshoppers, May beetles (June bugs, whose young are the white grubs), cutworms and other injurious kinds. On such evidence as this would not an unprejudiced jury acquit the crow?

The best way to establish the crow in this new and true relationship to the farmer, is to interest the boys and girls in studying crows and their ways. To make a fair judgment, one must collect evidence. Mere hearsay is not always to be depended on. Justice and truth are worth working for. The case of the Crow *vs.* the Farmer, will give opportunity for the practice of both of these virtues

Winter Birds.*

The winter is not so devoid of life as we sometimes think. There are mammals in the woods and coverts, fishes in the lakes and deep brooks, birds in the forest and the open. Let us devote one early midwinter lesson to the birds. Have the children make particular observations on the English sparrow. Other birds may be observed, as, for example, our old friend the crow. All these birds touch the life of the farmer and the nature-lover. Those students who are so situated that a study of crows is impossible may substitute English sparrows, chickadees, woodpeckers or any other winter birds.

A bulletin entitled "The Common Crow" was issued by the U. S. Department of Agriculture in 1895. Students in this course can obtain one copy each by sending ten cents to Superintendent of Documents, Union Building, Washington, D. C. Do not send stamps.

Do crows winter in your vicinity?

Are you able to verify the statements made in the lesson concerning the flight in opposite directions in morning and evening? Give observations made since receiving this lesson.

Is there a crow dormitory in your vicinity? (Inquire of old residents and keep a close watch.)

Watch a crow on the wing. If he is flying low, try to count the big wing feathers. Note here any peculiarities of this bird's way of flying.

How does a crow hold on to a limb when asleep?

What characteristics have crows and chickens in common?

How do they differ?

Compare feathers, bills and feet of chickens and crows.

Look for crow tracks in the snow. Where have you seen them? Can you always tell which way the bird was going? How? Sketch the tracks on separate sheet.

How long is the longest toe, including the claw? Which toe is this?

Is the track ever longer than the toe itself? If so, why?

Have you ever seen the scratches in the snow made by the stiff wing feathers when the crow takes its flight from the ground?

Count the scratches.

---

* Quiz on Lesson No. 27, December, 1902.

What food have you seen crows eating?

Watch during the whole month and mention any new items you can add to their bill of fare.

Have you ever seen crow's nests? Where? When?

Describe the nest, eggs and nestlings, if you have seen them. (These are things to look for during the spring and summer.)

Does the plumage of the yearling crow differ from that of the older birds?

Do males and females differ in color?

Crows are said to possess remarkably well developed brains. What evidence have you of their sagacity, fearlessness, cunning or greed?

What other winter birds have you seen this year?

Give on separate sheet an account of a winter walk.

LEAFLET XXVIII.

HOW A SQUASH PLANT GETS OUT OF THE SEED.*

By L. H. BAILEY.

IF one were to plant seeds of a Hubbard or Boston Marrow squash in loose warm earth in a pan or box, and were then to leave the parcel for a week or ten days, he would find, upon his return, a colony of plants like that shown in Fig. 189. If he had not planted the seeds himself or had not seen such plants before, he would not believe that these curious plants would ever grow into squash vines, so different are they from the vines which we know in the garden. This, itself, is a most curious fact,— this wonderful difference between the first and the later stages of nearly all plants, and it is only because we know it so well that we do not wonder at it.

It may happen, however,— as it did in a pan of seed which I sowed a few days ago — that one or two of the plants may look like that shown in Fig. 190. Here the seed seems to have come up on top of the plant ; and one is reminded of the curious way in which beans come up on the stalk of the young plant. If we were to study the matter, however, — as we may do at a future time — we should find a great difference in the ways in which the squashes and the beans raise their seeds out of the ground. It is not our purpose to compare the squash and the bean at this time, but we are curious to know why one of these squash plants brings its seed up out of the ground whilst all the others do not. In order to find out why it is, we must ask the plant, and this asking is what we call an experiment. We may first pull up the two

Fig. 189.
Squash plant
a week old.

---

*Teacher's Leaflet No. 1, December, 1896. The first Cornell nature-study leaflet. For a discussion of the title of this leaflet and what it signifies pedagogically, consult " The Integument Man," in " The Nature-Study Idea." (Doubleday, Page & Co.)

plants. The first one (Fig. 189) will be seen to have the seed-
coats still attached to the very lowest part of the stalk below the
soil, but the other plant has no seed at that point. We
will now plant more seeds, a dozen or more of them,
so that we shall have enough to examine two or three
times a day for several days. A day or two after the
seeds are planted, we shall find a little point or root-
like part breaking out of the sharp end of the seed, as
shown in Fig. 191. A day later this root
part has grown to be as long as the seed
itself (Fig. 192), and it has turned
directly downwards into the soil. But
there is another most interesting
thing about this germinating seed.

Fig. 191. Germi-
nation just begin-
ning.

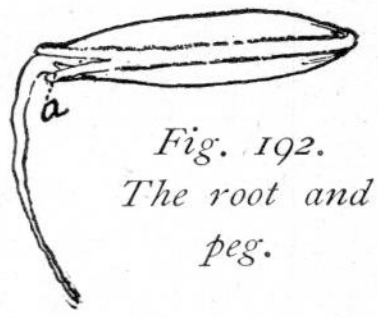

Just where the root is breaking out of the seed (shown
at *a* in Fig. 192), there is a little peg or projection. In
Fig. 193, about a day later, the root
has grown still longer, and this peg
seems to be forcing the seed apart.
In Fig. 194, however, it will be seen
that the seed is really being forced
apart by the stem or stalk above the
peg for this stem is now growing longer. The lower
lobe of the seed has attached to the peg (seen at *a*, Fig. 194), and
the seed-leaves seem to be backing out of the seed. Fig. 195

Fig. 190.
*Squash plant
which has
brought the
seed-coats
out of the
ground.*

Fig. 192.
*The root and
peg.*

shows the seed a day later.
The root has now pro-
duced many branches and
has thoroughly established
itself in the soil. The top
is also growing rapidly and
is still backing out of the seed, and the
seed-coats are still firmly held by the
obstinate peg.

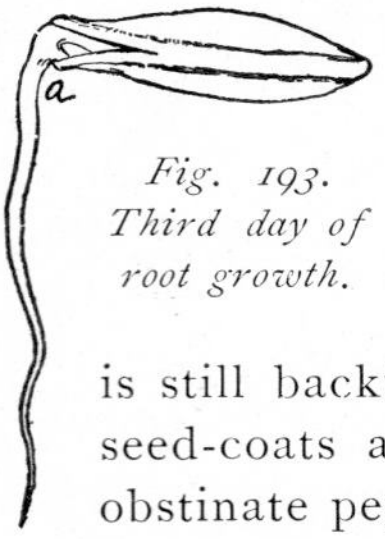

Fig. 193.
*Third day of
root growth.*

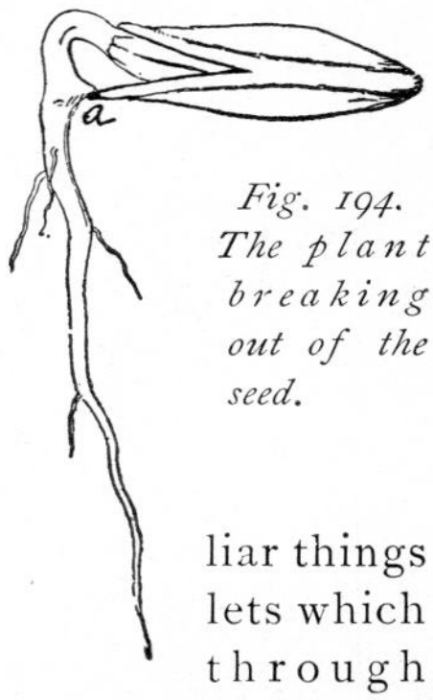

Fig. 194.
*The plant
breaking
out of the
seed.*

Whilst we have been seeing all these pecu
in the seeds which we have dug up, the plant
we have not disturbed have been coming
the soil. If we were to see the plant in Fig. 195, as it was "coming up," it would look like Fig. 196. It is tugging away in getting its head out of the bonnet which is pegged down underneath
the soil, and it has "got its back up" in the operation. In Fig.

liar things
lets which
through

197 it has escaped from its trap and it is laughing and growing in delight. It must now straighten itself up, as it is doing in Fig. 197, and it is soon standing proud and straight, as in Fig. 189. We now see that the reason why the "seed" came up on the plant in Fig. 190, is that in some way the peg did not hold the seed-coats down (see Fig. 195), and the expanding leaves,

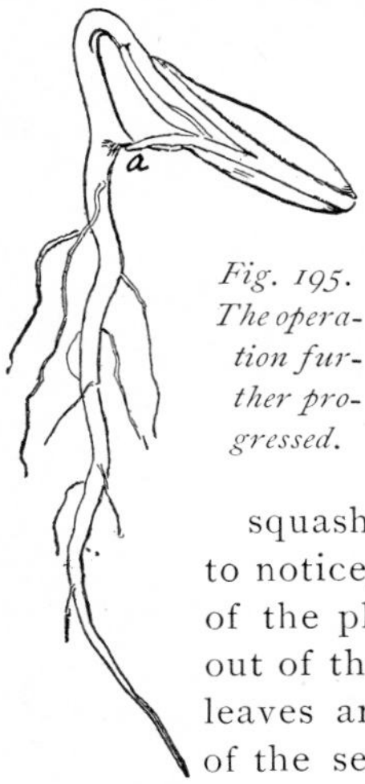

Fig. 195. The operation further progressed.

being pinched together must get themselves loose as best they can.

There is another thing about this interesting

Fig. 196. The plant just coming up.

squash plant which we must not fail to notice, and this is the fact that these first two leaves of the plantlet came out of the seed and did not grow out of the plant itself. We must notice, too, that these leaves are much smaller when they are first drawn out of the seed-coat than they are when the plantlet has straightened itself up. That is, these leaves increase very much in size after they reach the light and air. The roots of the plantlet are now established in the soil and are taking in food which enables the plant to grow. The next leaves which appear will be very different from these first or seed leaves.

These later ones are called the true leaves. They grow right out of the little plant itself. Fig. 199 shows these true leaves as they appear on a young Crookneck squash plant, and the plant now begins to look much like a squash vine.

Fig. 197. The plant liberated from the seed-coats.

We are now curious to know how the stem grows when it backs out of the seeds and pulls the little seed-leaves with it, and how the root grows downwards into the soil. Now let us pull up another seed when it has sent a single root about two inches deep into the earth. We will wash it very carefully and lay it upon a piece of paper. Then we will lay a ruler alongside of it, and make an ink mark one-quarter of an inch from the tip, and two or three

Fig. 198. The plant straightening up.

other marks at equal distances above (Fig. 200).* We will now carefully replant the seed.   Two days later we will dig it up,

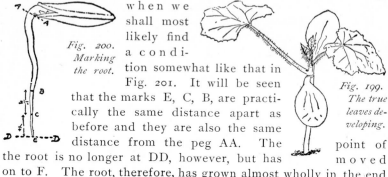

when we shall most likely find a con di- tion somewhat like that in Fig. 201.   It will be seen that the marks E, C, B, are practi- cally the same distance apart as before and they are also the same distance from the peg AA.   The point of the root is no longer at DD, however, but has moved on to F.   The root, therefore, has grown almost wholly in the end part.

Fig. 200. Marking the root.

Fig. 199. The true leaves de- veloping.

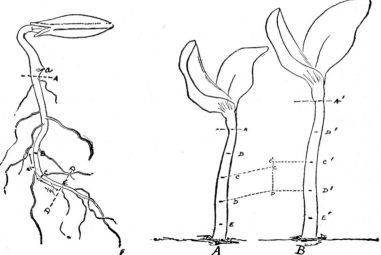

Fig. 201.   The root grows in the end parts.

Fig. 202.   The marking of the stem, and the spreading apart of the marks.

---

*NOTE.—Common ink will not answer for this purpose because it "runs" when the root is wet; indelible ink, used for marking linen or for drawing, should be used.   It should also be said that the root of the common pumpkin and of the summer bush squashes is too fibrous and branchy for this test.   It should be stated also that the root does not grow at its very tip, but chiefly in a narrow zone just back of the tip; but the determination of this point is rather too difficult for the beginner, and, moreover, it is foreign to the purpose of this tract.

Now let us make a similar experiment with the stem or stalk. We will mark a young stem, as at A in Fig. 202 ; but the next day we shall find that these marks are farther apart than when we made them (B, Fig. 202).   The marks have all raised themselves above the ground as the plant has grown.   The stem, therefore, has grown between the joints rather than from the end.   The stem usually grows most rapidly, at any given time, at the upper or younger part of the joint (or internode) ; and the joint soon reaches the limit of its growth and becomes stationary, while a new one grows out above it.

LEAFLET XXIX.

HOW THE TREES LOOK IN WINTER.*

By L. H. BAILEY.

NLY the growing and open season is thought to be attractive in the country. The winter is bare and cheerless. The trees are naked. The flowers are under the snow. The birds have flown. The only bright and cheery spot is the winter fireside. But even there the farmer has so much time that he does not know what to do with it. Only those who have little time, appreciate its value.

But the winter is not lifeless and charmless. It is only dormant. The external world fails to interest us because we have not been trained to see and know it ; and also because the rigorous weather and the snow prevent us from going afield. In the spring, summer, and fall, the hours are full to over-

---

To the teacher.—We want the country child to have a closer touch with nature in the winter time. Teach him to see, to know, and to care for the trees when they are leafless. This leaflet will suggest how you may interest him.

You can also intensify his interest in the subject, and at the same time increase his knowledge of drawing, by having him make skeleton or outline drawings of the trees about the schoolhouse or the home. Leaflet XXX gives suggestions for drawing.

You can correlate this work with geography by giving the distribution or range of the different kinds of trees. Indicate the limit of distribution northward, southward, eastward, westward ; also the regions in which the species is most abundant. The common manuals of botany will help you in this work ; or you may consult the many excellent special books on trees.

In teaching nature-study, remember that a great part of its value lies in the enthusiasm and zeal with which you handle it. Try, also, to develop the æsthetic sense of the pupil ; but do not teach mere sentiment.

---

*Teacher's Leaflet No. 12, January, 1899.

flowing with life and interest. On every hand we are in contact with nature. If the farmer's winter is to be more enjoyable the farmer must have more points of contact with the winter world. One of the best and most direct of these points of sympathy is an interest in the winter aspects of trees.

Fig. 204. Pignut Hickory. This and Fig.
Fig. 203. Small-fruited Shagbark Hickory.   *203 are from " Lessons with Plants."*

a. The Structure of the Tree-top.

In the summer time we distinguish the kinds of trees chiefly by means of the shape and the foliage. In winter the foliage is gone ; but the shape remains, and the framework of the tree is also conspicuous. Trees are as distinct in winter as in summer ; and in some respects their characters are more apparent and pronounced.

Observe the outline of a tree against the dull winter sky. It does not matter what kind of tree it is. Note its height, shape, and size of top, how many branches there are, how the branches are arranged on the main trunk, the direction of the branches, whether the twigs are few or many, crooked or straight.

Having observed these points in any tree, compare one kind of tree with another and note how they differ in these features. Compare an apple tree with an elm, an elm with a maple, a

Fig. 205.   Slippery Elm.   The expression is stiff and hard.

basswood with a pine, a poplar with a beech, a pear tree with a peach tree.

Having made comparisons between very dissimilar trees, compare those which are much alike, as the different kinds of maples, of elms, of oaks, of poplars. As your powers of observation become trained, compare the different varieties of the same kind of fruit trees, if there are good orchards in the vicinity. The different varieties of pears afford excellent contrasts. Contrast the Bartlett with the Flemish Beauty, the Kieffer with the Seckel. In apples, compare the Baldwin with the Spy, the King with the Twenty Ounce. The sweet and sour cherries show marked differences in method of branching. Fruit men can tell many varieties apart in winter. How?

Fig. 206. Swamp White Oak.

Two common hickories are shown in Figs. 203 and 204. How do they differ? Do they differ in length of trunk? General method of branching? Direction of branches? Character of twig growth? Straightness or crookedness of branches?

Contrast the slippery elm (Fig. 205) and the common or American elm (Fig. 211). The former has a crotchy or forked growth, and long, stiff, wide-spreading branches. The latter is more vase-like in shape. The branches are willowy and graceful, with a tendency to weep.

Compare the oaks. The white and scarlet oaks have short trunks when they grow in fields, and the main branches are comparatively few and make bold angles and curves. The swamp white oak (Fig. 206), however, has a more continuous trunk, with many comparatively small, horizontal, and tortuous branches.

With Fig. 206 compare the pepperidge (Fig. 207). This is one of the most unusual and interesting of all our native trees. It grows in swales. It has a very tough-grained wood. The autumn foliage is deep red and handsome. The peculiarities of the tree are the continuation of the trunk to near the summit, and the many lateral, short, deflected, tortuous branches.

Consider the structure of the sassafras in Fig. 208. The great branches stand off nearly at right angles to the trunk, and are bushy and twiggy at the ends. Each large branch if cut off at its base and stood upright would look like an independent tree, so tree-like are its branches. Observe how much more bushy the sassafras is than any of the other trees already figured. Compare it in the method of branching and the twigginess with the slippery elm (Fig. 205).

But there is still greater brushiness in the thorn-apple (Fig. 209). In twigginess Figs. 208 and 209 are very unlike, however. Pick out the differences. Observe the very short and spur-like twigs in the thorn-apple ; also notice how soon the trunk is lost in the branches.

With all the foregoing pictures compare the steeple-like

Fig. 207. *Pepperidge or Sour Gum. The oddest of New York trees.*

form of the Lombardy poplar (Fig. 210). The tree is frequent along roadsides and about yards. What is its structure? Observe it as it stands against the winter sky. There is nothing else in our northern landscape so straight and spire-like. If you know a beech tree standing in a field, contrast it with the Lombardy poplar. These two trees represent extremes of vertical and of horizontal branching.

Aside from the general structure of the tree-top, the pupil will become interested in the winter color of the tree and in the character of the bark. How does the bark differ between elms and maples, oaks and chestnuts, birches and beeches, hickories and walnuts? Why does the bark separate in ridges or peel off in strips? Is it not associated with the increase in diameter of the trunk? The method of breaking of the bark is different and peculiar for each kind of tree.

Look at these things ; and think about them.

THE EXPRESSION OF THE TREE.

Consciously or unconsciously, we think of trees much as we think of persons. They suggest thoughts and feelings which are

Fig. 208. Sassafras. Type of a bushy-topped tree.

also attributes of people. A tree is weeping, gay, restful, spirited, quiet, sombre. That is, trees have expression.

The expression resides in the observer, however, not in the tree. Therefore, the more the person is trained to observe and to reflect, the more sensitive his mind to the things about him, and the more meaning the trees have. No one loves nature who does not love trees. We love them for what they are, wholly aside from their uses in fruit-bearing or shade-giving. A knowledge and love of trees binds one close to the external world.

Fig. 209.   Thorn-apple.   One of the most picturesque objects in the winter landscape.

How shall one increase his love of trees? First, by knowing them. He learns their attributes and names. Knowing them in winter, as already suggested, is one of the ways of becoming acquainted. Second, by endeavoring to determine what thought or feeling they chiefly express. The slippery elm is stiff and hard. The American elm is soft and graceful. The Lombardy

ONE WAY OF DRAWING TREES IN THEIR WINTER ASPECT.*

By C. W. FURLONG.

THE few suggestions which are set forth in these pages are based upon two assumptions : — first, that the teacher has some knowledge of the most salient principles of elementary perspective ; and second, that she has a love for all things beautiful. It is feasible to deal here not to any extent with art in either its abstract or its concrete form, but only with drawing.

Drawing, in its simplest analysis, is the ability to record objects as they appear to the normal eye.

Art is more complicated. It includes many elements, a few of which are composition, expression of movement, and action. The very thought, feeling, and refinement of the artist must be expressed in his work. He must tell not only what he sees, but also what he feels. He interprets nature through his own moods.

There are no outlines in nature. The boundaries, shapes, and character of various forms are determined by the difference of their color values, and the contrasts of light and shade. Yet an outline drawing is the simplest means of representing form and proportion. Although inadequate in many respects, this somewhat conventional rendering is important to the beginner, for it is necessary that the child be taught to observe forms and proportions correctly ; and these impressions may be recorded most simply and definitely by outline drawings. Michael Angelo emphasized its importance in these words : "The science of drawing or of outline is the essence of painting and all the fine arts, and the root of all the sciences."

To a great extent, one may show in an outline drawing the character and texture of surfaces. Our main object should be to train the boys and girls to observe in order to acquire a correctness of perception, for "education amongst us consists too much in telling, not enough in training."

---

* Teacher's Leaflet, No. 12, January, 1899.

Fig. 211. The American Elm, one of the most typical of vase-form trees.

One of the greatest difficulties is to impress upon the minds of beginners the fact that they must think while they look and draw. Insist upon the pupil's looking repeatedly at the object. It is better to observe for five minutes and draw for one, than to observe for one and draw for five.

Make the drawing lesson more interesting by telling the class something about the object which they are to draw, involving in the story facts that will impress upon their minds some of the most salient characteristics of the object. Encourage the children to discuss the object, drawing out facts for their own observation. Certain kinds of trees, like certain races of people, have a general similarity, yet every single tree has an individuality of its own.

Apply a few essential questions that will help to determine at least the kind of tree it is, the race to which it belongs ; for first we must get its general character, seeing its big proportions and shape ; and later must search for its individualities.

Is it tall for its greatest width ?

How far does the trunk extend before dividing ?

At what height do the lowest branches arise ?

What is their general direction ?

Do they appear to radiate from the trunk ?

How do they appear to radiate from the trunk ?

How do the main branches compare in size with the trunk ?

Are they crooked or straight ?

The manner of branch growth must be studied carefully.

We see in our elm (Fig. 211) that the trunk divides at about a fourth of its height into several main branches, while in the case of the pepperidge (Fig. 207) the trunk extends to the very top of the tree, the branches being small in proportion to the trunk, not varying much in size, and taking an oblique downward direction. Notice the weird expression of these trees with their crookedly bent tops, one side of each trunk being almost devoid of branches.

The trunk of the sassafras (Fig. 208) continues nearly to the top of this tree, while the large branches, though unsymmetrical, give it a well-balanced appearance.

Again in our picture of the thorn-apple (Fig. 209), we are at once impressed with its irregular form, the branches on the left taking a more oblique direction than those of the other side, the trunk dividing a little short of half the height of the tree.

For an example, let our subject be an elm tree (Fig. 211) ; our drawing to be rendered in outline.

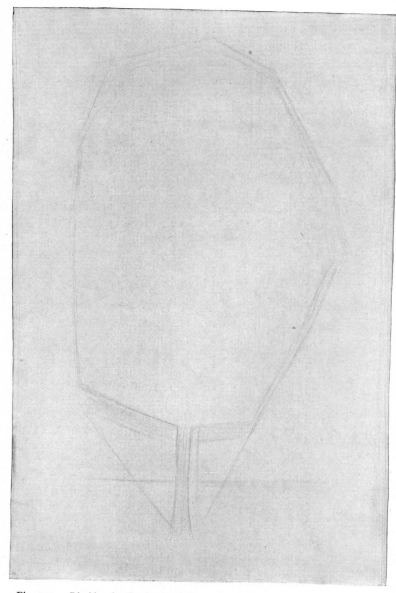

Fig. 212. *Blocking-in the elm tree (Fig. 211).* *The first work which the artist does when he draws the tree.*

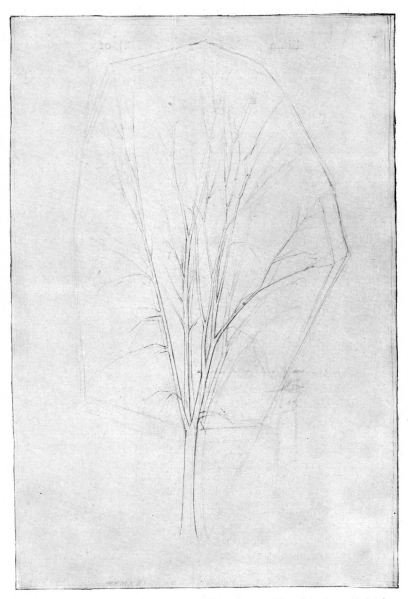

Fig. 213. *Working in the details with sharp lines. The original pencil sketch is not followed exactly.*

Material.— Almost any good drawing paper, white or buff in color, will answer our purpose ; 9x12 is a good size. Our pencil should be of medium grade lead (F. or HB.) of any standard make, Kohinoor preferred.

If procurable, we should have a light drawing board 17x22 inches (here is an opportunity for the carpenters) to place the paper on, otherwise a very stiff piece of cardboard ; or a large geography book might answer. It is best, however, to fasten our paper, which we cannot do in using the book. For fastening the paper use four thumb tacks for the corners.

A Faber or multiplex pencil eraser is needed ; also a sponge eraser with which to remove the light lines and clean the drawing before lining it in.

Our position.— Our point of view will depend upon our subject, but it is not well to be so near as to necessitate raising the head in order to see the top of the tree. If we take longer than one sitting for our drawing (which I do not think advisable, as we must not choose too complicated a subject), we must mark our position in order to obtain again the same point of view.

Position of the drawing-board.— Our paper must be placed on the board with its edges parallel to those of the board. The drawing-board should be held perpendicular, or nearly so, to the direction in which it is seen, for if the board is tilted far backward, it will be fore-shortened and our tree will probably have been drawn longer than it should be.

How to look.— The tendency of the beginner is to see and draw too much in detail. It is most essential that we look first for the large shapes, the greatest dimensions ; next for the smaller ones ; last for detail. It is not well for the pupils to work too close to their drawings. They should occasionally sit well back in their seats or get up and stand behind the seats to obtain the general effect of their drawing, to see that the big shapes are right and that the character of the tree has not been lost.

As an aid to placing our drawing so as best to fill the space it has to occupy, we may use what the French call a *cherche-motif,* the English, a finder. This is nothing more than a small piece of stiff paper or cardboard about 5x8 inches, in which is cut a small rectangular opening about ¾x1 inch ; the size and proportion may vary somewhat. We may look through this opening, the card acting as a frame to our picture. This will help us to decide whether our subject will look better placed the horizontal or the vertical way of the paper and how much of the subject to include and where to place it in that space. We may include more or less in the finder by varying its distance from the eye.

Now, I am sure we should not place ourselves within a dozen yards of our tree if we wished to get its general effect ; therefore, we must have plenty of foreground in our drawing. We must give the eye a chance to look, allowing plenty of space between the lowest point of our drawing and the lower edge of our paper.

As the height of tree we are to draw (Fig. 211) is greater than its greatest width, we find that it will fill the space best if placed the vertical way of the paper. After indicating the extreme height and width by four light marks, before carrying the drawing further we must test these proportions by comparing the width with the height, always testing the shorter dimension into the longer, viz. :

To test the drawing.— Close one eye. The pencil may be used to test the drawing by holding it in front of you at arm's length (as in Fig. 214) perpendicular to the direction in which the object is seen ; also revolving it in a plane perpendicular to the direction in which the object is seen, in order to compare one dimension with another. For example, hold your pencil horizontally at arm's length so that its blunt end covers the outermost left-hand point of the elm. Slide your

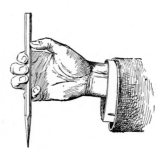

Fig. 214. How to test the drawing.

thumb along the pencil till it covers the extreme right-hand point ; retain that measurement (keeping the same position in your chair, pencil always at arm's length) ; revolve the pencil in the same plane until it coincides with the height of the elm, at the same time lowering it so that the end of the thumb covers the lowest point of the tree ; note carefully the point that the blunt end covers ; raise the pencil so that the end of the thumb covers that point, noting again where the blunt end occurs and notice how many times, and how much over, the width goes into the height. In our elm (Fig. 211) we find that the width goes about once and six-sevenths into the height, or a little short of twice. If the latter statement is preferred, we must bear in mind the proportion left over.

Do not use the scale side of a ruler or marks on the pencil or object used in order to test the proportions, and never transfer measurements from the object used in testing to your paper. A scale or other mechanical means should not be used in free-hand drawing. The teacher should have a spool of black thread and should give a piece about 2 feet 6 inches long to each pupil. An eraser, a knife, or some small article may be attached to one end of the thread. By holding the weighted thread as a plumb-line in front of us, we have an absolutely vertical line ; so by having it intersect a desired point of our tree we may obtain the relative positions to the right and left of other points above and below this intersected point.

Blocking-in.— We may conceive of the general shape of our elm by looking at it with half closed eyes. It appears in silhouette. Now imagine lines joining its outermost points ; this will give the general mass or shape of our tree. Now if we represent the outermost points contained in these lines by sketching lightly these " blocking-in " lines, as they are called, we obtain the general shape of the elm (Fig. 212). We must emphasize the fact that these blocking-in lines are to be sketched in lightly by holding the pencil near the blunt end, using a free-arm motion. Now before going farther we again test these new points to see if they occupy their correct positions in relation to the height and width. Do not, however, transfer the measurements from the pencil to the paper. This test is only to obtain the proportion of one dimension to another. Having tested these smaller dimensions we may draw lightly the main branches.

After having indicated their general direction and character of growth, we may indicate some of the smaller branches and twigs (Fig. 213). All this work should be carried out without erasing ; all corrections should be made by slightly darker lines.

Let us now sharpen our pencils to a good point and go over the drawing with a fine dark line, carefully studying the character and spirit of the tree. Now erase the lighter and superfluous lines, as the dark lines remain distinct enough to indicate our drawing.

Lining-in.— We may now take our pencil nearer the point and proceed to line-in the drawing, going over it with a definite, consistent line. If desirable, we may accent and bring out certain parts of the tree more strongly than others by darker or shade lines and short, strong markings called accents. These are especially effective at the junction and underside of branches, and where

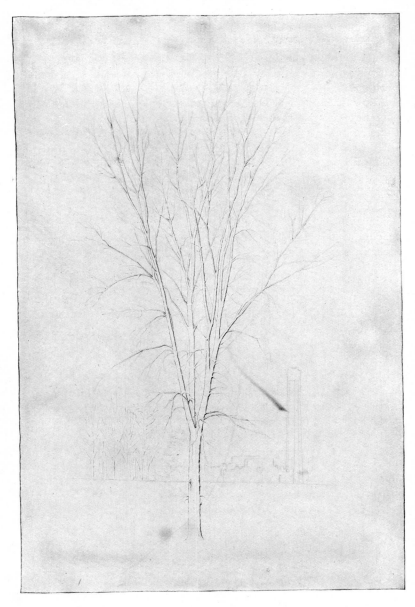

Fig. 215.   The outline drawing complete, and the first pencil marks erased.

one wishes to give the object a nearer appearance. A soft, broad, grey line may be obtained by using a softer pencil (B) and the drawing given variety by breaking lines here and there. We should be cautious in using them, however; but lack of space does not permit further discussion of the subject of accented outlines.

Allow the pupils to make short ten- or fifteen-minute "time sketches" of trees. In these it is the spirit and general effect of the tree that we must strive for. Above all, we must allow our little draughtsmen to give their own interpretation of the tree. A helpful suggestion as to proportion, etc., would be in place, but we must allow their individuality to have as much play as possible.

The suggestions given on these pages are necessary for the beginner. Some of them are hard facts; but it lies with the teacher to develop the æsthetic and artistic qualities lying dormant in the pupil, ready to be moulded and started in the right direction.

If you have confined the pupils to the flat copy, break away from it; allow them to create. Let them see the beautiful things all about them. They will respond. Let them draw from nature and still life. Train them to observe.

The early summer days, just before school closes, with their bright sunlight and strong shadows, make many subjects interesting as light-and-shade drawings. Fall, with its brilliant coloring, gives us a chance to use the color-box, while the early winter twilights will bring many an interesting silhouette before our boys and girls, and next day during the drawing hour these impressions may be carried out in pen and ink.

The most successful teacher will be the one of sympathetic nature whose love reaches out to the boys and girls, as well as to all things beautiful. The most successful teacher will be the one who endeavors to place the children where they may view nature sympathetically and in the most intimate relationship.

LEAFLET XXXI.

FOUR APPLE TWIGS.*

By L. H. BAILEY.

AS I walked through an apple orchard the other day for the first time since the long winter had set in, I was struck by the many different shapes and sizes of the limbs as I saw them against the blue-gray of the February sky. I cut four of them in passing, and as I walked back to the house I wondered why the twigs were all so different ; and I found myself guessing whether there would be any apples next summer.

I have had pictures made of these four little apple limbs. Let us look them over and see whether they have any story to tell of how they grew and what they have set out to do.

I.

One of these twigs (Fig. 216) was taken from a strong young tree which, I remember, bore its first good crop of apples last year. This simple twig is plainly of two years' growth, for the " ring " between the old and new wood is seen at B. That is, the main stem from the base up to B grew in 1895, and the part from B to the tip grew in 1896. But the buds upon these two parts look very unlike. Let us see what these differences mean.

We must now picture to ourselves how this shoot from B to 10 looked last summer while it was growing. The shoot bore leaves. Where ? There was one just below each bud ; or, to be more exact, one bud developed just above each leaf. These buds did not put out leaves. They grew to their present size and then stopped. The leaves fell.

What are these buds of the tip shoot preparing to do in 1897 ? We can answer this question by going back just one year and seeing what the buds on the lower (or older) part of the shoot did in 1896. On that part (below B) the buds seem to have increased in size. Therefore, they must have grown larger last year. There were

---

* Teachers' Leaflet No. 3, March, 1897.

no leaves borne below
leaves came out of
these leaves expanded
that is, each bud grew
came each of these
continue the growth in
be simple buds at 2, 3,

But the strangest
has not yet been seen,

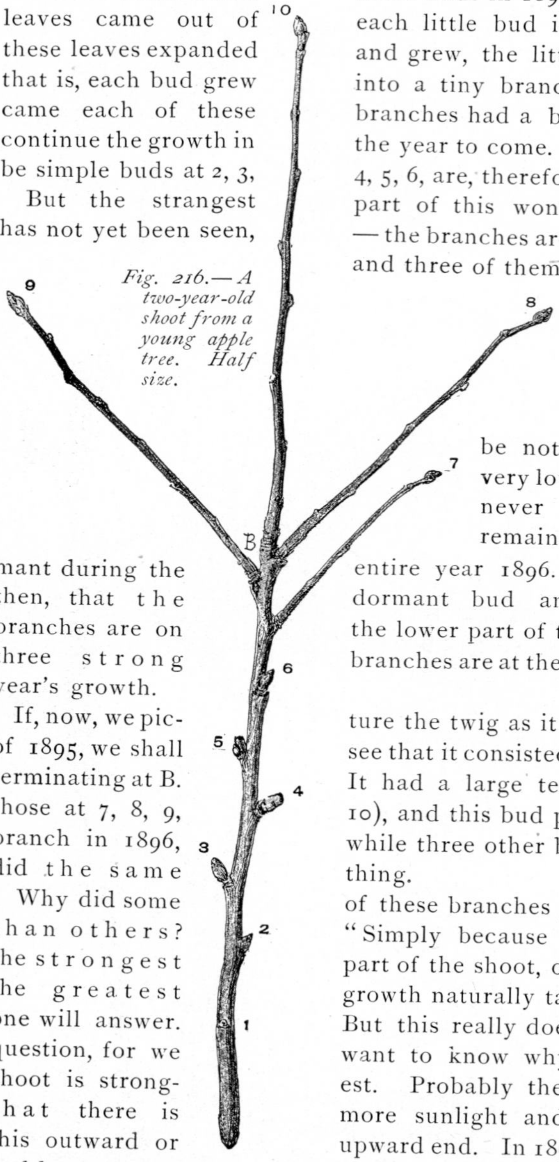

Fig. 216.— A two-year-old shoot from a young apple tree. Half size.

mant during the
then, that the
branches are on
three strong
year's growth.

If, now, we pic-
of 1895, we shall
terminating at B.
those at 7, 8, 9,
branch in 1896,
did the same

Why did some
than others?
the strongest
the greatest
one will answer.
question, for we
shoot is strong-
that there is
this outward or

these buds in 1896, but a cluster of
each little bud in the spring. As
and grew, the little bud grew on;
into a tiny branch, and when fall
branches had a bud on its end to
the year to come. What we took to
4, 5, 6, are, therefore, little branches.
part of this wonderful little twig
— the branches are of different sizes,
and three of them (7, 8, 9) have so
far outstripped
the others that
they seem to be
of a different
kind. It should
be noticed, too, that the
very lowermost bud (at 1)
never grew at all, but
remained perfectly dor-
entire year 1896. It will be seen,
dormant bud and the smallest
the lower part of the shoot, and the
branches are at the very tip of the last

ture the twig as it looked in the fall
see that it consisted of a single shoot,
It had a large terminal bud (like
10), and this bud pushed on into a
while three other buds near the tip
thing.
of these branches grow to be larger
"Simply because they were upon
part of the shoot, or that part where
growth naturally takes place," some
But this really does not answer the
want to know why this part of the
est. Probably the real reason is
more sunlight and more room on
upward end. In 1897,— if this shoot

had been spared — each of these four largest twigs (7, 8, 9, 10)
would have done the same thing as the parent twig did in 1896:

each would have pushed on from its end, and one
or two or three other strong branches would probably have started from the strong side-buds near
the tips, the very lowest buds would, no doubt,
have remained perfectly inactive or dormant for
lack of opportunity, and the intermediate buds
would have made short branches like 2, 3, 4, 5, 6.
In other words, the tree always tries to grow
onward from its tips, and these tip shoots
eventually become strong branches, unless some
of them die in the struggle for existence. What,
now, becomes of the little branches lower down ?

II.

From another apple tree I took the twig shown
in Fig. 217. We see at once that it is very unlike
the other one. It seems to be two years old, one
year's growth extending from the base up to 7,
and the last year's growth extending from 7 to
8 ; but we shall see upon looking closer that this
is not so. The short branchlets at 3, 4, 5, 7 are
very different from those in Fig. 216. They seem
to be broken off. The fact is that the broken
ends show were apples were borne in 1896. The
branchlets that bore them, therefore, must have
grown in 1895, while the main branch, from 1 to 7,
grew in 1894. It is plain, from the looks of the
buds, that the shoot from 7 to 8 grew last year,
1896.

Starting from the base, then, we have the main
twig growing in 1894 ; the small side branches
growing in 1895 ; these little branches bearing
apples in 1896 ; and the terminal shoot also growing in 1896. Why was there no terminal shoot
growing in 1895 ? Simply because its tip developed a fruit-bud (at 7) and therefore could not
send out a branch ; for there are two kinds of
buds, — the small, pointed leaf-bud and the thick,
blunt fruit-bud. If the branchlets 3, 4, 5, 7 are
two years old, the dormant buds — 1, 2 — must
be of the same age. That is, for two long years

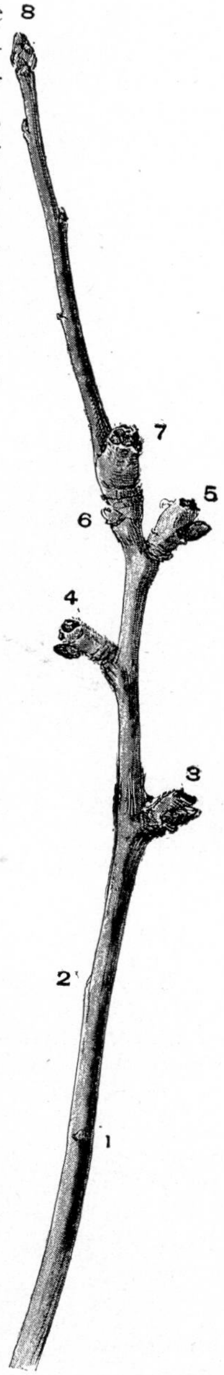

Fig. 217. A three-year-
old shoot and the fruit-
spurs. Half size.

these little buds have been waiting (if I may use the expression) for some bug to eat off the buds and leaves above, or some accident to break the shoot beyond them, so that they might have a chance to grow ; but they have waited in vain.

We have now found, therefore, that the little side shoots upon apple twigs often become fruit-branches or fruit-spurs, while the more ambitious branches above them are making a great display of stem and leaves.

But will these fruit-spurs bear fruit again in 1897 ? No. The bearing of an apple is hard work, and these spurs did not have enough vitality left to make fruit-buds for the next year ; but as they must perpetuate themselves, they have sent out small side buds which will bear a cluster of leaves and grow into another little spur in 1897, and in that year these new spurs will make

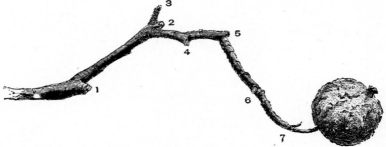

Fig. 218.—A fruit-spur which has borne six apples. Half size.

fruit-buds for bearing in 1898. The side bud is plainly seen on spur 5, also on spur 4, whilst spur 7 has sown a seed, so to speak, in the bud at 6. It is plain, therefore, why the tree bears every other year.

III.

There was one tree in the orchard from which the farmer had not picked his apples. Perhaps the apples were not worth picking. At any rate, the dried apples, shriveled and brown, are still hanging on the twigs, and even the birds do not seem to care for them. I broke off one of these twigs (Fig. 218). Let us see how many apples this interesting twig has borne. We can tell by the square-cut scars. An apple was once borne at 1, another at 2, another at 4, another at 5, another at 6, and another at 7,— and at 7 there will be a scar when the apple falls. Six apples this modest shoot has borne ! And I wonder how many of them got ripe, or how many were taken by the worms, or how many were eaten by the little boys and girls on their way to school!

A peculiar thing happened when the fruit was growing at 2. Two side buds started out, instead of one, and both of them grew the next year. But one of the little branchlets fell sick and died, or a bug nipped off its end, or it starved to death ; and its memory is preserved by the little stick standing up at 3. The other branchlet thrived, and eventually bore apples at 4, 5, 6, and 7.

I have said that these fruit-spurs bear only every other year ; then, if this branch has borne six apples consecutively, it must be twelve years old. The truth is that it is about twenty years old, for some years it failed to bear ; but the age cannot be traced out in the picture, although any little boy or girl with bright eyes could soon learn to trace out yearly rings on the shoot itself.

IV.

The last shoot that I got that day has a whole volume of history in it, and I cannot begin to tell its story unless I should write a small book. But we will trace out its birthdays and see how many apples it has borne. It is shown in Fig. 219, and because it is so long I have had to break it into several pieces to get it on the page. It begins at A, and is continued at B, C, D, E, and F.

Let us count the yearly rings and see how old the whole limb is. These rings are at 28, 26, D, 12, 1,—five of them ; and as the shoot grew one year before it made any ring, and another year made no increase in length — as we shall presently see — the whole branch must be seven years old. That is, the limb probably started in 1890.* Let us begin, then, at A, and follow it out.

1890. Started as a spur from the main branch, A, and grew to 1.

1891. Apple borne at 1. This apple did not mature, however, as we can readily see by the smallness of the scar. In this year, two side buds developed to continue the spur the next year.

---

* It is really impossible to tell whether the shoot started from the limb A in 1889 or 1890, without knowing the age of A ; for the spur may have developed its blossom bud at the end in either the first or second year of its life. That is, young fruit-spurs sometimes make a blossom bud the very year they start, but they oftener "stand still" the second year and delay the blossom bud until that time.

21

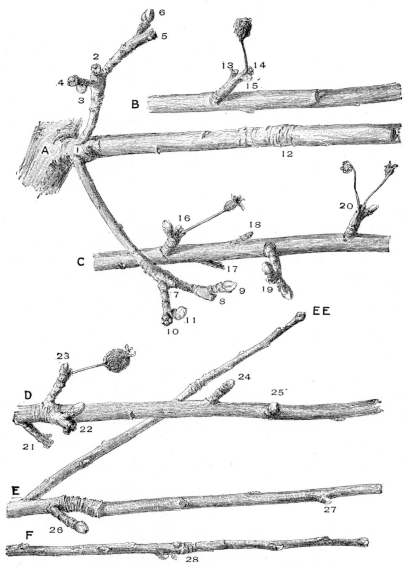

Fig. 219. A seven-year-old apple twig and its curious history. (Half size.)

1892. Ceased to be a fruit-spur, and made a strong growth on to
12. For some reason, it had a good chance to grow. Perhaps
the farmer pruned the tree, and thereby gave the shoot an
opportunity ; or perhaps he plowed and fertilized the land.

In the meantime, one of the side buds grew to 3, and the
other to 7, and each made a fruit-bud at its end.

1893. Shoot grew lustily,— on to D.

The fruit-bud at 3 bore an apple, which probably matured,
as shown by the scar 2. Two side buds were formed beneath
this apple, to continue the spur next year.

The fruit-bud at 7 bloomed, but the apple fell early, as
shown by the small scar. Two side buds were formed.

The buds upon the main shoot — 1 to 12 — all remained
dormant.

1894. Shoot grew from D to beyond E.

Side bud of 2 grew to 4, and made a fruit-bud on its end ;
the other side bud grew on to 5, and there made a fruit-bud.

Side bud of 7 grew on to 10, and the other one to 8, each
ending in a fruit-bud.

Buds on old shoot — 1 to 12 — still remained dormant.

Some of the buds on the 1893 growth — 12 to D,— remained
dormant ; but some of them made fruit-spurs,— 14, 16, 17, 18,
19, 20, 21, 22, 23.

1895. Shoot grew from beyond E to 28.

Flowers were borne at 4 and 5 ; but at 4 the fruit fell early,
for the five or six scars of the flowers can be seen, showing
that no one of them developed more strongly than the other ;
that is, none of the flowers "set." A fairly good fruit was
probably borne at 5. At the base of each, a bud started to
continue the spur next year.

Upon the other spur, flowers were borne both at 8 and 10.
At 10 none of the flowers set fruit, but a side bud developed.
At 8 the fruit partially matured, and a side bud was also
developed.

The buds upon the old stem from 1 to 12 still remained
dormant.

Some of the spurs on the 1893 growth — 12 to D — developed fruit-buds for bearing in 1896.

Some of the buds on the 1894 growth — D to beyond E —
remained dormant, but others developed into small fruit-
spurs. One of these buds, near the top of the 1894 growth,

threw out a long shoot, starting from E ; and the bud at 26
also endeavored to make a long branch, but failed.

1896.   Main shoot grew from 28 to the end.

The side bud below 4 (where the fruit was borne the year
before) barely lived, not elongating, as seen above 3.   This
branch of the spur is becoming weak and will never bear
again.   The side bud of 5, however, made a fairly good spur
and developed a fruit-bud at its end, as seen at 6.

The side bud of 10 grew somewhat, making the very short
spur 11.   This branchlet is also getting weak.   The bud of 8,
however, developed a strong spur at 9.   Both 11 and 9 bear
fruit-buds, but that on 11 is probably too weak ever to bear
fruit again.   In fact, the entire spurs, from 1 to 6 and 1 to 9,
are too weak to be of much account for fruit-bearing.

This year several of the spurs along the 1893 growth — 12
to D -- bore flowers.   Flowers were borne from two buds on
the first one (at 13 and 14), but none of the flowers "set."
One of the little apples that died last June still clings to the
spur at 14.   A side bud (15) formed to continue the spur in
1897.   Flowers were borne at 16, 20, 21, and 23, but no apples
developed.   Upon 16 and 20 the flowers died soon after they
opened, as seen by the remains of them.   Upon 23, one of the
flowers set an apple, but the apple soon died.   The spurs 17
and 18 are so weak that they have never made fruit-buds, and
they are now nearly dead.   The spurs 19 and 22 have behaved
differently.   Like the others, they grew in 1894 and would
have made terminal fruit-buds in 1895, and would have borne
fruit in 1896 ; but the terminal buds were broken off in the
fall or winter of 1894, so that two side buds developed in
1895, and each of these developed a fruit-bud at its end in
1896 in the spur 19, but only one of them developed such a
bud in 22.   Upon these spurs, therefore, the bearing year has
been changed.

Upon the growth of 1894 — D to beyond E — only three spurs
have developed, nos. 24, 25, 26.   These started out in 1895, and
two of them — 25 and 26 — have made large fat buds which are
evidently fruit-buds.   The shoot at E grew on to EE, and all
the buds on its lower two-year-old portion remained dormant.

On the 1895 growth — from beyond E to 28 — all the buds
remained dormant save one, and this one — 27 — made only
a very feeble attempt to grow into a spur.

The buds upon the 1892 growth — 1 to 12 — are still dormant and waiting for an opportunity to grow.

What an eventful history this apple twig has had! And yet in all the seven years of its life, after having made fifteen efforts to bear fruit, it has not produced a single good apple! The fault, therefore, does not lie in the shoot. It has done the best it could. The trouble has been that the farmer either did not give the tree enough food to enable it to support the fruit, or did not prune the tree so as to give the twig light and room, or allowed apple-scab or some other disease to kill the young apples as they were forming. I am wondering, therefore, whether, when trees fail to bear, it is not quite as often the fault of the farmer as it is of the trees?

LEAFLET XXXII.

THE BURST OF SPRING.*

By L. H. BAILEY.

SPRING is coming! The buds will burst and the birds will sing!

How do the buds burst? Watch them as the spring opens; or, if you are impatient, cut long twigs and place them in bottles of water in a living-room, and the buds will swell. First, notice what the winter buds are like, — that they are spherical, or oblong, or conical bodies lying close to the limb and tightly covered with scales. Notice that there is a mark or scar beneath the bud, showing where a leaf was borne.

It is excellent practice to collect winter twigs of different kinds of trees and bushes, and to compare the form and color of the shoots, and the size, shape, color, and make-up of the buds. Lay the twigs side by side on the table and notice how one differs from the other. What part of the twig grew last year? Notice the "ring" at the base of the last year's growth. After all the differences are noted, put the twigs in water, as you would a bouquet. Sometimes flowers and leaves will appear. If the twigs are two or three feet long, the buds are more likely to grow, for then there is sufficient supply of food in them. Change the water frequently, and cut off the lower ends of the twigs so that a fresh surface will be exposed to the water. It will be two to five weeks before the buds open, depending mostly on the kind of plant.

Mark one bud on a maple, or apple, or lilac, or other plant, by tying a string about the twig. Look at it carefully from day to day: observe how it opens, and what comes out of it.

The pupil should know that a winter twig has interest.

* * *

* Nature-Study Quarterly No. 4, Leaflet 17, March, 1900.

The bud may be peach or apricot. Soon the bud begins to swell
at its top. The scales open. A white lining appears. This lining
soon protrudes (Fig. 220). Soon the lining opens. We see that
it is a flower. Or perhaps the peach bud sends out a green shoot

rather than a flower. There must be two kinds of
peach and apricot buds,—a flower-bud and a leaf-bud.
Can you tell them apart? The flower-bud is thicker
and rounder. Usually one stands on either side of a
leaf-bud. But the leaf-bud may stand alone. Find
one: any peach tree or apricot tree will have leaf-buds,
but all may not have flower-buds. As the bud expands

Fig. 220. and the flower or leaf appears, notice that the bud-
Opening scales fall away. Do these scales leave scars? And
of an do not these scars, standing together, make the "ring"
apricot which marks the beginning of the new growth?
bud.

*   *   *

Observe a pear bud. Notice that the scales elongate as the bud
swells. You can see the white bases of the scales, marking the
new growth (Fig. 221). If it is a leaf-bud the scales
may become three-fourths of an inch long before they
fall. But sooner or later, they are cast, and their
places are marked by scars. If it is a flower-bud,
notice that several flowers come out of it. In the apricot and peach, there is only one flower in each bud.

Each of these little pear
flowers is closed up like
a bud and elevates itself   *Fig. 221.*
on a stalk before it opens: *Opening*
and this stalk becomes   *of a pear*
the stem of the pear fruit.   *bud.*

But this pear flower-bud contains
leaves as well as flowers. Fig. 222
shows what comes out of a pear
bud. This, then, is a mixed flower-
bud,—it contains both leaves and
flowers. The apricot and the peach
bear true or simple flower-buds.

*Fig. 222. What came out of a pear
bud.*

*   *   *

Watch apple buds. The scales do
not elongate as in the pear, but the flower-buds are mixed.
Fig. 223 shows the expanding cluster from an apple flower-bud.

Four flowers will open; and there are six leaves. If the buds
are made to open in the
house on severed twigs, the
leaves do not grow so large
before the flowers expand,
for the twig does not contain sufficient food. Fig.
224 is a photograph of an
apple twig which I had in
my window one winter's
day.

* * *

Examine a hickory twig.
The illustration (Fig. 225)

Fig. 223. Opening of an apple bud.

shows the "ring" mark-
ing the beginning of the
annual growth. See the
large leaf-scars. Notice
that the terminal bud is
much the largest. It is
the one which will grow.
The other buds will re-
main dormant unless
they are forced into
growth by the death of
the terminal bud or by
other unusual circum-
stances. Notice that buds
differ in size on shoots of
all plants; consider that
not all the buds are to
grow : there is a struggle
for existence. When the
hickory bud expands,
some of the scales fall

Fig. 224. Apple flowers in midwinter.

away; but some of the inner parts enlarge into leaf-like bodies,
as shown in Fig. 226. In some hickories these bodies become
two or three inches long before they fall. Hickories open very
late in the season. The Norway maple, commonly planted on
lawns, behaves in a similar way. Observe the sugar maple.

* * *

A twig of the common elm is shown
in Fig. 227. Notice the "ring." See
the two kinds of buds. We suspect
that the three larger ones are flower-
buds. With the very first warm days
— before the robin has built her nest
— these three buds will burst; soon
the red-brown tassels will hang on the
leafless twigs. Each tassel is a flower.
Several flowers come from each bud.
We see them in Fig. 228; and the
leaf-buds have elongated somewhat.
Watch for the fruits or seeds that
blow about the walks so early in
spring; and note how the leaves come
out.

Fig. 225. Shoot of a hickory.

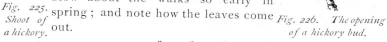

Fig. 226.   The opening of a hickory bud.

*   *   *

With the first breath of spring, the "pussy willows" come.
And what are the "pussies"? They are clusters of flowers. So

Fig. 227.   Twig of elm.

Fig. 228.   Blossoms of the elm.

snugly are the little flowers wrapped in wool, that the "pussies"
are silken-soft as they begin to expand. Fig. 229 is a willow
shoot. Find one when the buds first begin to burst. Notice the
big brown-black scale that covers the bud as a shield and falls
when the "pussy" first begins to appear.

*   *   *

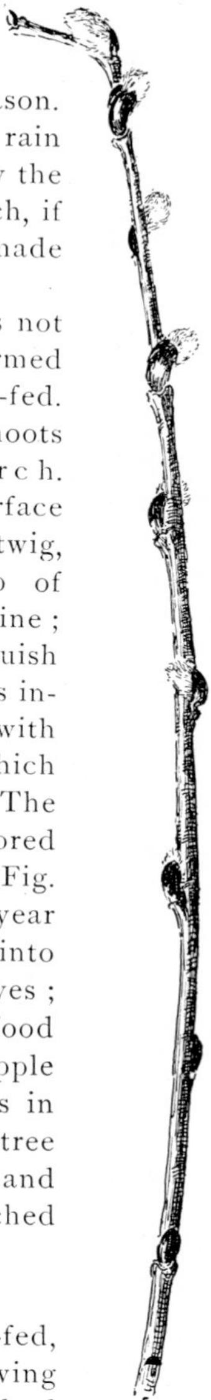

And now what is a winter bud? It is a miniature shoot or flower, resting for the time, and snugly
wrapped for the long winter. It was made last season.
It is ready to leap into growth the moment the warm rain
of spring wakens it. A good hand lens will show the
embryo branch, if
a section is made
of the bud.

This bud is not
only ready-formed
but is ready-fed.
The winter shoots
contain s t a r c h.
On a cut surface
of a dormant twig,
apply a drop of
tincture of iodine ;
n o t e the bluish
color, which is in-

Fig. 230.   Bloom of azalea.

dicative of starch. This starch is insoluble ; but with
the first awakening of life, it changes into sugar, which
is soluble and is transferred to the growing part. The
burst of spring is made possible by means of this stored
food. Notice the azalea in the florist's window (Fig.
230). The large flower-buds were formed the year
before, and it is a short operation to "force" them into
bloom. The flowers come in advance of the leaves ;
therefore these leaves could not have made the food
required for the bloom. The blooming of the apple
twig (Fig. 224) in the winter shows that the food is in
the twig and buds. Once I drew a branch of a tree
into a room and fastened it there. It made leaves and
began to grow while the tree to which it was attached
was perfectly dormant (Fig. 231).

*   *   *

Not only are the buds ready-formed and ready-fed,
but they are covered. Snugly is the tender, growing
part protected. Pull away the scales of a winter bud
one by one. Observe how closely they are placed.
Often the chinks are filled with a packing of wool, or
are sealed with varnish. Dip the bud in water : then

Fig. 229.
The opening
of a pussy
willow.

see whether the water permeates the covering.   The chief value of
the bud covering is not to protect from freezing, as commonly
supposed, but to prevent the soft growing parts from drying out.
    The plants are waiting for spring.   They are ready.

*Fig. 231.   Branch of a tree bearing leaves inside a window, when
the tree itself is dormant.*

LEAFLET XXXIII.

EVERGREENS AND HOW THEY SHED THEIR LEAVES.*

By H. P. GOULD.

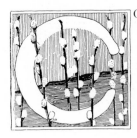

CONE–BEARING evergreens are familiar to everyone ; yet this familiarity is usually with the trees as entire objects. We do not often stop to analyze a tree in order to find out what gives it its characteristic appearance or to see what makes it look as it does.

We shall often find, if we stop to look, that much of the character of a tree,— that is, its general appearance or the way in which it impresses us,— is due to the leaves and to their arrangement on the branches. This is true of many of the evergreen trees.

Why are certain kinds of trees called evergreen in distinction from those which are said to be deciduous ? The reason is obvious. One kind is always green from the presence of foliage, while the other sheds all of its leaves every season. The evergreen trees, like the pines and the spruces and the firs, always appear to be well covered with foliage ; hence it does not often occur to us that these trees shed their leaves. And yet perhaps we can recall

Note to the teacher.— This leaflet has two particular objects : to teach how evergreens shed their leaves, and to enable you to distinguish a few of the evergreens which are most commonly met. These studies (and those suggested in Leaflet No. XXIX) should be the means of adding much cheer to the winter. Encourage pupils to make collections of cones, to observe when they shed their seeds, and how long (how many seasons) they remain attached to the branch. Remember that mere identification of the kinds of trees is not the highest type of nature-study.

Cones are good subjects for free-hand drawing. Beginners should draw them in outline, omitting the shading. Encourage pupils to draw single leaf-clusters of the different pines, cautioning them to show the right number of leaves in each case.

* Teacher's Leaflet No. 13, February, 1899.

happy hours when we used to play beneath some large pine tree where the ground was carpeted with pine "needles."

The falling of the leaves of the maple trees or the oaks is a familiar sight, but who has seen the spruce leaves fall, and who can tell when the pine needles drop?

That the evergreen trees do shed their foliage, as truly as the maples and the elms do, we will not question, for we can see the fallen leaves under any tree. Look up into the top of a spruce or pine. See that the interior is bare of foliage. The leaves are towards the ends of the branches, where they receive sunlight. Yet the branches which are now in the interior once bore leaves, for we can see the leaf-scars.

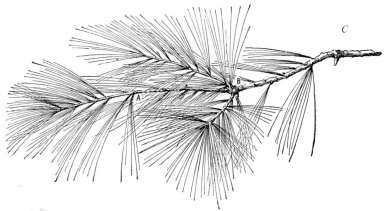

Fig. 232. Shoot of the common white pine, one-third natural size.

It will be interesting to find out something about the leaves of our common evergreens. Let us look at some of them.

THE WHITE PINE.

In Fig. 232 is shown a white pine branch. Notice that the leaves are borne in bunches or clusters of five. Each bunch of leaves is produced in the axil (or angle) of a minute scale-like body, but this scale can best be seen and studied on the very young growth. It has been worn away or broken from the older growth by the wind and the rain and the other forces of nature.

Another strange fact should be well observed. The leaves of the maples and other deciduous trees are borne only on the present season's growth ; but this is not the case in the pines, and kindred trees. If we trace back the growth of the past two or three years, we may find that there are as many leaves on the wood that is two years old as there are on the last season's growth ; and in many cases we can find leaves on the part of the branch that is three years old. This means that the pine leaves or needles are two and sometimes three years old when they fall. The Fig. 232 shows the falling of the leaves from the different years' growth. The part of the branch between the tip and A is the last season's growth ; between A and B it is two years old ; the part between B and C is three years old. The part that grew four seasons ago — beyond C — has no leaves.

The different seasons' growth is in- dicated not by distinct " rings " as in the case of deciduous trees, but by the branching. Each whorl of branches about a limb represents the end of a season's growth. A young pine tree, or the younger limbs of an old tree, shows this character very plainly.

Fig. 233.   Cone of white pine. It has shed its seeds. Half natural size.

Do the leaves of the pines and of the other evergreen trees fall at the end of the growing season, as the leaves of most of the deciduous trees do ? Or do they gradually become lifeless and fall at any season, from the force of the wind and other natural forces ? Tie a large sheet of cloth in the top of some evergreen tree, in such a way as to form a receptacle to catch the leaves. Do you catch leaves in winter as well as in summer ? Do you find leaves on the snow ?

As there are several different kinds of pines, we must picture carefully in our minds the foliage of the white pine, for it is dif- ferent from that of any others. The leaves are soft and very slender, and from three to four inches long. The base of each cluster of leaves is at first surrounded by a small sheath. A scar is left when the leaves drop and these scars can often be seen on parts of the branches that are eight or ten years old. Do the leaves of other kinds of trees make a scar when they fall?

The white pine cones, in which the seeds are borne, are conspicuous objects. They are five or six inches long and slightly curved. It will be interesting to find out whether the seeds ripen the same year in which they are formed. Perhaps a cone still containing seeds can be secured. Carefully tear it apart and see where the seeds are attached. Red squirrels sometimes eat the pine seeds. A white pine cone, which has shed its seeds, is shown in Fig. 233.

Fig. 234. Shoot of common pitch pine. One-half natural size.

This kind of pine is found widely scattered in New England, New York, and westward to Minnesota and Iowa and along the Alleghany Mountains as far south as Georgia; also in some parts of Canada. It is a valuable lumber tree.

THE PITCH PINE.

This kind of pine is very different, in many respects, from the white pine. Let us find some of the differences. Instead of having leaves in bunches of five, it has them in clusters of three, and the base of each cluster is inclosed by a scaly sheath which does not fall away as in the case of the white pine; neither does the little scale-like body upon the branch, in the axil of which the leaf-cluster is borne, fall away, but it may be found just below the leaf, and even on branches that are several years old. Sometimes a sheath is found with only two leaves. We shall want to know, too, how old the leaves are when they fall. Do they remain on the tree longer than the white pine leaves do?

Fig. 235. Cone of pitch pine. One-half natural size.

Again, instead of being soft and slender as the white pine leaves are, we shall find that these leaves are rigid and thick in comparison, and stand out straight from the branches. The shape of the leaves is also distinct from that of the white pine needles. See whether you can find any other differences.

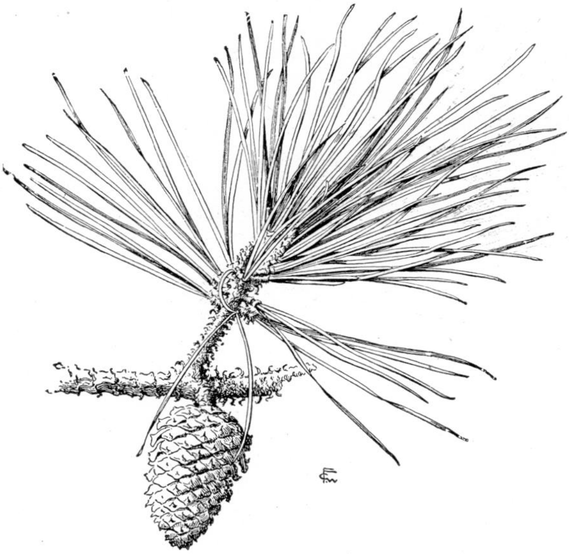

Fig. 236. Pitch pine. One-third natural size.

A pitch pine branch is shown in Fig. 234. The part between the tip and A is the past season's growth. Observe the foliage on the part that is two years old. Part of it has fallen. We often find it on growth which is older than this; but in this specimen there are no leaves on the three-year wood.

The cone of the pitch pine is very unlike that of the white pine. Fig. 235 gives a good idea of one that has shed its seeds. Compare this with Fig. 233; or, better, examine the two kinds of cones side by side. The pitch pine cones are sometimes borne in clusters of two or more and they persist,—that is, remain on the tree for several years after the seeds have ripened and scattered.

Notice how the new cones are borne with reference to last season's growth. Are they attached to the tip of a branchlet? Or are they closely attached to the side of a branch? Figs. 236 and 237 will help us answer this question. The little cones in Fig. 237 near the tip of the twig, are just beginning to form.

The pitch pine usually grows in sandy or rocky soil and is found in the United States along the Atlantic coast to Virginia,

Fig. 237. Pitch pine, showing young cones. Half natural size.

along the mountains to Georgia, westward to Western New York, Eastern Ohio, Kentucky, and Eastern Tennessee. It has little value as timber, because it does not grow large enough.

SCOTCH AND AUSTRIAN PINES.

In the same manner other pines may be studied. Fig. 238 shows a cone and a bit of foliage of the Scotch pine, and Fig. 239 the Austrian pine. These cones grew the past season and are not yet mature.   After they ripen and shed the seeds which they contain, they will look somewhat like the cone in Fig 235.   The Scotch pine has short and blue-green needles.   The Austrian pine is coarser, and has long dark-green needles.

There are but two leaves in a cluster on these kinds of pines and we shall find that the sheath which incloses the base of the leaf-cluster is more conspicuous than in either the white or the pitch pine.   Do the leaves persist in the Scotch and Austrian pines

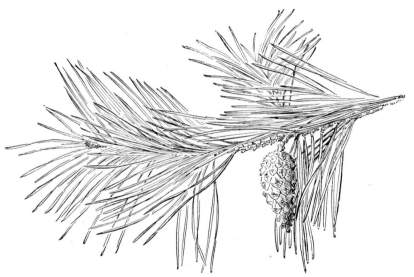

Fig. 238.   Scotch pine.   Half natural size.

longer than they do in the others we have examined ?   Study the cones of these and other pines.

The Scotch and Austrian pines are not native to this country, but are much grown for ornament.   They can be found in almost any park and in many other places where ornamental trees are grown.

THE NORWAY SPRUCE.

The leaves of spruce trees are borne very differently from those of the pines.   Instead of being in clusters of two or more, they are single and without a sheath at the base ; neither are there   scale-like bodies on the branches where the leaves are borne.   Notice, too, that the leaves have a very short stem or petiole.

The leaves of the Norway spruce are about one inch long, although the length varies more or less in different parts of the tree and in different trees. They are rather stiff and rigid and sharp-pointed. In a general way, the leaves are four-sided, though indistinctly so.

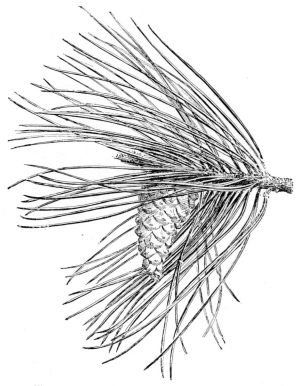

Fig. 239. Austrian pine. One-third natural size.

It will be interesting to study the position which the leaves take on the branches. A hasty glance might give us the impression that the leaves are not produced on the under side of the branches; but a more careful examination will convince us that there are nearly as many on the under side as on the upper. The leaves are all pointing outward from the branch and as nearly upward as is possible. In other words, the leaves grow toward the light.

We must not forget to see how long the leaves of the Norway spruce persist and to find out when the leaf-scars disappear. We can find leaves that must surely be six or seven years old and sometimes we can find them even older than this. The leaf scars, too, remain a long time. The falling of the leaves is illustrated in Fig. 240. It shows the extremities of a limb which is eight years old. The part between the tip and A is last season's growth; between A and B it is two years old; and beyond B is a part that grew three seasons ago.   The section beyond C is six years old ; from C to D is seven years of age.   The four years' growth of this limb not shown in the drawing was as densely covered with foliage as is the part shown in the upper figure ; but there are not many leaves between C and D (seven years old) and none on the eight-year-old wood (except those on the branchlets, and these are younger).

The cone of the Norway spruce is nearly as long as that of the white pine, but it is not so rough and coarse as the white pine cone is.   The cones are usually borne on the tips of small branchlets, although occasionally one is borne in the manner shown in Fig. 241.   The cones usually fall the first winter.

Fig. 240.   Twig of the common Norway spruce.   Half natural size.

The Norway spruce is not a native of this country, but like the Scotch and Austrian pines, it was introduced from Europe and is grown very widely as an ornamental tree.   It is the commonest evergreen in yards and parks.

THE BLACK SPRUCE AND ITS KIN.

There are several different kinds of spruces which we find growing in our forests and swamps, and sometimes these are planted for ornament.   A sprig of foliage and a cone of one of these,— the black spruce, — is shown in Fig. 242.   The foliage is not very unlike that of the Norway spruce, but the cones are very small in comparison. They are about one inch long, though they vary considerably in size. Before they open they are oval or plum-shaped ; but when mature and the scales of the cone have expanded, they are nearly globular. They are often borne in clusters, as well as singly, and persist for many years after the seeds have fallen. The position of the cones will depend upon their age. When young they point upward, but they gradually turn downward.

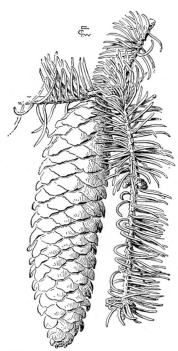

In general appearance the white spruce resembles the black very closely. The leaves of the white spruce have a whitish or dusty looking tinge of color and when crushed or bruised give forth a peculiar, disagreeable odor. The cones vary in length from an inch to two inches, and in shape are more cylindrical or finger-shaped than the cone of the black spruce.

The foliage of the red spruce lacks the whitish tinge of color of the white spruce and the cones, which are from one inch to two inches in length, are obovate in shape — that is, the widest place is through the upper part of the cone, and from this point it gradually tapers to the tip. They seldom persist longer than the second summer.

Fig. 241. Cone of Norway spruce. Half size.

The leaves of all these different kinds of spruces vary greatly in length, thickness, and sharpness of point, according to the part of the tree on which they grow, and their surroundings. The shedding of the leaves on these or other spruces can be determined as easily as in the Norway spruce.

These three spruces like a cold climate and grow in many sections of the northern United States and Canada and farther south in the mountains. They are sometimes all found growing together, but the black spruce likes best the damp, cold swamps, while the others grow best on the drier and better drained lands. The black spruce is commonest. The red spruce is least known.

The Balsam Fir.

This is another evergreen tree which grows naturally in the cold, damp grounds of the northern United States and Canada, and to some extent in the eastern states as far south as West Virginia.

The foliage is borne in much the same manner as that of the spruces ; yet there are interesting differences in the characters of these two kinds of leaves. Perhaps the most noticeable difference is in the shape ; and the color of the fir leaves will attract our attention because the under side is a silvery color, while the upper side is green.   What is the nature of the tip of the leaf and

Fig. 242.— Black spruce.   Half natural size.

how does it compare with the pines and spruces in this respect ? Does the leaf have a stem or petiole or is it attached directly to the branch without any stem ?   How are the leaves shed ?

The cones are about three inches long and present a rather delicate appearance.   It will be interesting to determine the position of the cones, that is, the direction in which they point, and to learn whether it is the same when they are young as it is after they have matured.

The grayish colored bark of the trunk and limbs bears many " blisters " from which Canada balsam is obtained.

The Hemlock.

A hemlock twig is an interesting object. It may have many characters in common with the spruce and fir ; yet the impression which we get from it, or from a large hemlock tree, is entirely distinct. The arrangement of the leaves and the gracefulness of the drooping branchlets are most pleasing.   We are led to examine it more closely.   We notice that the leaves appear to be borne in two more or less regular rows,—one on each side of the branch or twig; but in reality they come from all sides of the branch, and it is the position which the leaves assume that gives this two-rowed appearance.

The leaves have a short stalk or petiole, and this stalk rests along the side of the branchlet in such a direction that the leaves are placed in single rows on either side of the branch. The petioles of the leaves are nearly parallel with the branch while the leaves often make a decided angle with the petiole. This fact can best be brought out by carefully examining a small twig.

While we are noting the arrangement of the leaves on the branchlets, we should also notice the points of similarity and difference between these leaves and those of the spruces and firs.

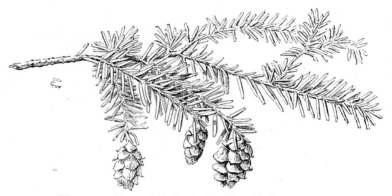

Fig. 243. Spray of the hemlock. Two-thirds natural size.

We shall find that there is more in common, at least so far as shape and color are concerned, between the hemlock and the fir than between the hemlock and the spruce.

The small, delicate cones, borne on the tips of the branchlets, will also attract our attention (Fig. 243.) We may wonder at their small size, for they are only about three-quarters of an inch long, and very delicate; yet a second glance at the tree will impress us with the number of cones which the tree bears, and we conclude that, although the cones may be small, yet there are so many of them that there will be no lack of seeds.

It is more difficult to trace the age of a hemlock limb than of many other kinds of trees, yet we can easily determine that many of the leaves are several years old when they fall.

The bark of the hemlock is used in tanning hides for leather. The tree is much used for lumber.   Where does it grow ?

The Arbor-vitæ.

One might almost wonder, at first sight, if the arbor-vitæ (often, but wrongly, called the white cedar) has any leaves at all.   It does possess them, however, but they are very different in size and shape from any of the others that we have examined.   They are small scale-like bodies, closely pressed together along the sides of the branchlets, in four rows.   Leaves pressed to the branches in this manner are said to be "appressed."   The leaves of the arbor-vitæ are so close together that they overlap one another. The leaves are of two distinct shapes, sometimes known as the

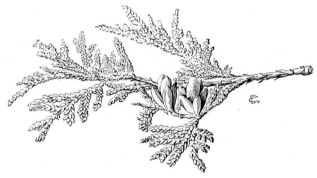

Fig. 244.   The Arbor-vitæ.   Nearly full size.

surface leaves and the flank leaves.   The former are located on what appears to be the flattened surface of the branchlets, while the latter are on the sides or edges.   See Fig. 244.

If we carefully look at the leaves, we shall notice a raised spot near the point or tip.   This is said to be a resin gland.   This gland can be seen more plainly on the surface leaves that are two years old.

Most of the leaves persist for at least two and sometimes three years ; but even older ones can be found.   These older leaves, however, exist not as green, active leaves, but merely as dried and lifeless scales.   These lifeless leaves are probably detached from the branches by the forces of nature.

The cones are even smaller than the hemlock cones.   They are borne in the axils of the leaves in the same manner as the branchlets and are not conspicuous unless one is close to the tree.

The arbor-vitæ is much planted for hedges and screens, as well as for other ornamental purposes. There are many horticultural varieties. The tree is abundant in a wild state in New York.

SUMMARY OF THE KINDS OF COMMON EVERGREENS.

The white pine (Pinus Strobus).— Leaves in clusters of five, soft and slender ; cones five or six inches long, slightly curved ; bark smooth except on the trunks and larger limbs of old trees, where it is fissured.

The pitch pine (Pinus rigida).— Leaves in clusters of three, from three to four inches long, rather rigid ; cones two to three inches long, often in clusters of two or more but frequently borne singly, persisting long after the seeds have been shed ; bark more or less rough on the young growth and deeply fissured on the trunks of old trees.

The Scotch pine (Pinus sylvestris).— Leaves usually in clusters of two, from two to four inches long, rigid, of a bluish-green hue when seen in a large mass on the tree ; cones two to three inches long and the scales tipped with a beak or prickle.

The Austrian pine (Pinus Austriaca).— Leaves in clusters of two, five or six inches long and somewhat rigid, dark green in color, and persisting for four or five years ; cones about three inches long, conical in shape ; and scales not beaked or pointed as in the Scotch pine.

The Norway spruce (Picea excelsa).— Leaves borne singly, about one inch long, dark green, four-sided ; cones about six inches long, and composed of thin scales, and usually borne on the tips of branchlets. The small branches mostly drooping.

The black spruce (Picea nigra).— In general appearance, this is not very unlike the Norway spruce, but the small branches stand out more horizontally and the cones are only one or one and one-half inches long, recurving on short branches. The cones persist for several years after shedding the seed.

The white spruce (Picea alba).— Leaves about one inch long, having a glaucous or whitish tinge ; twigs stout and rigid, of a pale greenish-white color ; cones from one to two and one-half inches long, more or less cylindrical or " finger-shaped," and easily crushed when dry.

The red spruce (Picea rubra).— The foliage lacks the whitish tinge of the white spruce and is of a dark or dark yellowish color ; twigs stouter than those of the black spruce and not so much inclined to droop ; cones about one inch long, obovate, and usually falling by the second summer.

The hemlock (Tsuga Canadensis).— Leaves about one-half inch long, flat with rounded point, green on the upper side, whitish beneath, and borne on short appressed petioles ; cones about three-quarters of an inch long, oval or egg-shaped, and borne on the ends of small branchlets and often persisting for some time.

The balsam fir (Abies balsamea).— Leaves narrow, less than one inch long, borne singly, very numerous and standing out from the branchlets in much the way of the spruce ; cones about three inches long, cylindrical, composed of thin scales, and standing upright on the branches, or recurved ; bark smooth, light green with whitish tinge.

The arbor-vitæ (Thuya occidentalis).— Leaves very small, scale-like, and over-lapping one another in four rows, adhering closely to the branchlets ; the cones oblong and small,— a half-inch or less in length,— and composed of but few scales.

LEAFLET XXXIV.

THE CLOVERS AND THEIR KIN.*

By ANNA BOTSFORD COMSTOCK.

The pedigree of honey does not concern the bee,
A clover any time to him is aristocracy.
— EMILY DICKINSON.

White clover.

HERE is a deep-seated prejudice that usefulness and beauty do not belong together ; — a prejudice based obviously on human selfishness, for if a thing is useful to us we emphasize that quality so much that we forget to look for its beauty. Thus it is that the clover suffers great injustice ; it has for centuries been a most valuable forage crop, and, therefore, we forget to note its beauty, or to regard it as an object worthy of æsthetic attention. This is a pitiful fact ; but it cheats us more than it does the clover, for the clover blossoms not for us, but for the bees and butterflies as well as for itself. As I remember the scenes which have impressed me most, I find among them three in which clover was the special attraction. One was a well-cultivated thrifty orchard carpeted with the brilliant red of the crimson clover in bloom. One was a great field of alfalfa spread near the shore of the Great Salt Lake, which met our eyes as we came through the pass in the Wasatch Mountains after days of travel in dust-colored lands ; the brilliant green of that alfalfa field in the evening sunlight refreshed our eyes as the draught of cold water refreshes the parched throat of the traveller in a desert. And another was a gently undulating field in our own State stretching away like a sea to the west, covered with the purple foam of the red clover in blossom ; and the fragrance of that field settled like a benediction over the acres that margined it. But we do not need landscapes to teach us the beauty of clover. Just one clover blossom studied carefully and looked at with clear-seeing eyes, reveals each floweret beautiful in

* Home Nature-Study Course, Vol. V, No. 8, May, 1904.

color, interesting in form, and perfect in its mechanism for securing pollination.

The clover is especially renowned for its partnerships with members of the animal kingdom. It readily forms a partnership with man, thriftily growing in his pastures and meadows, while he distributes its seed. For ages it has been a special partner of the bees, giving them honey for carrying its pollen. Below the ground it has formed a mysterious partnership with microbes, and the clover seems to be getting the best of the bargain.

For many years clover was regarded as a crop helpful to the soil, and one reason given was the great length of the roots. Thus the roots of red clover often reach the depth of several feet, even in heavy soil, which they thus aerate and drain, especially when they decay and leave channels. But this is only half the story ; for a long time people had noted that on clover roots were little swollen places or nodules, which were supposed to have come from some disease or insect injury. The scientists became interested in the supposed disease, and they finally ascertained that these nodules are filled with bacteria, which are the underground partners of the clovers and other legumes. These bacteria are able to fix the free nitrogen of the air, and make it available for plant-food. As nitrogen is the most expensive of the fertilizers, any agency which can extract it from the free air for the use of plants is indeed a valuable aid to the farmer. Thus it is that in the modern agriculture, clover or some other legume is put on the land once in three or four years in the regular rotation of crops, and it brings back to the soil the nitrogen which other crops have exhausted. An interesting fact about the partnership between the root bacteria and the clover-like plants is that the plants do not flourish without this partnership, and investigators have devised a method by which these bacteria may be scattered in the soil on which some kinds of clover are to be planted, and thus aid in growing a crop. This method is to-day being used for the introduction of alfalfa here in New York State. But the use of clover as a fertilizer is not limited to its root factory for capturing nitrogen ; its leaves break down quickly and readily yield the rich food material of which they are composed, so that the farmer who plows under his second-crop clover instead of harvesting it, adds greatly to the fertility of his farm.

The members of three distinct genera are popularly called clovers : The True Clovers (*Trifolium*), of which six or seven species are found in New York State, and more than sixty species are found in the United States. The Medics (*Medicago*), of which four species are found here. The Melilots (*Melilotus*), or sweet clovers, of which we have two species.

THE TRUE CLOVERS. (*Trifolium.*)

The Red Clover (*Fig. 245*). (*Trifolium pratense.**) — This beautiful dweller in our fields came to us from Europe, and it is also a native of Asia. It is the clover most widely cultivated in New York State for fodder, and is one of our most important crops. Clover hay often being a standard of ex-cellence by which other hay is measured. The export of clover seed from the United States has sometimes reached the worth of two million dollars per year, and this great industry is supposed to be carried on with the aid of that other partner of the red clover, the bumblebee. Bum-blebees had to be imported into Australia before clover seed could be produced there. The whole question of the rela-tion of the bumblebee to the pollination of clover no doubt needs to be re-studied, for re-cent observations have led to the contesting of prevailing opinions. It has been sup-posed that the failure of the clover seed crop in some places

Fig. 245. *The common red clover.*

---

* Pronounced *Trifol' -ium praten' -se*, the second or specific name with three syllables.

is due to the destruction of bumblebees; whether this is true or not, we are certain that bumblebees visit clover blooms, and the teacher can observe for himself.

There is a more perennial form of red clover, known as variety *perenne*. It is distinguished from the common form of red clover by its taller growth and mostly less hairy herbage, and by the fact that the flower-head is usually somewhat stalked. Some persons regard it as a hybrid of red and zig-zag clover.

Zig-Zag Clover. (*T. medium.*)—This is another species of red clover, resembling the one just discussed, except that its flower-head rises on a long stalk above the upper leaves, while the red clover has the flower-head set close to these leaves. The color of the blossom is darker than in red clover, and the flower-head is looser. The stems of the zig-zag clover are likely to be bent at angles and thus it gets its name. It is a question whether this species is really grown on farms. It is probable that some or all of the clover that passes under this name is *Trifolium pratense* var. *perenne*. At all events, the zig-zag clover seems to be imperfectly understood by botanists and others.

Crimson Clover — *Scarlet Clover* (*Fig. 246*). (*T. incarnatum.*)— While this beautiful clover grows as a weed in the southern parts of our State, it has only recently begun to play an important part in our horticulture. It is an annual, and its home is the Mediterranean region of Europe. It thrives best in loose, sandy soils, and in our State is chiefly used as a cover-crop for orchards, and to plow under as a fertilizer. It usually has bright, crimson flowers, arranged in a long, pointed head, and its brilliant green fan-shaped leaves make it the most artistically decorative of all our clovers.

Fig. 246. Crimson clover.

Buffalo Clover (*Fig. 247*). (*T. reflexum.*)—This is sometimes taken for a variety of the red clover, but only a glance is needed to distinguish it. While the head is perhaps an inch in diameter the flowerets are not directed upward and set close as in the red clover, but each floweret is on a little stalk, and is bent abruptly backward. The flowers are not pink. The standard is red, while the wings and keel are nearly white. The leaves are blunt at the tip. It grows in meadows in western New York and westward. This species is native to this country.

Alsike Clover. (*T. hybridum.*)—This is a perennial and grows in low meadows and waste places from Nova Scotia to Idaho. It was introduced from Europe. It is especially valuable in wet meadows, where the red clover would be drowned. The blossoms of the alsike look like those of the white clover except that they are a little larger and are pink; but the long branching mostly upright stems are very different in habit from the creeping stems of the white clover ; the blossoms are very fragrant.

Fig. 247. Three clovers, respectively, Buffalo, Yellow, and Rabbit-foot clover.

The White Clover. (*T. repens.*)—This beautiful little clover, whose leaves make a rug for our feet in every possible place, is well known to us all. It is the clover best beloved by honey-bees, and the person who does not know the distinct flavor of white clover honey has lost something out of life. While in hard soil the white clover lasts only two or three years, on rich, moist lands it is a true perennial. While it was probably a native in the northern part of America, yet it is truly cosmopolitan and may be found in almost all regions of the temperate zones. Very likely the common stock of it is an introduction from Europe. By many this is considered to be the original shamrock.

The Yellow, or Hop Clover (*Fig. 247*). (*T. agrarium.*) — This friendly little plant, filling waste places with brilliant green leaves and small yellow flower-heads, is not considered a clover by those

23

who are not observant. But if the flowerets in the small, dense heads are examined, they will be seen to resemble very closely those of the other clovers. The stems are many-branched and often grow a foot or more in height. The flowers are numerous, and on fading turn brown, and resemble the fruit of a pigmy hop vine, whence the name. Its leaves are much more pointed than those of the medics, with which it might be confused because of its yellow flowers.

Low Hop Clover, or Hop Trefoil. (*T. procumbens.*) — This resembles the above species, except that it is smaller and also more spreading, and the stems and leaves are more downy.

The Least Hop Clover. (*T. dubium.*) — This may be readily distinguished from the above species by the fact that its yellow flowerets occur from three to ten in a head. This is said by some to be the true shamrock, although the white clover is also called the shamrock.

The Rabbit-Foot, or Stone Clover (*Fig. 247*). (*T. arvense.*) — This is another clover not easily recognized as such. It grows a foot or more in height and has erect branches. The leaflets are narrow and all arise from the same point. The flowerets occur in long, dense heads. The calyx is very silky, and the lobes are longer than the white corollas, thus giving the flower-head a soft, hairy look, something like the early stages of the blossom of the pussy willow. Because of its appearance it is often called " pussy clover."

THE MEDICS. (*Medicago.*)

Alfalfa (*Fig. 248*). (*Medicago sativa.*) — This is the veteran of all the clovers, for it has been under cultivation for twenty centuries. It is a native of the valleys of western Asia. In America it was first introduced into Mexico with the Spanish invasion. It was brought from Chile to California in 1854, where it has since been the most important hay crop. In fact, there is no better hay than that made from alfalfa. It was probably introduced into the Atlantic States from southern Europe, and has grown as a weed for many years in certain localities in New England and the Middle States; only recently has it been considered a practicable crop for this climate, although it was grown in Jefferson Co., N. Y., in 1791. Its special value is that it is a true perennial, and may be cut three times or more during a season, and when once established it withstands hot, dry weather. It is of marvelous value to the semi-arid regions. The alfalfa flower is blue or violet, and grows in a loose raceme. The plant grows tall and its stems are many branched. This and all these medics are introduced from Europe.

Black or Hop Medic. (*M. lupulina.*) — This would hardly be called a clover by the novice. The long stems lie along the ground, and the tiny yellow flower-heads do not much resemble the clover blossom. It is a common weed in waste places in our State. It is perennial.

The Toothed Medic. (*M. denticulata.*) — Instead of having the yellow flowerets in a dense head, this species has them in pairs or perhaps fours, or sometimes more. It is widely distributed as a weed, and is also introduced as a pasture plant for early grazing. It is of little value as hay.

The Spotted Medic. (*M. Arabica.*) — This very much resembles the preceding species except that the leaves are likely to have on them conspicuous dark spots near the center. Like the preceding species it is an annual and a weed, and has

Fig. 248. Alfalfa, foliage and flowers.

also been introduced as a plant for early grazing. This and the toothed medic are known to farmers under the name of bur-clover. The reason for this name is found in the seed-pod, which is twisted in a spiral and has an outer margin of curved prickles.

THE MELILOTS, OR SWEET CLOVERS. (*Melilotus.*)

In driving or walking along the country roads, we may find ourselves suddenly immersed in a wave of delightful fragrance, and if we look for the source we may find this friendly plant flourishing in the most forbidding of soils. Growing as a weed, it brings sweet perfume to us, and at the same time nitrogen, aeration and

drainage to the hopeless soil, making rich those places where
other weeds have not the temerity to attempt to grow. When the
soil is generous, the sweet clover often grows very tall, sometimes
as high as ten feet. It is a cheerful, adaptable and beneficial
plant, and I never see it without giving it a welcome, which, I am
sorry to say, I cannot always grant to other roadside wayfarers.
The sweet clovers are European.

The White Sweet Clover (*M. alba*) is sometimes called Bokhara
clover and has white flowers (Fig. 249).

The Yellow Sweet Clover (*M. offici-
nalis*) has yellow blossoms. It has
interesting old English names, such as
Balsam Flowers, King's Clover and
Heartwort.

QUESTIONS ON THE CLOVERS.

*Two general kinds of types of studies
are to be made of the clovers : identification studies, whereby you will come to know
the kinds of clover ; life history studies,
whereby you will come to know under
what conditions the plants live and thrive.
The latter is the more important, but the
former usually precedes it, for one is better
able to discover and discuss the biological
questions when he is acquainted with the
species. The following questions will bring
out some of the important biological aspects :*

1. How many of the true clovers, the
medics, and the sweet clovers do you
know ?

Fig. 249. White sweet clover.

2. Send me properly labelled pressed
specimens of the leaves and blossoms of the clovers that you have
been able to find.

3. Dig a root of red clover and find the nodules on it. Please
describe them.

4. What methods does the U. S. Department of Agriculture
employ to inoculate the soil with bacteria so that alfalfa may grow ?

5. How do clover roots protect the land from the effects of
heavy rains ?

6. How do the clover plants conserve the moisture in the soil?

7. How does this conservation of moisture aid the farmer and orchardist?

8. What is a cover-crop, and what are its uses?

9. Why do farmers sow red clover with grass seed?

10. How do the habits of the stems of white clover differ from those of other clovers?

11. Why is white clover so desirable for lawns?

12. Compare the floweret of the red clover with the sweet pea blossom and describe the resemblance.

13. Study a head of white clover from the time it opens until it is brown, and tell what changes take place in it day by day.

14. What has happened to the flowerets that are bent downward around the stalk?

15. Watch one of these flowerets deflect, and describe the process.

16. How many flowerets do you find in a head of red clover? Of white clover? Of alsike?

17. Which flowerets open first in a head of red clover?

18. Describe a clover seed. Describe a seed of alfalfa.

19. What insects do you find visiting the red clover blossoms? The white clover blossoms?

Alfalfa, or Lucerne.*

The alfalfa plant is just now coming into great prominence in New York State. Every teacher, particularly in the rural schools, will need to know the plant and to have some information about it.

What alfalfa is.—It is a clover-like plant. It is perennial. It has violet-purple flowers. The leaves have three narrow leaflets. It sends up many stiff stems, 2 to 3 feet high. The roots go straight down to great depths.

Why it is important.—It is an excellent cattle food, and cattle-raising for dairy purposes is the leading special agricultural industry in New York State. In fact, New York leads all the States in the value of its dairy products. Any plant that is more nutritious and more productive of pasture and hay than the familiar clovers and grasses will add immensely to the dairy industry, and therefore to the wealth of the State. Alfalfa is such a plant. It gives three cuttings of hay year after year in New York State, thereby yielding twice as much as clover does. In

---

* Home Nature-Study Course, New Series, Vol. I, No. 1, October, 1904.

the production of digestible nutrients per acre ranks above clover as 24 ranks above 10. When once established it withstands droughts, for the roots grow deep.

Alfalfa is South European. It was early introduced into North America. It first came into prominence in the semi-arid West because of its drought-resisting qualities, and now it has added millions of dollars to the wealth of the nation. Gradually it is working its way into the East. It is discussed in the agricultural press and before farmers' institutes. Last year the College of Agriculture offered to send a small packet of seeds to such school children in New York State as wanted to grow a little garden plat of it. About 5,000 children were supplied. The teacher must now learn what alfalfa is.

In nearly every rural community, sufficient alfalfa can be found for school purposes. In many places it has run wild along roadsides.

On these plants make the following observations:

1. Under what conditions have you found alfalfa growing? How did the plant come to grow there,— sown, or run wild?

2. Describe the form of the root. How does the root branch?

3. Do you find the little tubercles or nodules on the roots? On what part of the roots? How large? How numerous?

4. The crown of the plant (at the surface of the ground), — describe it, and how the tops and the roots start from it.

5. The stems,— how many from each crown, whether erect or prostrate, how they branch.

6. The leaves,— simple or compound? Form? Edges entire or fine toothed? Do the leaves "sleep" at night, as those of clover do?

7. Do you find any distinct spots on the leaves? What do you think is the cause of them?

8. Flowers,— how borne (whether singly or in clusters), color, form, resemblance to any other flowers you may know. Do they vary in color?

9. If possible, find the seed-pods and seeds, and describe.

10. Make inquiries as to whether alfalfa is becoming well known in your vicinity.

Agricultural Account of Alfalfa.

You may be asked some practical questions about alfalfa; therefore we give you a brief agricultural account of it. If you desire further information, write to the College of Agriculture, Ithaca, N. Y., for Bulletin 221, "Alfalfa in New York."

Alfalfa is grown mostly for hay. It is not adapted to pasture, because the new growth springs from the crown at the surface of the ground, and if this is destroyed the growth will not be renewed vigorously. New York is a hay-producing State. Grain feeds can be grown more cheaply in the West. It is of great importance to the State, therefore, if a better hay-producing plant can be found. We have seen that New York leads the States in dairy cattle. Other livestock also is abundant. Last year more than half a million horses and mules were fed in the State.

Success has not attended efforts to grow alfalfa in all parts of New York. This is due to two principal reasons: (1) farmers have not known the plant and its habits well enough to give it the care and treatment it demands; (2) the soils of many localities, because of their physical condition or composition, are not suitable for the plant.

The alfalfa seedling is not a strong plant. It cannot compete with weeds nor overcome adverse conditions of moisture; it cannot adapt itself to conditions resulting from poor preparation of land, and it is not vigorous in its ability to get food from any source. Care must be given to the preparation of the land in order that sufficient moisture may be supplied during the early stages of growth and that there may be an abundance of quickly available plant-food. After growth has started, alfalfa has the power to get some of its nitrogen from the air through the nodules which grow upon its roots; yet during the early stages of growth it is essential that the soil be supplied with all elements of plant-food in available form.

While alfalfa requires an abundance of moisture for its best growth and development, yet it will not grow in soils that hold water for any considerable length of time. Such soils are usually those with an impervious subsoil or hard-pan, or those of clay or silt structure which retain free water to the exclusion of air. Therefore, it is important that alfalfa soils be well and uniformly drained, either by natural conditions or by underground drains. One other essential of prime importance is that the soil be neutral or alkaline in its reaction; in other words, that it contain no free acid. Limestone or blue-grass soils are ideal in this regard for alfalfa. If acid is present, the difficulty may be corrected either wholly or in part by the application of 500 to 2,000 pounds of lime per acre.

As in most other legumes (members of the family Leguminosæ, including peas, beans, clovers), there is a peculiar relationship existing between the plant and excrescences or nodules upon its roots. These nodules are essential to the normal growth and development of the plant. They contain bacteria, and these bacteria have the power of "fixing" or appropriating the free atmospheric nitrogen in the soil. Legumes are "nitrogen-gatherers," whereas most other plants secure their nitrogen only from decomposing organic matter. Failure to have the soil inoculated with the proper bacteria for alfalfa is the cause for many failures with the crop. In most instances when the plants do not make satisfactory growth, or have a yellow, dwarfed appearance, the trouble can be traced to the absence of these bacteria from the soil, and hence to a lack of nodules on the roots. The relationship existing between the plant and the organism is one of mutual benefit. Each kind of leguminous plant seems to have its characteristic bacterium, which grows on no other plant, although this question is not thoroughly settled.

Farmers are becoming aware of this requisite in alfalfa culture and usually supply it in two different ways. The older method is to take the surface soil from an old alfalfa field, where the plants have grown well and where nodules are to be found on the roots, and to sow it on the land to be seeded at the rate of one hundred or more pounds per acre. In this way the soil becomes inoculated with the bacteria, and as the young plants spring into growth the bacteria develop on the roots. Another method is to inoculate the seed before sowing with artificial cultures of the bacteria. Both of these methods are usually successful, and if soil conditions are right the chances for failure are few.

Alfalfa should be cut when it opens into flower. At this time the stems and leaves contain their highest percentage of nutrients, the leaves do not so easily fall off in curing, and the stems are not so woody. Besides these reasons, if cutting be delayed until after flowering, the plant may not spring quickly into subsequent growth.

Disease does not spare the alfalfa plant. Both leaves and roots are attacked, the leaf spot being serious. The parasitic dodder is a serious enemy in some parts of New York State.

LEAFLET XXXV.

HOW PLANTS LIVE TOGETHER.*

By L. H. BAILEY.

O the general observer, plants seem to be distributed in a promiscuous and haphazard way, without law or order. This is because he does not see and consider.

The world is now full of plants. Every plant puts forth its supreme effort to multiply its kind. The result is an intense struggle for an opportunity to live.

Seeds are scattered in profusion, but only the few can grow. The many do not find the proper conditions. They fall on stony ground. In Fig. 250 this loss is shown. The trunk of an elm tree stands in the background. The covering of the ground, except about the very base of the tree, is a mat of elm seedlings. There are thousands of them in the space shown in the picture, so many that they make a sod-like covering which shows little

Fig. 250.   A carpet of young elms, all of which must perish.

detail in the photograph. Not one of these thousands will ever make a tree.

* Nature-Study Quarterly No. 6 : Leaflet 19, October, 1900.

Since there is intense competition for every foot of the earth's surface that is capable of raising plants, it follows that every spot will probably have many kinds of plant inhabitants.   Plants must live together.   They associate ; they become adapted or accus-

Fig. 251.   A plant society waiting for the spring.

tomed to each other.   Some can live in shade ; they thrive in the forest, where sun-loving plants perish.   Others prefer the sun, and thereby live together.   There are plant societies.

Every distinct or separate area has its own plant society.   There

Fig. 252.   Weak, narrow-leaved grasses grow in the cat-tail forest.

is one association for the hard-tramped door-yard,—knot-weed and broad-leaved plantain with interspersed grass and dandelions ; one for the fence-row,— briars and choke-cherries and hiding weeds; one for the dry open field,—wire-grass and mullein and scattered docks ; one for the slattern roadside,— sweet clover, ragweed, burdock ; one for the meadow swale, — smartweed and pitchforks ; one for the barnyard, — rank pigweeds and sprawling barn-grass ; one for the dripping rock-cliff,— delicate bluebells and hanging ferns and grasses. Indefinitely might these categories be extended. We all know the plant societies, but we have not considered them.

In every plant society there is one dominant note. It is the individuality of one kind of plant which grows most abundantly or overtops the others. Certain plant-forms come to mind when one thinks of willows, others when he thinks of an apple orchard, still others when he thinks of a beech forest. The farmer may associate "pussly" with cabbages and beets, but not with wheat and oats. He associates cockle with wheat, but not with oats or corn. We all associate dandelions with grassy areas, but not with burdock or forests.

It is impossible to open ones eyes out-of-doors, outside the paved streets of cities, without seeing a plant society. A lawn is a plant society. It may contain only grass, or it may contain weeds hidden away in the sward. What weeds remain in the lawn? Only those which can withstand the mowing. What are they? Let a bit of lawn grow as it will for a month, and see what there is in it. A swale, a dry hillside, a forest of beech, a forest of oak, a forest of hemlock or pine, a weedy yard, a tangled fence-row, a brook-side, a deep quiet swamp, a lake shore, a railroad, a river bank, a meadow, a pasture, a dusty roadway,— each has its characteristic plants. Even in the winter, one may see these societies,— the tall plants still

Fig. 253. The wild grape covers the treetop, and the children play in the bower. The grape is searching for light.

asserting themselves, others of less aspiring stature, and others snuggling just under the snow (Fig. 251).

Often these societies are in the nature of overgrowth and undergrowth — one society living beneath another. Of such are forest societies. Few woods are so dark that some plants do not grow on the ground, unless they are evergreen or coniferous woods. Even in humbler communities, the overgrowth and

undergrowth are usually apparent if one looks closely.   Separate
the cat-tails in the dense swamp and see the weak and narrow-
leaved grasses growing between (Fig. 252).   Note the clover,
young grasses, and other plants between the grass in the meadow :
the farmer says that his meadow has good " bottom."

Some plants even grow on top of other plants.   It is their way
of getting light.   Of such are the climbers.   Note the mantle
which the wild grape throws over the trees (Fig. 253).   Often the
supporting tree is smothered and killed.

When an area is newly cleared, many plants rush for it.
Quickly it is covered
with ambitious
growths,—pokeweeds,
fireweeds, thistles, bri-
ars, nettles.   Often
each plant occupies
large places alone,
making clumps or
patches.   These
patches are plant colo-
nies,—made up mostly
of one species or kind
(Fig. 254).   But as the
struggle tightens,
other plants insinuate
themselves into the
colony and it is broken
up ; a mixed popula-

Fig. 254.   A colony of clotbur.

tion results.   Sometimes these colonies are broken up by the shade
of trees and tall bushes which have come up near them, for all neglected areas, in this part of the world, tend to return to forest if
they are not mown, pastured or burned.   Mown and pastured
areas run into grass, for the grass withstands the cutting and
grazing.   In burned areas the struggle begins anew when the fire
has passed.

Plant societies are easy to study for the school.   The study of
them appeals to the desire for exploration and adventure, and adds
zest to the excursion.   Go to a swale, swamp, roadside, forest,
weedy field, or other place, and ask the pupil to note : (1) that
the flora of the place is unlike that of places with different
physical features ; (2) that these particular plants grow together

because they can all survive under similar conditions; (3) what
these conditions are,—whether sun, shade, dry soil, wet soil,
sand, clay, rock; (4) what particular plant is most abundant or
gives character to the society.

Fig. 255.   Two plant societies,— the close-bitten sward and the rushy pond.

Study one society thoroughly.   Make lists of the kinds of
plants and of the relative numbers of each.   If the names of the

*Fig. 256.   The edge of the road.   Trees and bushes crowd the drive-way, and a
ribbon of grass and weeds has pushed itself to the very margin.*

plants are not known, call them by numbers; make dried specimens of them for reference.   When another society is visited,
repeat these observations, and compare one society with another.
  Ask every plant why it grows there.

LEAFLET XXXVI

PLANTING A PLANT.[*]

By L. H. BAILEY.

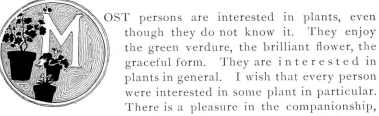

OST persons are interested in plants, even though they do not know it. They enjoy the green verdure, the brilliant flower, the graceful form. They are interested in plants in general. I wish that every person were interested in some plant in particular. There is a pleasure in the companionship, merely because the plant is a living and a growing thing. It expresses power, vitality. It is a complete, self-sufficient organism. It makes its way in the world. It is alive.

The companionship with a plant, as with a bird or an insect, means more than the feeling for the plant itself. It means that the person has interest in something real and genuine. It takes him out-of-doors. It invites him to the field. It is suggestive. It inculcates a habit of meditation and reflection. It enables one to discover himself.

I wish that every child in New York State had a plant of his own, and were attached to it. Why cannot the teacher suggest this idea to the pupils? It may be enough to have only one plant the first year, particularly if the pupil is young. It matters little what the plant is. The important thing is that it shall be alive. Every plant is interesting in its way. A good pigweed is much more satisfactory than a poor rosebush. The pupil should grow the plant from the beginning. He should not buy it ready grown, for then it is not his, even though he own it.

It is well to begin with some plant that grows quickly and matures early. One is ambitious in spring, but his enthusiasm may wither and die in the burning days of summer. If possible, grow the plant in the free open ground; if this is not feasible, grow it in a pot or box or tin can. Take advantage of the early spring enthusiasm. Choose hardy and vigorous plants: sow the seeds when the "spirit moves."

[*] Nature-Study Quarterly, No. 8 : Leaflet 21, January, 1901.

cuttings be made of the soft or growing wood, of which the "slips" of geraniums and coleus are examples. Others grow equally well from cuttings of the hard or mature wood, as currants and grapes ; and in some instances this mature wood may be of roots, as in the blackberry. Somewhat different principles underlie the handling of these two kinds of cuttings ; and these principles we may now consider. We shall find it excellent practice to set the pupils to making cuttings now and then. If we can do nothing more, we can make cuttings of potatoes, as the farmer does ; and we can plant them in a box in the window.

Fig. 257. Geranium cutting. One-half natural size.

THE SOFTWOOD CUTTING.

The softwood cutting is made from tissue which is still growing, or at least from that which is not dormant. It must not be allowed to wilt. It must, therefore, be protected from direct sunlight and dry air until it is well established ; and if it has many leaves, some of them should be removed, or at least cut in two in order to reduce the evaporating surface. Keep the soil uniformly moist ; and avoid soils which contain much decaying organic matter, for these soils are breeding places of fungi which attack the soft cutting and cause it to "damp off."

For most plants, the proper age of maturity of wood for the making of cuttings may be determined by giving the twig a quick bend ; if it snaps and hangs by the bark, it is in proper condition ; if it bends without breaking it is too young and soft or too old ; if it splinters, it is too old and woody.

Fig. 258.   Carnation cutting. Natural size.

The tips of strong upright shoots usually make the best cuttings. Preferably each cutting should have a joint or node near its base ; and if the internodes are short, it may comprise two or three joints. Allow one to three leaves to remain at the top. If these leaves are large, cut them in two.

Insert the cutting half or more its length in clean sand or gravel. Press the earth firmly about it. Throw a newspaper over the bed to exclude the light — if the sun strikes it — and to prevent too rapid evaporation. See that the soil is moist clear through, not on top only.

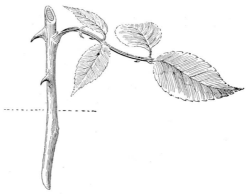

Mason's sand is good earth in which to start cuttings. Or fine gravel — sifted of most of its earthy

Fig. 259. Rose cutting. More than one-half natural size.

matter — may be used. If the cuttings are to be grown in a window, put three or four inches of the earth in a shallow box or a pan. A soap box cut in two lengthwise, so that it makes a box four or five inches deep — like a gardener's flat — is excellent.

Fig. 260. Cutting-bed, showing carnations and roses.

If the box does not receive direct sunlight, it may be covered with a pane of glass to prevent evaporation; and then the children may see the plants more readily. But take care that the air is not kept too close, else the damping-off fungi may attack the cuttings and they will rot at the surface of the ground. See that the pane is raised a little at one end to afford ventilation ; and if water collects in drops on the under side of the glass, remove the pane for a time. Cuttings of common plants, as geranium, coleus, fuchsia, carnation, should be kept in a living-room temperature.

The pictures are better than words. The line across them shows where the soil comes. There are softwood cuttings of the geranium (Fig. 257), the carnation (Fig. 258), and the rose (Fig. 259) ; and there is a gardener's cutting bed (Fig. 260) with cuttings of carnations and roses.

Be patient. As long as the cuttings look bright and green, they are safe. It may be a month before roots form. When roots have formed, the plants will begin to make new leaves at the tip. Then they may be transplanted into other boxes or into pots. The verbena in Fig. 261 is just ready for transplanting. Each child will want a plant.

Fig. 261. Verbena cutting ready for transplanting. Two-thirds natural size.

It is not always easy to find growing shoots from which to make the cuttings.

The best practice is to cut back some old plant severely, then keep it warm and well watered, and thereby force it to throw out new shoots. The old geranium plant from the window garden, or the one taken up from the lawn bed, may be served this way. See Fig. 262. This may seem hard treatment, but that is all the old plant is good for ; it has passed its usefulness for bloom. The best plants of the geranium and the coleus and many window plants are those which are not more than one year old. The cuttings that are made in January, February, or March will give compact blooming plants for the next winter ; and thereafter new ones take their place.

Some plants may be propagated by means of cuttings of leaves. The Rex begonias or " beefsteak geraniums " are the commonest examples. The large, nearly mature leaf is divided into triangular pieces, each piece containing at its point a bit of the leaf-base (top of the leaf-stalk). This kind of cutting is shown in Fig. 263.

This base is sometimes split (as at o) by gardeners to hasten the formation of roots. Only the tip of the cutting is stuck into the sand ; otherwise it is treated like other softwood cuttings.

THE HARDWOOD CUTTING.

Many plants grow readily from cuttings of ripe or dormant wood. The willows cast their branchlets in snow and wind, and these, falling in pleasant places propagate their kind ; and thus the river sides and the lake shores become willow-crowned.

Grapes, currants, gooseberries, poplars readily take root from the hardwood. Fig. 264 shows a currant cutting. It has only one bud above the ground.

The best results are attained when the cuttings are made in the fall, and then buried until spring in sand in the cellar. They are not

Fig. 262. Old geranium plant cut back to make it throw out shoots from which cuttings can be made.

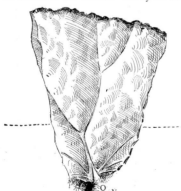

Fig. 263. Begonia leaf cutting. Natural size.

idle while they rest. The lower end calluses or heals, and the roots form more readily when the cutting is planted in the spring. But if the children are interested, take cuttings at any time in winter, plant them in a deep box in the window, and watch. They will need no shading or special care.

When plants of any variety are scarce, the cuttings may be shorter. Sometimes they are reduced to a single " eye " or bud, with an inch or two of wood attached ; and these single-eye cuttings are planted much as one plants seeds.

The Graft.

If the cutting were planted in a plant rather than in the soil, we should have a graft ; and the graft might grow.   In this case, the cutting would not make roots, but it would grow fast to the other plant, and the twain would become one.   When the cutting is inserted in a plant it is no longer called a cutting, but a cion ; and the plant in which it is inserted is called the stock.   The completed thing — the cion growing in the stock — is a graft.

Plants are particular as to their companions, when it comes to such close relationships as these. They choose the stocks upon which they will grow ; but we can find out what their choice is only by making the experiment.   There are queer things about it. The pear grows well on the quince, but the quince does not grow so well on the pear.   The pear grows on some of the hawthorns, but it is an unwilling sub- ject on the apple.   Tomato plants will grow on potato plants and potato plants on tomato plants.   When the potato is the root, both tomatoes and potatoes may be produced ; when the tomato is the root, neither potatoes nor tomatoes will be produced.   Chestnuts are said to grow on some kinds of oaks.

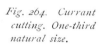

Fig. 264.   Currant cutting. One-third natural size.

Fig. 265. Cion for cleft-grafting. One-half natural size.

Why do we graft ? Think a bit. If I sow seeds of a Baldwin apple, I shall probably have as many kinds of apples as I have trees.   Some of these apples may be like the Baldwin, and they may not.   That is, apple seeds do not reproduce the particular variety.   They will not be held to any stricter account than merely to produce apples ; these apples may range all the way from toothsome kinds to Ben Davis.   The nurseryman knows this, and he does not wait for the trees to bear in the hope that they will produce something to his liking.   So he grafts them when they still are young, — takes a cion from the kind which he wishes to perpetuate.   So it happens that all the Baldwins and the Kings and the Russets, and all other named varieties, are growing on alien roots; and what kinds of fruits these stocks would have produced no one will ever know, because their heads were cut off in youth and other heads were put on to order. In this way apples and pears and plums and peaches and cherries and apricots are propagated, for they will not grow readily from cuttings. But raspberries and blackberries and gooseberries and currants and grapes grow willingly from cuttings, and they are not grafted by the nurseryman.

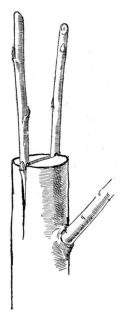

The forming, growing tissue of the trunk is the cambium, lying on the outside of the woody cylinder, beneath the bark. In order that union may take place, the cambium of the cion and the stock must come together. Therefore, the cion is set in the side of the stock. I once knew a man who believed that everything was designed for some useful purpose. The hole in the pith bothered him, until he discovered that a cion just filled it. He grafted his trees accordingly; but the experiment was productive of nothing except pithy remarks.

Fig. 266. Cleft-graft. One-half natural size.

Fig. 267. The graft waxed.

There are many ways of shaping the cion and of preparing the stock to receive it. These ways are dictated largely by the relative sizes of cion and stock, although many of them are matters of mere personal preference. The underlying principles are two: see that there is close contact between the cambiums of cion and stock; cover the wounded surfaces to prevent evaporation and to protect the parts from disease.

On large stocks the common form of grafting is the cleft-graft.

The stock is cut off and split ; and in one or both sides a wedge-shaped cion is firmly inserted. Fig. 265 shows the cion ; Fig. 266, the cions set in the stock ; Fig. 267, the stock waxed. It will be seen that the lower bud — that lying in the wedge — is covered by the wax ; but being nearest the food supply and least exposed to weather, it is the most likely to grow : it pushes through the wax.

Fig. 268. Shield-budding. One-half natural size.

The wax is made of beeswax, resin, and tallow. The hands are greased, and the wax is then worked until it is soft enough to spread. For the little grafting which any school would do, it is better to buy the wax of a seedsman. However, grafting is hardly to be recommended as a general school diversion, as the making of cuttings is ; and this account of it is inserted chiefly to satisfy the general curiosity on the subject. But we hope that now and then a youngster will make the effort for himself, for nothing is more exciting than to make a graft grow all by one's self.

Cleft-grafting is done in spring, as growth begins. The cions are cut previously, when perfectly dormant, and from the tree which it is desired to propagate. The cions are kept in sand or moss in the cellar. Limbs of various sizes may be cleft-grafted — from one-half inch up to four inches in diameter ; but a diameter of one inch is the most convenient size. All the leading or main branches of a tree top may be grafted. If the remaining parts of the top are gradually cut away and the scions grow well, the entire top will be changed over to the new variety in three or four years. Each cion may be a different variety ; but there is no difference in the operation or the treatment of the tree.

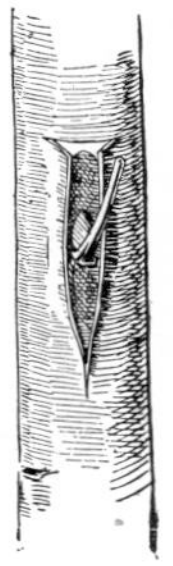

Fig. 269. The bud set in the matrix. One-half natural size.

On young or small stocks, like nursery trees, the cleft-graft is not practicable, and a different form of grafting is employed ; but the teacher will not care to be confused with further details.

We have seen that a cutting may be reduced to a single bud ; so may a cion. If the bud-cion has very little or no wood attached, and is inserted underneath the bark, the operation is known as budding. The commonest form of budding is shown in Figs. 268, 269, 270. This is the method known as shield-budding,

because the bud, with its attached bark, is shield-shaped (Fig. 268).
A T-shape incision is made in the stock, and under the bark the
bud is inserted (Fig. 269) ; then the wound is tightly bound with
soft cord or bast (Fig. 270). Budding may be performed whenever
the bark will "slip" and when well grown buds can be secured,—
that is, either in spring or late summer. It is usually performed
at the latter season ; and then the bud does not throw out a shoot
the same season, but merely grows fast to the stock.
The next spring it throws out a shoot and makes a
trunk ; and in the meantime the stock has been cut
off just above the bud. That is, the bud-shoot takes
the place of the top of the stock.

Shield-budding is performed only on small and
young stocks. It is usually exclusively employed
in the propagation of stone fruits, as cherries,
peaches, plums, apricots, for experience has proved
that it is preferable to other forms of grafting. It
may also be employed for other fruit trees.

*Fig. 270. The
bud tied.*

How is a peach tree made? In 1898 a pit or
seed is saved. In the spring of 1899 it is planted.
The young tree comes up quickly. In August, 1899, the little
stock has one bud — of the desired variety — inserted near the
ground. In the spring of 1900 the stock is severed just above the
bud : the bud throws out a shoot which grows to a height of four
or six feet ; and in the fall of 1900 the tree is sold. It is known
as a year-old tree ; but the root is two years old.

How is an apple tree made? The seed is saved in 1898, planted
in 1899. The seedlings do not grow so rapidly as those of the
peach. At the end of 1899 they are taken up and sorted ; and in
the spring of 1900 they are planted. In July or August, 1900,
they are budded. In the spring of 1901 the stock is cut off above
the bud ; and the bud-shoot grows three or four feet. In 1902
the shoot branches, or the top begins to form ; and in the fall of
1902 the tree may be sold as a two-year-old, although most persons prefer to buy it in 1903 as a three-year-old. In some parts
of the country, particularly in the west, the little seedling is
grafted in the winter of 1899–1900 in a grafting-room ; and the
young grafts are set in the nursery row in the spring of 1900, to
complete their growth.

I have now given my reader an elementary lesson in horticulture ; but I shall consider it of little avail if it is not trans-

formed into practice for the children. February is the gardener's time for the starting of his cutting-beds, in which to grow plants for the summer bloom. Ask the children to bring the old geraniums and fuchsias and coleus, and other favorites. Keep them in a warm window ; cut them back ; see that they are well watered ; then take the cuttings when the time comes. The children will be interested to watch the fortunes of the different cuttings. They will be interested in Vergil's couplet, as set to rhyme in old-fashioned English :

> Some need no root, nor doth the Gardner doubt,
> That Sprigs though headlong set, will timely sprout.

LEAFLET XXXVIII.

A CHILDREN'S GARDEN.*

By L. H. BAILEY.

E want every school child in the State to grow a few plants. We want every one of them to learn something of why and how plants grow ; and the best and surest way to learn is to grow the plants and to watch them carefully. We want everyone to become interested in everything that lives and grows. It does not matter so very much just what kinds of plants one grows as it does that he grows something and grows it the best that he knows how. We want the children to grow these plants for the love of it,— that is, for the fun of it,— hence we propose that they grow flowers ; for when one grows pumpkins and potatoes, and such things, he is usually thinking of how much money he is going to make at the end of the season. Yet, we should like some rivalry in the matter in every school, and we therefore propose that a kind of a fair be held at the school-house next September, soon after school begins, so that each child may show the flowers which he has grown. What a jolly time that will be !

Now, we must not try to grow too many things or to do too much. Therefore, we propose that you grow sweet peas and China asters. They are both easy to grow, and the seeds are cheap. Each one has many colors, and everybody likes them Now let us tell you just how we should grow them.

1. The place.— Never put them — or any other flowers — in the middle of the lawn,— that is, out in the center of the yard. They do not look well there, and the grass roots run under them and steal the food and the moisture. I am sure that you would not like to see a picture hung up on a fence-post. It has no background, and it looks out of place. The picture does not mean anything when hung in such a spot. In the same way, a flower

---

* Teachers' Leaflet No. 4, April, 1897.

379

bed does not mean anything when set out in the center of a lawn.
We must have a background for it, if possible,—a wall upon
which to hang it. So we will put the flower bed just in front of
some bushes or near the back fence, or alongside the smoke-house,
or along the walk at the side of the house or in the back yard.
The flowers will not only look better in such places, but it will
not matter so much if we make a failure of our flower bed ; there
are always risks to run, for the old hen may scratch up the seeds,
the cow may break into the yard some summer night, or some
bug may eat the plants up.

Perhaps some of the children may live so near to the school-
house that they can grow their plants upon the school grounds,
and so have sweet peas and asters where there are usually docks
and smartweeds. Grow them alongside the fence, or against the
school-house if there is a place where the eaves will not drip on
them.

2. How to make the bed.— Spade the ground up deep. Take out
all the roots of docks and thistles and other weeds. Shake the
dirt all out of the sods and throw the grass away. You may need
a little manure in the soil, especially if the land is either very
hard or very loose and sandy. But the manure must be very fine
and well mixed into the soil. It is easy, however, to make sweet
pea soil so rich that the plants will run to vine and not bloom
well.

Make the bed long and narrow, but not narrower than three feet.
If it is narrower than this the grass roots will be likely to run under
it and suck up the moisture. If the bed can be got at on both
sides it may be as wide as five feet.

Sow the seeds in little rows crosswise the bed. The plants can
then be weeded and hoed easily from either side. If the rows are
marked by little sticks, or if a strong mark is left in the earth, you
can break the crust between the rows (with a rake) before the
plants are up. The rows ought to be four or five inches further
apart than the width of a narrow rake.

3. How to water the plants.— I wonder if you have a watering-
pot ? If you have, put it where you cannot find it ; for we are
going to water this garden with a rake ! We want you to learn, in
this little garden, the first great lesson in farming,— how to save
the water in the soil. If you learn that much this summer, you
will know more than many old farmers do. You know that the
soil is moist in the spring when you plant the seeds. Where does

this moisture go to? It dries up,—goes off into the air. If we could cover up the soil with something, we should prevent the moisture from drying up. Let us cover it with a layer of loose, dry earth! We will make this covering by raking the bed every few days,—once every week anyway, and oftener than that if the top of the soil becomes hard and crusty, as it does after a rain. Instead of pouring water on the bed, therefore, we will keep the moisture in the bed.

If, however, the soil becomes so dry in spite of you that the plants do not thrive, then water the bed. Do not *sprinkle* it, but *water* it. Wet it clear through at evening. Then in the morning, when the surface begins to get dry, begin the raking again to keep the water from getting away. Sprinkling the plants every day or two is one of the surest ways to spoil them.

4. When and how to sow.—The sweet peas should be put in just as soon as the ground can be dug, even before frosts are passed. Yet good results can be had if the seeds are put in as late as the 10th of May. In the sweet pea garden at Cornell last year, we sowed the seeds on the 20th of April. This was about right. The year before, we sowed them on the 30th. If sown very early, they are likely to bloom better, but they may be gone before the middle of September. The blooming can be much prolonged if the flowers are cut as soon as they begin to fade.

Plant sweet peas deep,—two or three or sometimes even four inches. When the plants are a few inches high, pull out a part of them so that they will not stand nearer together than six inches in the row. It is a good plan to sow sweet peas in double rows,— that is, put two rows only five or six inches apart,—and stick the brush or place the chicken-wire support between them.

China asters may be sown from the middle of May to the first of June. In one large test at Cornell, we sowed them the 4th of June, and had good success; but this is rather later than we would advise. The China asters are autumn flowers, and they should be in their prime in September and early October.

Sow the aster seed shallow,—not more than a half inch deep. The tall kinds of asters should have at least a foot between the plants in the row, and the dwarf kinds six to eight inches.

Sometimes China asters have rusty or yellow spots on the undersides of their leaves. This is a fungous disease. If it appears, have your father make some ammoniacal carbonate of copper solution and then spray them with it; or Bordeaux mixture will do just as well or better, only that it discolors the leaves and flowers.

5. What varieties to choose.— In the first place, do not plant too much. A garden which looks very small when the pussy willows come out and the frogs begin to peep, is pretty big in the hot days of July. A garden four feet wide and twenty feet long, half sweet peas and half asters, is about as big as most boys and girls will take care of.

In the next place, do not get too many varieties. Four or five kinds each of peas and asters will be enough. Buy the named

Fig. 271. A clump of weeds in the corner by the house,— motherworth and Virginia creeper. How pretty they are !

varieties,— that is, those of known colors,— not the mixed packets. If you are very fond of reds, then choose the reddest kinds ; but it is well to put in at least three colors. The varieties which please you may not please me or your neighbor, so that I cannot advise you what to get.

Of China asters, the Comet type — in various colors — will probably give the most satisfaction. They are mostly large-growing kinds. Other excellent kinds are the Perfection and Peony-flowered, Semple or Branching, Chrysanthemum-flowered, Washington, Victoria, and, for early, Queen of the Market. Odd varieties are Crown, German Quilled, Victoria Needle, and Lilliput. Very dwarf kinds are Dwarf Bouquet or Dwarf German, and Shakespeare.

One of the chief merits of the China aster is the lateness of bloom, allowing the flowers to be used in the schools after they open in the fall. An excellent flower for sowing during May is the common annual Phlox (*Phlox Drummondii* of the catalogues). Poppies are also satisfactory, but the flowers do not last long. Petunias are excellent and Balsams, Clarkias, Coreopsis (or Calliopsis), and Zinnias may be sown.

Now, let us see how many boys and girls in New York State will raise sweet peas and China asters this year! And we should like them to write us all about it.

A HILL OF POTATOES.*

By I. P. ROBERTS,

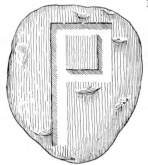

LANT a hill of potatoes. You can do it in the school-room. Plant in a box or a flower-pot. Keep the box warm, and do not let the soil dry out. Plant whole tubers and pieces of tubers. Plant pieces of various sizes. Plant some that have no "eyes." Plant shallow — so that the tuber is just covered with soil — and deep. Watch the results.

All plants are abundantly supplied with means for reproducing their kind: some by seed, some by multiplication at the crown or base or by roots, others by means of underground stems; and some, as the potato, have two or more means of reproduction. In its wild or partially improved state the potato is abundantly supplied with fruit, "seed balls," borne on the top of the stalks. The seeds of a single ball will often produce many varieties of potatoes; but they cannot be depended upon to reproduce the parent stock. Farmers seldom attempt to raise potatoes from the seeds; when they do it is for the purpose of securing new varieties. The common method of reproduction is to plant a part or all of an enlarged underground stem, that is, a part of the "potato" or tuber.

When the soil is reasonably porous and fertile, a strong root may start at the seed-piece and descend more or less directly into the subsoil. In most cases, however, the roots spread laterally. This is a good illustration of how plants may vary in their root habits in order to adapt themselves to their environment. Notice where the roots form on the plants you are growing. Few farmers know where they form. Distinguish the true or feeding roots from the underground stems. Determine how many tubers form on each underground stem. Dig up a hill of potatoes from the garden before school closes.

---

* Nature-Study Quarterly, No. 7: Leaflet 20, January, 1901.

A single eye, with a portion of the tuber attached to furnish nourishment to the bud until sustenance can be secured from newly formed rootlets, may produce one, occasionally more,

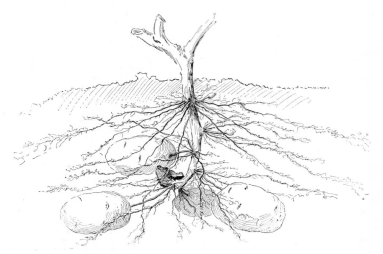

Fig. 272. Underground part of potato plant in mellow soil.

strong upright stems. A most interesting study of manifold reproduction may be made even in the winter time by planting in a fertile soil a piece of potato containing a single eye (Fig. 273).

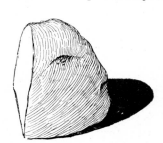

Fig. 273. Piece of tuber for planting, bearing a single eye.

As soon as the rootlets begin to start, divide each eye and piece into two parts and re-plant. In a few days after the rootlets have again started, divide the two pieces into four and re-plant. This operation may be performed again and again, until many plants suitable for transplanting in the open may be secured from a single eye.

Demonstrate that the potato contains starch. This can be done by applying a drop of dilute iodine to a freshly cut surface of the tuber: the starch grains turn blue-black. Five cents' worth of iodine purchased at the drug-store will be sufficient for many tests. Dilute it about one-half with water. This starch, after being changed to sugar, supplies the young plant with nourishment. Dig up the pieces you have planted and see which start first, shoots or roots.

The "potato" is an enlarged underground stem provided with numerous buds similar to those on the stems of plants above ground. These buds are placed spirally on the underground stem or tuber with a considerable degree of uniformity. As on the stems of other plants, the buds are less numerous and weaker at the base and most numerous and vigorous at the top or upper end. On a smooth well developed long potato, the spiral arrangement of the buds may be illustrated by sticking a tooth-pick or pin in each eye, beginning at the base or stem end, and connecting the pins with a string (Fig. 274).

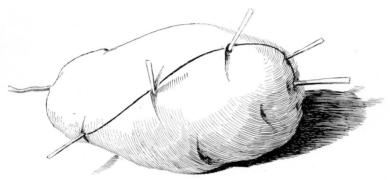

Fig. 274. How to illustrate the spiral arrangement of the eyes.

Farm Notes on the Potato.

Now that we have seen the potato growing in the school-room, some information may be given respecting its treatment in the field as a crop.

Potatoes are easily raised, even under adverse conditions, although they respond quickly to superior fertility and tillage. The average yield in the United States during the last ten years was 76.6 bushels an acre, although from three to four hundred bushels an acre are not uncommon under superior tillage when soil and climate are at their best.

The area devoted to potatoes during the last decade was two and a half million acres annually. Potatoes do best on a moderately moist and deep soil and in a climate relatively cool.

Since the period of growth is short, varying from three to five months, they should be planted in soil which has an abundance of readily available plant-food. Notice in Fig. 272 that most of the underground stems which have produced potatoes leave the main stem about four inches below the surface and but a short distance above the seed-piece. This suggests that the seed should be planted about four inches deep. To produce three hundred bushels of potatoes requires the exhalation of over three hundred tons of water : therefore water or moisture is of quite as much importance in securing large yields as plant-food.

It is best to prepare the land deeply, to plant deep, and then to practice nearly or quite level culture. The practice of hilling up potatoes, so common in most parts of the country, is to be discouraged, usually, because it is wasteful of moisture and the tubers do not grow in the coolest part of the soil. For very early potatoes, hilling-up may be allowable. Till the soil very often to save the moisture. For the philosophy of this, see Leaflet No. IX.

Not infrequently the potato is seriously injured by blights which attack the leaves. The early blight, which usually appears in June, may destroy some of the foliage, thereby checking growth. The late blight, which also attacks the foliage, is far more serious. It differs little in outward appearance from the early blight. In rare cases the vines are so seriously injured that no potatoes are formed. The potato rot or blight did great damage to the potato in many localities in the United States in 1845. In 1846 the blight appeared in Ireland and virtually destroyed the entire crop. Before this date the potato had become the chief food supply of the peasantry. The cultivation of oats as a food crop had been universal before the introduction of the potato, but oats furnished so little food on a given area as compared to the potato that the cultivation of them at the time the blight appeared had been very largely abandoned. The loss of the potato crop produced widespread famine. The most conservative estimate of the numbers who perished for want of food or by disease caused by a meager diet of unhealthy and innutritious food is set down at six hundred thousand during the two years of the potato blight. This disease was not so destructive in 1847 as in 1846 ; and by 1848 it had virtually disappeared. Some one has said that if Great Britain had expended one dollar for investigating the diseases of potatoes where she had spent a thousand dollars for perfecting the engines of war, the terrible famine might have been averted. We now think it a relatively easy matter to keep the blight in check by thorough spraying with Bordeaux mixture.

How the Potato Has Been Improved.

All plants have their origin in pre-existing plants. While the young plant is always similar to the one from which it was derived, it is never exactly like its parent in every detail. This arises from the fact that all of the conditions under which the parent plant and its offspring grow are never exactly alike. The variations or differences in the plants are usually exceedingly small in a single generation; but occasionally they are wide, in which case they are called "sports" and are usually difficult to perpetuate. If successive generations of plants are reared under continuously improved conditions, there will be a continuous and accumulating variation from generation to generation, which in time may come to be so great as to make it difficult to discover a marked similarity between the wild and the cultivated forms of the same plant.

When conditions are undisturbed by man there is found to be a fierce struggle for existence. The hardiest or those best suited to the conditions preponderate, and this without any reference to the wants of mankind. The farmer steps in and selects those plants which give promise of being most useful or most beautiful and then decreases or eliminates the struggle for these selected plants, by destroying the plants which are least desirable, by fertilizing and tilling the soil, by conserving moisture, and by improving the physical conditions of the land, thereby making it more comfortable for the plants which he has chosen. The selected or "improved" plant, by reason of being more comfortable and better nourished, tends to vary in one or more directions from the wild and unimproved types. Whenever these variations tend towards greater productiveness, better quality or enhanced beauty, selection is again made of such specimens as give promise of supplying the wants and gratifying the desires of civilized man. The bettered conditions of the plant, by reason of man's effort, do not usually result in producing like variation along all lines. One part of the plant as the flower, the fruit, or the stem, varies more than the other parts. All this tends to break up a single type or stock into many varieties. There are hundreds of varieties of potatoes all traceable to a single wild species. The kind and quantity of nourishment supplied plays the most important part of any single factor in producing variation.

The general character of the cultivated potato plant as to leaf, stem, root, and habit of growth, is virtually the same as the wild plant, variation having been directed and accentuated along the line of increasing the size and quality of the underground tubers. This habit of producing enormously enlarged underground stems has been operating so long that the plant has inherited the power of transmitting this acquired quality to the succeeding plants. The most improved varieties seldom produce seed balls, because growth has been directed so largely toward enlarging and multiplying the tubers. By selecting tubers with shallow buds or eyes and avoiding those with deep, sunken eyes, varieties have been produced with few eyes or buds, and these set not in deep indentations but nearly even with the surface of the potato.

As a school-room subject, the potato is not very tractable, unless we study merely the tubers. If the school is in session in summer, the growing plant may be had. Then it will be found to be an interesting and profitable exercise to set the children at the problem of determining the root-system of the potato plant. How do the roots look? Does the plant have a tap-root, or do the roots spread laterally? Are the tubers borne on roots? Or on underground stems? Why do you think so? Does the tuber terminate the branch? What relation, in position, do the tuber-bearing branches bear to other parts of the underground system? Do you think that the tuber-bearing branches aid in collecting food from the soil?

The top of the plant may be studied in the same spirit,— branching, leaves, flowers, berries.

If the growing plant cannot be had, study tubers. Compare as to size, shape, color, character of eyes, whether scabby or smooth. Use them as objects in drawing.

Plant tubers in the school-room, in boxes or flower pots. This Leaflet will suggest some interesting observations.

How important is the potato crop in the State and nation? The pupil can use his mathematics here.

LEAFLET XL.

THE HEPATICA.*

By ANNA BOTSFORD COMSTOCK.

AS children are always especially interested in the wild flowers in spring, I have thought best to study a few of the woodland blossoms. The wonderful processes of plant life are as well shown in these as in any. The hepatica is among the first which greets us in the spring, and we will study this first.

There are several ways of getting acquainted with a plant : one is to go-a-visiting, and another is to invite the plant to our own home, either as guest on the window-sill, or as a tenant of the garden. When we visit the hepatica in its own haunts it is usually with the longing for spring in our hearts that awakens with the first warm sunshine and which is really one of the subtlest as well as greatest charms of living in a climate that has a snowy winter. As we thread our way into the sodden woods, avoiding the streams and puddles that are little glacial rivers and lakes from fast disappearing snow-drifts still heaped on the north sides of things, we look eagerly for signs of returning life. The eye slowly differentiates from the various shades of brown in the floor of the forest a bit of pale blue or pink purple that at first seems as if it were an optical delusion ; but as we look again to make sure, lo ! it is the hepatica. There it is, rising from its mass of purple brown leaves, leaves that are always beautiful in shape and color and suggest patterns for sculpture like the acanthus or for rich tapestries like the palm-leaf in the Orient. There the brave little flower stands with its face to the sun and its back to the snow-drift and looks out on a gray brown world and nods at it and calls it " good."

It is when the hepatica is our guest that we have a better opportunity for studying its form and features. Take up a hepatica root in the fall and pot it and place it in a cool cellar

---

* Home Nature-Study Course, Vol. IV, No. 30, March, 1903.

until March 1. Then give it light, warmth, and moisture on your
table and see how gladly it will blossom and tell its secrets. Or
perhaps if we are not sufficiently forehanded to get the root in
the fall we can get it during a thaw in March when we go foraging
for spring feelings in winter woods.

When finally a bud has uncuddled and lifted itself into a flower,
it will tell us the story of leaves in different disguises, and we
may be able to notice whether the pollen ripens and is all distributed when the flower begins to fade and fall. We may note

Fig. 275. Hepatica, harbinger of spring.

also the number of seeds and examine one of them with a lens.
It is what the botanists call an akene, which simply means just
one seed with a tight envelope about it. We have a careless habit
of forgetting all about plants after their blossoms fade unless
their fruits or seed are good to eat or good to look at. This is as
inconsistent as it would be to lose all interest in the farm before
the fields were planted. After the flower is gone the plant must
mature its seeds and somehow must sow them. We will study the

hepatica through the summer and autumn, for we must know what is happening to it every month.

QUESTIONS CONCERNING THE HEPATICA TO BE ANSWERED DURING MARCH AND APRIL.

1. In what situations are the hepaticas found?

2. How does the hepatica prepare for the winter and store up energy for blossoming early in the spring?

3. How early do you find blossom buds down in the center of the plant? Did you ever look for these buds in the fall?

4. Do the flowers come out of the crown bud?

5. Are the leaves that come up late in the spring as fuzzy when they first appear as those that come up early?

6. Make out as complete a life-history of the hepatica as you can,— how it sows itself, where it grows, how long it lives, with what plant it keeps company.

LEAFLET XLI.

JACK-IN-THE-PULPIT.*

By ANNA BOTSFORD COMSTOCK.

" Jack-in-the-Pulpit preaches to-day
 Under the green trees, just over the way.
 Squirrel and song sparrow high on their perch
 Hear the sweet lily bells ringing to church.
 Come, hear what his reverence rises to say,
 In his low, painted pulpit this calm Sabbath day,
 Fair is the canopy over him seen,
 Penciled by nature's hand, black, brown, and green."

J. G. Whittier.

Fig. 276.   Jack-in-the-Pulpit.

* Home Nature-Study Course, Vol. IV, No. 31, April, 1903.

T one time or another, perhaps all of us **are** given to the belief that all flowers blossom for our especial enjoyment. It is hard to think back for a thousand years and imagine hepaticas blooming on our New York hills; yet no doubt, they blossomed then in far greater numbers than they do to-day. Many of our native plants played their part in sustaining the lives of the native Americans, and that little preacher, Jack-in-the-pulpit, was a turnip long before he was a preacher. Indian turnip was his name in the days of our ancestors because the Indians boiled his bulb-like root and the ripe berries, thus making them a less peppery and a more palatable food.

The St. Nicholas Magazine was for so many years the organ through which Jack preached so many sermons to children all over our land that he is even to-day one of the best loved of the woodland flowers. Whittier, in his "Child Life," and Lucy Larcom have both celebrated Jack-in-the-pulpit in song, and these verses should be given to the children when they are studying the habits of this interesting plant.

Jack-in-the-pulpit is a wild cousin of the over-civilized calla lily. It is interesting to study the way the flowers resemble each other, and this you and the children will be able to study for yourselves. It will teach you that the showy parts of a blossom may be merely a protection, and an advertisement for the true flower hidden within.

QUESTIONS CONCERNING JACK-IN-THE-PULPIT.

1. Where do you find this plant, in dry or in wet locations?

2. What is the shape of the root? Is is pleasant to the taste?

3. How do the leaves look when they first appear above the ground?

4. How far are the leaves developed when the flowers appear?

5. Does the tip of the hood fold over at first?

6. Do you see a resemblance to the calla lily when you bend the tip of the hood backward? Compare or contrast the two plants.

7. How many leaves has Jack-in-the-pulpit? Are they simple or compound?

8. What are the colors of the "pulpits" in your locality?

LEAFLET XLII.

INDIAN CORN.*

By ANNA BOTSFORD COMSTOCK.

" Hail! Ha-wen-ni-yu! Listen with open ears to the words of thy people. Continue to listen. We thank our mother earth which sustains us. We thank the winds which have banished disease. We thank He-no for rain. We thank the moon and stars which give us light when the sun has gone to rest. We thank the sun for warmth and light by day. Keep us from evil ways that the sun may never hide his face from us for shame and leave us in darkness. We thank thee, oh, mighty Ha-wen-ni-yu that we still live. We thank thee that thou hast made our corn to grow. Thou art our creator and our good ruler, thou canst do no evil. Everything thou doest is for our happiness."

HUS prayed the Iroquois Indians when the corn had ripened on the hills and valleys of New York State long before it was a state, and even before Columbus had turned his ambitious prows westward in quest of the Indies. Had he found the Indies with their wealth of fabrics and spices he would have found there nothing so valuable to the world as has proved this golden treasure of ripened corn.

The origin of Indian corn, or maize, is shrouded in mystery. There is a plant which grows on the tablelands of Mexico which is possibly the original species, but so long had maize been cultivated by the American Indians that it was thoroughly domesticated when America was discovered. In those early days of American colonization it is doubtful, says Professor John Fiske, if our forefathers could have remained here had it not been for Indian corn. No plowing nor even clearing was necessary for the successful raising of this grain. The trees were girdled, thus killing their tops to let in the sunlight; the rich earth was

---

* Home Nature-Study Course, Vol. IV, No. 32, May, 1903.

scratched a little with a primitive tool and the seed put in and covered ; and the plants that grew therefrom took care of themselves. If the pioneers had been obliged to depend alone upon the wheat and rye of Europe which would only grow with good tillage they might have starved before they had gained a foothold on our forest-covered shores. While maize has never been a popular grain in European countries outside of the southermost parts, yet on the great continents of Africa and Asia it was welcomed from the first, and is now largely grown. It has ripened for so many centuries on the slopes of the Himalayas that if you were to ask one of the natives to-day how long it had grown there he would answer you " always."

It is fitting that a grain which is so peculiarly adapted to be the aid and support of a great civilization should grow upon a plant of such dignity and beauty as is the maize. The perfect proportions of the slender stalk to the long gracefully curving leaves ; the plumed tassels swaying and bowing to every breeze and sending their pollen showers to the waiting skeins of silk hidden below ; the ripened ear with its exact rows of shining yellow grains wrapped in silken husks ; all these make the corn plant as delightful to the eye as it is intrinsically important to the welfare of nations. No more wonderful lesson in plant growth can we find for our study than this lesson of the Indian corn.

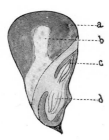

Fig. 277. Parts of corn kernel.

LESSON ON INDIAN CORN FOR SPRING AND SUMMER.

Secure a kernel of corn and cut it in halves (Fig. 277) and with the naked eye you will be able to see there the young plant pressed close to its stored up food, which, though largely composed of starch, also has in it proteids and oil. You will see that this food is dry and thus cannot be used by the young plant, for plants, whether young or old, must take their nourishment in a fluid condition. Soak the seed and see how soon the young plant passes on the moisture to soften the food so that it may imbibe it and grow. Fill a tumbler with earth and plant a grain of corn next to the glass so that you may be able to see how it grows.

CORN STALKS, LEAVES AND ROOTS.

1. Which appears first, root parts or leaf?

2. How does the leaf look when it first comes up?

3. How old is the corn when the blossom stalks begin to show above the leaves?

4. Does the stalk break more easily at the joints than elsewhere? Measure the distances between the joints in a stalk of young corn and two weeks later measure these distances again, and compare your figures. From these measurements tell whether the plant grows only at the top, or has it several growing places?

5. Are the joints nearer each other at the bottom or at the top?

6. Where do the bases of the leaves clasp the stalks?

7. Tell why this arrangement gives strength to the stalk.

8. Do you see a little growth at the base of the leaf that prevents the rain from flowing down between the stalk and the clasping leaf? This is called the rain-guard. How might it damage the plant if the water should get in between the leaf and stem?

9. What is the structure of the leaf and direction of the ribs?

10. How does this structure keep the long leaf from being torn to pieces by the wind?

11. Note the ruffled edge of the leaf. Lay such a leaf flat on a table and bend it this way and that, and note how this fullness allows it to bend without breaking the edges. What advantage is this to the plant?

12. Study the roots of a corn plant. How far do they extend into the ground? Describe them.

13. Study the brace roots that come off the stalk an inch or more above the ground. Of what utility are these to the plant?

14. Bend down a stalk of growing corn and place a stone on it near its base so as to hold it down, and note how it acts. Does it commence to lift itself up straight from the joint, or from a place between the joints?

15. Cut off the water supply from a plant, or watch the corn during a drought and tell how the leaves behave.

16. Do they offer as much surface to the air for evaporation when they are curled? Is this the way the plant protects itself by retaining this moisture during a dry time?

17. Do the stalks or leaves grow after the ears begin to form?

18. Do you find "suckers" growing; if so what is the variety?

FLOWERS.

There are two kinds of flowers on the corn: the tassels bearing the pollen, and the ears bearing the ovules which develop into seeds. Study first the tassel. Observe the flowerets through a lens if you have one and note that the pollen sacs open a little at one side instead of at the tip so that the wind is needed in order to shake out the pollen. It is estimated that on each corn plant there may be developed eighteen million pollen grains and two thousand ovules. The pollen-tube must penetrate the whole length of each thread of corn-silk in order to reach the ovules.

19. What agency carries the pollen grains to the ear?

20. What would happen to a field of corn if the farmer cut off all the tassels as soon as they were formed?

21. Find a tassel before it appears and study it. Secure an ear when only an inch or two long and study it. These should be studied as flower parts.

22. How early can you find the ear? Look at every joint and tell how many ears you find on a young stalk.

23. In studying the ear, take first the husk. Does it resemble the leaf in structure? What is the difference between the outer and the inner husks?

24. Do you believe that the husk is a modified leaf; if so why? In the young ear does each thread of silk extend out to the end of the ear; if so why?

25. Is there a thread of silk for each kernel in the ear?

26. Study corn when it is in the "milk." Is the taste sweet?

27. Does this sweet taste continue as the kernel matures?

28. How is the stalk modified to fit the ear?

ENEMIES.

The corn has many difficulties to contend with: there are heavy winds, too much or too little rain, hail, and, worst of all, frosts which not only kill it when it is first planted, but also hurt it before it is matured. The corn has living enemies also, such as wire-worms and cut-worms. Our forefathers were much troubled with the mischief which crows did in pulling corn. However, many of our observing farmers to-day say that only in rare instances do the crows injure corn much. The work done by cut-worms is often attributed to crows.

29. Please note in your locality what difficulties the corn has to contend with. If possible make a special study of the damage said to be done by crows. Give the results.

THE RIPENED CORN.*

BY ANNA BOTSFORD COMSTOCK.

VERY boy and girl living on a farm in New York State twenty-five years or more ago, has in memory a picture like this : a stubbly hill-side field beset with russet shocks of corn and constellations of orange pumpkins, whence might be seen wide valleys filled with purple haze, and far hills bedecked with autumn tapestries woven about emerald patches of new wheat.

To such a field, after the laggard sun had changed the hoar frost to dew, would they hasten of an October morning, to begin the corn-husking. The enthusiastic youngster, who had an eye to artistic unity in the situation, invariably selected a pumpkin for his seat, scorning his more sordid fellows who had brought milking-stools from the barn, when nature had placed so many golden thrones at their disposal. Too soon a discovery was made about this that applies as well to other thrones,— it proved an uneasy seat, and was abandoned for a sofa constructed of corn-stalks. Here, leaning back with a full sense of luxury, listening to the rustle of the dry leaves and husks and the monotonous song of the cricket, enlivened now and then by the lazy call of the crow from the hemlocks on the hill, the sweet note of the belated meadow-lark from the valley, or the excited bark of the dog as he chased a squirrel along the fence, the busy husker passed the autumn day. On either side of him were evidences of his labor. On the right stood great disheveled stooks of corn stalks bereft of their pockets of gold ; on the left lay in a heap the shining yellow ears, ready to be measured in the waiting bushel-basket ; in front was always a little pile of noble ears with some of the husks still attached,— the seed corn. Proud was the boy when he had learned to select successfully "the ear of good length, cylindrical rather than

---

* Home Nature-Study Course, Vol. V, No. 1, October, 1903.

pointed, the cob firm and well filled from butt to tip with grains uniformly large, of good color and in regular rows that showed no space between." Now-a-days, we challenge this ideal of the "perfect ear."

As "chore time" approached, came the wagon afield to gather the harvest of ears and take them to the cribs, where their gold gleaming between the boards gave comfortable assurance of peace and plenty. But the seed corn was stored in a way learned by our forefathers from the American Indians ; the ears were braided

Fig. 278. The Harvest of the Corn.

together by their husks, by the skilled farmer, who could make a braid two or three feet long, strong enough to hold the weight of the ears that hung a heavy fringe along each side ; this braid when completed was tied with a bit of soft, tow twine, long saved for the purpose, and then was hung on hooks on the granary walls. There, until spring, waited the elect of the cornfield, holding in perfect kernels all the future corn wealth of that farm.

From the first day's husking a bushel of ears was reserved from the crib and was spread on a chamber floor to dry quickly ; later this was taken to the mill and ground into samp, one of the prized luxuries of the autumn bill of fare. Other corn was ground into finer meal for the delicious Johnny-cake and the Indian bread, the latter reaching fullest perfection when baked in a brick oven.

To the tenants of the farm barns the corn meant even more than to those in the farm house. In August the cattle in dry pastures cast longing eyes and expressive voices toward the pale, green leaves and waving tassels of the sowed-corn, and great was their joy the first day they tasted this delicacy ; in November, they munched the dry leaves of the planted crop, leaving in the barn-yard an angular patterned carpet of bare, hard stalks. In winter the corn meal, in proper proportions, made for them a food that kept them warm despite the cold winds that clutched at them, through crevices, with fingers of drifted snow. And no less dependent on this important crop were the denizens of the fold, of the sty, and of the chicken-yard.

The old-time harvesting and husking are passing from the New York farm of to-day. The granary is no longer frescoed with braids of model ears, for the seed corn is now bought by the bushel from the seedsmen. The corn harvester has dissolved the partnership between corn and pumpkin and fells the stalks by the acre, doing away with the old-time stooks or shocks. Cornstalks now become silage and are fed in a green condition throughout the winter. How often do we lose something of picturesqueness when we gain the advantages of modern improvements ! Let us be thankful, however, that the corn harvester and the silo make efficient use of the great fields of corn.

Although there is but one species of corn recognized (*Zea Mays*), there have been an endless number of varieties developed from it. Seven hundred and seventy of these were sufficiently distinct to be recognized when the Department of Agriculture published its account of varieties. The importance of the corn crop to this country and to others is almost incalculable. In 1902, the United States produced more than two and a half billion bushels and the export price was $.60 per bushel. When the corn crop fails every man, rich or poor, in America, suffers from it, and every business is affected by it. Though the man working in the cornfield may think only of his own crop, yet he is the man that is helping maintain the prosperity of our country. He is working for us all.

QUESTIONS ON THE RIPENED CORN.

1. Is the corn crop in your vicinity good this year?

2. What affected it, beneficially or otherwise?

3. How many ears of corn are there usually on a mature stalk?

4. Are they on the same side of the stalk, or how are they disposed?

5. How many kinds of corn do you know?

6. Describe an average ear of each in the following particulars : shape and color of kernel ; number of rows of kernels on the cob ; number of kernels in a row ; length of cob. Are the rows in distinct pairs? Do any of the rows disappear near the tip ; if so, how many?

7. Study a cob with corn on it. Are the kernel-sockets of adjacent rows opposite each other or alternate?

8. Cut a kernel of pop-corn and a kernel of field corn across and compare the texture of the two. What has this texture to do with causing the kernel to "pop?"

9. How many foods do you know made from the grain of the corn?

10. How many products do you know made from stalks of the corn?

11. Do you know of any part of the corn that is used in constructing battleships?

12. What is the corn crop of New York State worth in dollars a year? (See U. S. Census Bulletin, No. 179.)

13. How many bushels of shelled corn are usually produced on an acre of well cultivated land?

14. Could the corn plant itself without the agency of man?

If you are able to draw, please make a sketch of a kernel of sweet corn and a kernel of field corn. Break an ear of corn in two and sketch the broken end, showing shape of the cob and its relation to the kernels.

NOTE ON THE NEW CORN BREEDING.*

The particular materials that give the corn kernel most of its value are the oil, the protein and the starch. For the production of corn oil — for which the demand is large — a corn that has a high oil content is, of course, particularly valuable ; while for the production of starch or for the feeding of bacon hogs, a relatively higher percentage of other materials is desirable. It is apparent, therefore, that races of corn should be bred for a particular content, depending on the disposition to be made of the grain. Equal economic results cannot be attained, however, in increasing the content of any of the three leading ingredients, since a pound of gluten is worth one cent, a pound of starch one and one-half cents, and a pound of oil five cents. The amounts of these ingredients in the corn kernel are amenable to increase or diminution by means of selection,— by choosing for seed the kernels of ears that are rich or poor in one or the other of these materials. Fortunately, the oil and starch and protein of the corn kernel occupy rather distinct zones. Next the outside hull is a dark and horny layer that is very rich in protein ; in the center is the large germ, very rich in oil ; between the two is a white layer of starch. It is found that the kernels on any ear are remarkably uniform in their content ; the dissection of a few kernels, therefore, enables the breeder to determine the ears that are rich in any one of the substances. Experiment stations in the corn-growing States are already making great headway in this new breeding of corn, and one private concern in Illinois is taking it up as a commercial enterprise. All this recalls the remarkable breeding experiments of the Vilmorins in France, whereby the sugar-content of the beet was raised several points. It is impossible to overestimate the value of any concerted corn-breeding work of this general type. The grain alone of the corn crop is worth about one billion dollars annually. It is possible to increase this efficiency several percentages ; the coming generation will see it accomplished.

An interesting cognate inquiry to this direct breeding work is the study of the commercial grades of grains. It is a most singular fact that the dealer's " grades " are of a very different kind from

---

* Extracted from an article by L. H. Bailey in Country Life in America, July, 1903.

the farmer's " varieties." In the great markets, for example, corn is sold as " No. 1 yellow," " No. 2 yellow," " No. 3 yellow," and the like. Any yellow corn may be thrown into these grades. What constitutes a grade is essentially a judgment on the part of every dealer. The result is that the grain is likely to be condemned or criticised when it reaches its destination. Complaints having come to the government, the United States Department of Agriculture has undertaken to determine how far the grades of grain can be reduced to indisputable instrumental measurement. The result is likely to be a closer defining of what a grade is ; and, this point once determined, the producer will make an effort to grow such grain as will grade to No. 1, and thereby attain to the extra price. Eventually, the efficiency points of the grower and the commercial grades of the dealer ought nearly or quite to coincide. There should come a time when corn is sold on its intrinsic merits, as, for example, on its starch content. This corn would not then be graded 1, 2 and 3, on its starch content, because that content would be assured in the entire product ; but the grade 1 would mean prime physical condition, and the lower grades inferior physical condition. Eventually, something like varietal names may be attached to those kinds of corn that, for example, grade fifteen per cent protein. The name would be something like a guarantee of the approximate content, as it now is in a commercial fertilizer.

The first thing that strikes one in all this new work is its strong contrast with the old ideals. The " points " of the plants are those of " performance " and " efficiency." It brings into sharp relief the accustomed ideals as to what are the " good points " in any plant, illustrating the fact that these points are for the most part only fanciful, are founded on a priori judgments, and are more often correlated with mere " looks " than with efficiency. An excellent example may be taken from corn. In " scaling " any variety of corn it is customary to assume that the perfect ear is one nearly or quite uniformly cylindrical throughout its length, and having the tip and butt well covered with kernels. Now, this ideal is clearly one of perfectness and completeness of mere form. We have no knowledge that such form has any correlation with productiveness in ears, hardiness, drought-resisting qualities, protein or starch content,—and yet these attributes are the ones that make corn worth growing at all. We only know that such ears may bear more kernels. An illustration also may be taken from string beans. The ideal pod is considered to be one of which the tip-projection is very short and only slightly curved. This, apparently, is a question of comeliness, although a short tip may be associated in the popular mind with the absence of "string" in the pod ; but it is a question whether this character has any direct relation to the efficiency of the bean-pod. We are also undergoing much the same challenging of ideas respecting the "points" of animals. Now, animals and plants are bred to the ideals expressed in these arbitrary points by choosing for parents the individuals that score the highest. When it becomes necessary to recast our "scales of points," the whole course of evolution of domestic plants and animals is likely to be changed. We are to breed not so much for merely new and striking characters, that will enable us to name, describe and sell a "novelty," as to improve the performance along accustomed lines. It may be worth while to produce a "new variety" of potato by raising new plants from the seed-bolls ; but it is much more to the point to augment the mealiness of some existing variety or to intensify its blight-resisting qualities. We are not to start with a variety, but with a plant.

LEAFLET XLIV.

THE USES OF FOOD STORED IN SEEDS.*

By ANNA BOTSFORD COMSTOCK.

"A mystery passing strange,
   Is the seed in its wondrous change;
   Forest and flower in its husk concealed,
   And the golden wealth of the harvest field."
                                 — LUCY LARCOM.

S is the case with our own babies, the first necessity of the infant plant is food close at hand to sustain this tiny speck of life until it shall be large and strong enough to provide for itself. If we study any seed whatever we shall find some such motherly provision for the plant baby or germ. Sometimes the germ is a mere speck with a large amount of food packed around it, as is the case with the nutmeg ; sometimes the baby is larger and its food is packed in a part adjacent to it, as is the case with the corn (Fig. 279) ; and sometimes the mother stuffs the baby itself so that it has enough to last it until its own little roots and leaves bring it mature food, as is the case with the squash seed. In any case this "lunch put up by the mother," to use Uncle John's words, is so close at hand that as soon as favorable conditions occur the little plant may eat and grow, and establish itself in the soil.

Nature is remarkable for her skill in doing up compact packages, and in no other place is this skill better shown than in storing food in seeds for the young plants. Not only is it concentrated, but it is protected and of such chemical composition that it is able to remain fresh and good for many years awaiting the favorable moment when it may nourish the starting germ. People often wonder why, when a forest is cleared of one species of trees, another species grows in its place. This often may have resulted from the seeds lying many years dormant awaiting the

* Home Nature-Study Course, Vol. V, No. 4, January, 1904.

opportunity. This preservation of the food in the seed is largely
due to the protecting shell that keeps out the enemies of all sorts,
especially mould. And yet, however strong this box may be, as it
is in the hard-shelled hickory nut, it falls apart like magic when
the germ within begins to expand.

Brain rather than brawn is the cause of man's supremacy in this
world. Of all the beings that inhabit the earth he knows best
how to use for his own advantage all things that exist. His progress from savagery to civilization is marked by his growing power
to domesticate animals and plants. Very early in his history man
learned the value to himself of the seeds of the cereals. He discovered that they may be kept a long time without injury ; that
they contain a great amount of nutrition for their bulk ; that they
are easily prepared for food ; that, when planted, they give largest
return. Thus, we see, the advantages the plant mother had developed for her young, man has turned to his own use. That the

food put up for the young plant is so protected and
constituted as to endure unhurt for a long time
gives the cereal grains their keeping quality. That
it is concentrated and well packed renders it convenient for man to transport. That the "box" is
easily separated from the "lunch" makes the preparation of food by crushing and sifting an easy
matter for man. That every mother plant, to insure
the continuation of the species, develops many
seeds, so that in the great struggle for existence at
least some shall survive, makes the cereals profitable for man to plant, and harvest the increase.

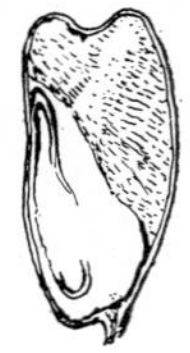

*Fig. 279. Section
of kernel of corn,
showing the em-
bryo, and the
food supply at
one side of it (at
the right).*

Think once, how few ears of corn it requires to plant an
acre.

Because of all these things there has grown up between domestic plants and man a partnership. Man relieves the plant of the
responsibility of scattering its seeds, and in return takes for himself that proportion of the seeds which would have died in the
struggle for existence had the plant remained uncultivated. This
partnership is fair to both parties.

Different plants store food materials in different proportions in
their seeds ; the most important of these food substances are
starch, oil, protein, and mineral matter. All of these materials are
necessary to man as food. In the cereals the seeds contain a
large proportion of starch, but in the nuts, like the butternuts and

walnuts, there is a predominance of oil. Let us for a moment examine a kernel of corn and a kernel of wheat and see how the food is arranged. Fig. 279 is a kernel of corn cut in two lengthwise; at the lower left-hand corner are the root parts and leaf parts of the young plant (the embryo); above the embryo is the loose starch material. Now we have the baby corn plant lying at one side, and its food packed about it. However, this food is in the form of starch, and must be changed to sugar before the young plant can partake of it and grow. There lies a connecting part between the germ and its food, the scutellum. This is so constituted that when soaked with water it ferments the starch and changes it to sugar for the young plant's use.

The germ itself is also a very nutritious food for man; hence the seed is eaten, " baby and all." In the corn, those kernels with the largest germs have the largest food value, and, therefore, to-day corn breeders are developing kernels with very large embryos.

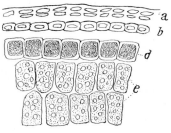

Fig. 280. Section of grain of wheat.

If we examine the microscopic structure of the food part of a grain of wheat (Fig. 280), we find that there are two outer layers, a and b. Next there is a row of cells d that divides these outer layers from the flour cells within. This is the aleurone layer. At e are the flour cells which constitute the central portion of the wheat kernel. They contain starch, and also gluten, and some oil, and some mineral substances. In grinding to make white flour, the miller tries to leave the aleurone layer of cells d with the outer layers a and b, for if it is mixed with the flour the latter spoils much sooner, and it is also darker in color. In the seed is a ferment that helps digest the food for the young plant.

In order to think more intelligently about our use of food, let us find out, if we can, which parts of the food stored up by the plant for its sustenance are used by us both for ourselves and our live-stock. The intelligent farmer gives his stock a carefully balanced ration, i. e., food that is well proportioned for the growth and product of the animal. If he wishes his cows to give more milk he may give them more proteids in their food, and less starch and fat. If he wishes to fatten them he may give them a greater amount of starch and fat and less of the proteids. In order to

know what these proteids and starch and fat mean, both to us and
to the plant, we have to know a little chemistry. The following
table may aid us in this :

Nutritive substances which contain nitrogen.	Proteids (casein, gluten, legumen, etc., albuminoids, gelatine, white of egg, etc.).
Nutritive substances which do not contain nitrogen.	The carbohydrates (sugar and starch). Fats (oils, butter).
Mineral substances.	Lime, phosphorus, sulfur, etc.

The substances mentioned in the above table are all needful to
sustain the life of man and beast. If we compare the body to a
steam engine, then we can see that its whole framework is built
out of the proteids, mineral matter and water. The starch and sugar
and fats constitute the fuel used to heat the boiler and make the
engine move. Strictly speaking the proteids are also used somewhat as fuel, as well as for framework. It is easily seen from this
that in order to be healthy we should try to give ourselves food
containing a proper amount of building material to repair the
breakage and wear and tear in the engine, and also give ourselves
enough fuel to make the boiler do its greatest possible work. For
if we do not have sufficient building material we break down, and
if we do not have sufficient fuel we lack energy. Food thus properly proportioned is called a " well balanced ration."

A well balanced ration per day for the average human being is
as follows :

Proteids, - - - - - - -	.40 lbs.
Starch, - - - - - - -	1.00 "
Fats, - - - - - - - -	.40 "
Mineral matter, - - - -	.10 "
	1.90 lbs.

The above is the amount of nutriment necessary, and in addition
to this there should be sufficient bulk to keep the digestive organs
healthy. We are just now entering upon the era of intelligence
in relation to our food. It seems strange that this intelligence
should first be applied to our domestic animals rather than to
man. As soon as the farmer discovered that to make his animals
pay better he must give them the right proportions of building

material and fuel for energy, he demanded that the agricultural chemists give him directions for mixing and preparing their food. But how few of the cooks in our land understand in the slightest degree this necessity for the proper proportions to our food! When they do we may look forward to entering upon an era of serene good health, when we shall have strength to bear and ability to do.

In answering the following list of questions you may be obliged to consult with the miller, or feed-dealer, but it is to be hoped that you will gain a clear conception of the parts of the seed used in making foods from cereals.

1. What is graham flour?   How does it differ from white wheat flour?

2. What is whole wheat flour?

3. What is bran?

4. What is cracked wheat?

5. What are shorts, middlings, or canaille?

6. Which of the above are considered the more nutritious and why?

7. What part of the corn kernel is hominy?

8. What is corn meal?

9. Is corn bran considered good food?

10. What is gluten meal?

11. What is germ meal?

12. Why is corn fattening to cattle?

13. How much of the oat grain is contained in oat meal?

14. What is a cotyledon?

15. Show by sketch or describe the cotyledon in the chestnut, the walnut or hickory nut, and the bean.

16. Describe or show by sketch the position of the germinal portion in each of these.

If you cannot find the germ in these, soak them in water for several days and then observe.

The following publications may be had from the Department of Agriculture, Washington, D. C., on application:

Circular No. 46, Revised — The Functions and Uses of Food. By C. F. Langworthy.

Circular No. 43, Revised — Food-Nutrients-Food Economy.

The Cost of Food as Related to its Nutritive Value.   By R. D. Milner.

A PROBLEM IN FEEDING.

As our knowledge increases, we give greater attention to the economical and efficient use of all feeds for live-stock. We cannot afford to feed even the corn stalks carelessly, either for the immediate concern of the pocket-book or for the good of the animal. The results of many experiments in feeding lead to the conclusion that a suitable daily ration for a cow giving milk and weighing 1,000 pounds should contain 24 pounds of dry matter, of which 2.5 pounds is digestible protein ; .4 pounds digestible fat ; and 12.5 pounds digestible carbohydrates. In such a ration, the ratio of digestible protein to digestible carbohydrates in the ration will be as 1 is to 5.4. In computing this ratio the amount of fat, multiplied by 2.4, is added to the carbohydrates. The fiber and the nitrogen-free extract constitute the carbohydrates. Individual animals vary so much in digestive capacity and in other respects that the foregoing standards may be frequently widely departed from to advantage. Thus many animals will profitably use more than 24 pounds of dry matter in a day and the ratio of protein to carbohydrates may vary from 1 : 5 to 1 : 6.5 without materially affecting the amount or character of the product. Standards are useful as guides. The art of feeding and the skill of the feeder consist in determining in how far the standard should be conformed to or departed from in each individual case.

Suppose a farmer has corn silage and timothy hay, and may purchase cotton seed meal, wheat bran and buckwheat middlings, how may they be combined so that the ration shall contain 24 pounds dry matter, and the ratio of protein to the carbohydrates shall be approximately 1 : 5.4 ? The following table gives the data :

	Water.	Protein.	Fiber.	Nitrogen-free extract.	Fat.
In 100 pounds of silage *.	79.1	1.2	4.3	7.4	.6
Timothy hay............ ..	13.2	3.4	16.8	28.4	1.2
Cotton seed meal.... ...	8.2	31.3	1.3	10.9	11.9
Wheat bran............	11.9	13.6	1.8	43.1	3.2
Buckwheat middlings...	13.2	22.	†	33.4	5.4

*Silage is often put up when the corn is more mature, and then the water content is less than here given.

†Included with nitrogen-free extract.

LEAFLET XLV.

THE LIFE HISTORY OF A BEET.*

By MARY ROGERS MILLER.

IF you are fond of a dish of "greens" made of young beet leaves in early summer, you must see to it that there are beets in the garden. What shall be planted? Seeds. Certainly; but where do the seeds come from? Most of us buy them from a seedsman, it is true; but somebody must grow them. They are not manufactured articles. If the beet plant produces seeds it must first have flowers. Have you ever seen the beet in blossom? When do the flowers come and how do they look?

Study the picture in Leaflet LII. Read the history beneath the picture. Better still, get a plump red beet from the cellar, and plant it in a can, a box, or a flower-pot. If no beets are to be had, a turnip, a carrot, or a parsnip will do as well. It seems that "plants" come from beet roots as well as from beet seed. The root you plant in the flower-pot grew last summer from a seed. When may we expect the plant to produce seeds of its own, thus multiplying according to its nature? If you keep a beet plant long enough it will answer this question.

Beet seeds are rather slow in germinating. For this reason it is common to soak them in warm water several hours or a day before planting in the garden. These facts are interesting in themselves; and instead of being discouraged should we not try to find out some reason why the beet seed should take more time than the corn or the bean? From a comparative study of a beet seedling and of a plant which comes from a beet root throughout a season, one may learn the whole life history of a beet. This story is not written down in books. Every stage of growth noted in the two plants should be regarded as typical of the life of an individual, for each plant must pass through all these stages in its development from seed to seed again.

The seedling beet pushes out roots and begins early to take

* Home Nature-Study Course, Vol. IV, No. 29, February, 1903.

food from the soil. One may even see the root-hairs through which the liquids enter the plant. Inquire if the plant growing from a beet root has put out new roots. Have not its old ones dried long ago in the cellar? It is a good idea to have more than one plant, so that investigation of a matter like this may go on without disturbing all. Where, if not from the soil through roots, does the food come from which nourishes those thick-ribbed leaves? From the stored-up material in the root, does it not? Is this not the plant's way of providing for the second half of its life, after a long resting period in the "beet" stage? When the "plant" or top has grown quite large, how does the old beet look?

We may read in the botany that certain plants are biennials, taking two seasons to pass through all the phases from seed to seed; but we shall not know the joy of gaining knowledge from original sources nor experience the mental training that comes with this "finding out" process until we have actually planted the beets or other things and watched them grow.

The following questions relate to the study of a beet plant. Any other available plant may be reported on. The important thing is that a minute study be made of some particular plant.

What plant are you making this special study of this month?

What care do you give it?

What conditions of temperature and moisture do you find most beneficial to its growth?

What other plants are related to it? (Mention a wild and a cultivated plant.)

What leads you to think them related? (Make this clear and definite.)

How do the plants which come from beet roots differ from those which come from the seed?

Of what utility to the plant is the fleshy root of beet, turnip, or carrot? When is this root made use of by the plant?

What becomes of the old beet as the plant grows larger and stronger?

What is the natural length of life of an individual beet plant?

Through how many changes of form does it pass? Which of these are "resting" stages?

Give the events in the life history of a beet in chronological order by seasons, beginning with a seed in the spring of 1903, and ending with the first crop of ripened seed.

PRUNING.*

By MARY ROGERS MILLER.

YOU should know how the trees in your school yard have been p r u n e d. Who did the work, nature or a man with a saw? Some people hold to the idea that pruning is unnatural, and therefore should not be practiced. Let us see if this is true. Have you ever gone into the deep woods after a storm? Who has been there, tearing and wrenching at the big limbs, twisting the small branches until the ground is strewn with wreckage? Nature has been pruning a few trees and she works with a fury which is awe-inspiring. But the trees are much the worse for their encounter with the forces they must obey without question. Their branches are broken; mere stubs are left. With the melting snow and the April rains germs of decay are likely to enter at every break in the bark. In a few years the trunk may be weakened and the monarch of the woods lie prone upon the forest floor.

We may learn the lesson of how not to prune by looking at this great pine tree torn by the storm (Fig 281).

"But why do we prune?" one asks. Let the horticulturist answer. In a Farmers' Reading-Course lesson on The Care of Trees, Professor Craig says: "Fruit trees must be pruned. If a tree in an open field is allowed to go unpruned, the crown soon becomes a dense mass of twigs and interlacing branches. Such a tree may produce as large a number of apples as a well-pruned, open-headed tree, but will there be the same percentage of merchantable fruit? The chief effort of every plant under natural conditions is expended in ensuring its own reproduction. This is chiefly effected by means of seeds. A small apple may contain

---

*Home Nature-Study Course, Vol. IV, No. 20, February, 1902.

as many seeds as a large one and even more.   The orchardist wants big fruits, and if they are nearly seedless so much the better."

In a tree top there is a sharp struggle for existence.   But few of the twigs which started from last year's buds will reach any considerable size.   One needs only to count the dead and the dormant buds on a branch, and the weak, stubby, or decayed side shoots to appreciate this fact.   If part of the branches are cut out, this struggle is reduced and energy is saved.   By judicious pruning the tree may be shaped to suit the needs of the owner. If a low tree is desired to make fruit-gathering easy pruning keeps the head down.   An open, spreading habit may be encouraged by cutting out such branches as tend to grow close to the main trunk.   A careful orchardist has an ideal in his mind and knows how to prune to bring the tree up to his standard.   He knows the habits of trees of different varieties.   He will not prune all alike.   He must prune some every year, or the trees will not carry out his plans.

Fig 281.   A pine tree pruned by the storm.

The pruner should not only know why he prunes, but how the work should be done.   He should be able to tell why he removes one limb and leaves another.   When I look at the trees in parks and along the streets I wonder at the careless pruning.   Judging from the way they are treated one would think that a tree could be produced in "a year or two or three at most."

Pruning should not be confined to fruit trees. It may be practiced with profit on all kinds of plants from shade trees to house plants. Pinching off the terminal bud of a young geranium makes the plant branch. Cutting the lower limbs of a young elm makes the tree more stately. Nature may do this, but broken branches leave wounds which the tree cannot heal. Small branches may be cut close with a sharp knife or pruning shears. The tree readily heals these places. It is little short of a crime to break or tear limbs from trees. The injury done to the trees is bad enough ; but does not such heedless treatment of living things also have a baneful influence on the mutilator?

Fig. 282. Close cutting results in prompt healing.

For larger branches, if these must come off, no tool is better than a sharp saw. The cut should be smooth and clean. No ragged edges of bark should be left. The branch should all be cut off, and care should be taken not to tear the bark about the wound. If a stub six or eight inches long, or even one inch, be left, the tree is likely to suffer. The branch started years ago from a bud on the side of the main trunk, then but a twig itself. The fibers of the branch are continuous with those of the trunk. In the air are the germs of decay. These take hold of the bare stub and soon make their way to the center of the tree itself. Try as it may, the tree cannot quickly heal a wound so far from the main paths traveled by the sap in the trunk.

Fig. 283. The long stub does not heal.

The two illustrations (Figs. 282, 283) show the right and the wrong way to remove a limb. When the branch is cut close, new growth takes place all around the cut surface and in a few years the wound is healed.

Bad pruning is worse than no pruning. Do you not think that nature students should use their influence to protect the trees in the school grounds, in the door yards, and along the streets? Trees have insect and fungous enemies enough without having to contend against carelessness and neglect.

QUESTIONS ON PRUNING.

1. Describe the results of some of the natural forces you have seen pruning trees. Observe willows after a storm.

2. Are all sorts of trees affected alike by wind, ice, and snow?

3. From your observations which kinds suffer most? Give your opinion as to why.

4. Nature does not always prune in this boisterous fashion. Silent forces are at work pruning out the weak buds and shoots, giving the strong ones a better chance. Select a very young tree, or a shrub like the lilac. Examine the tips of the branches. You will find healthy buds on last season's growth. See if you can find any dormant buds. Are there any weak-looking or dead twigs?

5. Compare the number of strong healthy shoots with the number which the plant started to make. How many of each?

6. Mention several good effects which may result from pruning.

7. What are some of the bad results of over-pruning? Of insufficient pruning?

8. Consult some orchard-owner concerning this subject. When does he prune to increase the production of fruit? When to increase the growth of the woody part of the tree?

9. If the lower branches of a tree are not removed, what is the effect on the shape of the tree?

10. For what kinds of trees is this form desirable?

11. What is your opinion as to the shearing of evergreens into fantastic shapes?

12. If a tree has a tendency to grow crooked, how should one prune to correct the habit?

13. Would you prune an elm tree just as you would an apple tree? Why?

14. Why does pinching off the terminal bud of a geranium produce a more bushy plant?

15. Discuss in full the reasons for cutting a limb off smoothly and close to the main trunk or larger branch. Look at every tree you pass to see whether it has been pruned well. Has it been able to cover its wounds by the healing process?

16. Is it correct to suppose that "anybody" can prune a tree?

17. The cut surfaces made by pruning large limbs from trees are often covered with thick paint, tar, or Bordeaux mixture. What is the purpose of this?

18. Why is it better to prune a little every year than a great deal once in five years?

19. When is the best time to prune shade trees? Why?

20. Does a tree carry the bases of its branches upward as it grows higher, or does the base of every branch remain at the level from which it started originally? Observe many trees in different situations before making up your mind on this point.

LEAFLET XLVII.

A STUDY OF A TREE.*

By ANNA BOTSFORD COMSTOCK.

The Sugar Maple.

The maple puts her corals on in May,
While loitering frosts about the lowlands cling,
To be in tune with what the robins sing,
Plastering new log-huts 'mid her branches gray;
But when the autumn southward turns away,
Then in her veins burns most the blood of Spring,
And every leaf, intensely blossoming,
Makes the year's sunset pale the set of day.
— LOWELL.

LIKE a friend is a tree, in that it needs to be known season after season and year after year in order to be truly appreciated. A person who has not had an intimate, friendly acquaintance with some special tree has missed something from life. Yet even those of us who love a tree because we find its shade a comfort in summer and its bare branches etched against the sky a delight in winter, may have very little understanding of the wonderful life-processes which have made this tree a thing of beauty. If we would become aware of the life of our tree we must study it carefully. We should best begin by writing in a blank book week after week what happens to our tree for a year. If we keep such a diary, letting the tree dictate what we write, we shall then know more of the life of our tree.

In selecting a tree for this lesson I have chosen the sugar maple, for several reasons. It is everywhere common ; it is beautiful ; it is most useful ; and it has been unanimously chosen as the repre-

*Home Nature-Study Course, Vol. V, No. 2, November, 1903.

sentative tree of the Empire State. Let each of us choose some maple tree in our immediate vicinity that shall be the subject

Fig. 284. Sugar maple.

for our lesson now, and again in the winter, and again in the spring. Our first thought in this study is that a tree is a living being, in a measure like ourselves, and that it has been confronted with many difficult problems which it must have solved successfully, since it is alive. It has found breathing space and food; it has won room for its roots in the earth and for its branches in the light; and it has matured its seeds and planted them for a new generation.

BRIEF PHYSIOLOGY OF THE TREE.

The tree lives by breathing and by getting its daily food. It breathes through the numerous pores in its leaves, and green bark, and roots. The leaves are often

Fig. 285. A sugar maple grown in an open field.

called the lungs of the tree, but the young bark also has many openings into which the air penetrates, and the roots get air that is present in the soil. So the tree really breathes all over its active surface, and by this process takes in oxygen from the air. It gives off carbon dioxid as we do when we breathe.

While the leaves act as partial lungs they have two other most important functions. First, they must manufacture the food for the entire tree. "Starch factories" is the name that Uncle John gives to the leaves when he talks to children, and it is a good name. The leaf is the factory; the green pulp in the leaf cells is part of the machinery; the machinery is set in motion by sunshine power instead of steam or water power; the raw materials

Fig. 286. Silver maple.

are taken from the air and from the sap sent up from the roots; the first product is usually starch. Thus, it is well when we begin the study of our tree to notice that the leaves are so arranged as to gain all sunlight possible, for without sunlight the starch factories would be obliged to "shut down." It has been estimated that on a mature maple of vigorous growth there is exposed to the sun nearly a half acre of leaf surface. Our tree appears to us in an unfamiliar light when we think of it as a starch factory covering half an acre. Plants are the original starch factories. The manufactories that we build appropriate the starch that plants make from the raw materials.

Starch is plant-food in a convenient form for storage ; but as it cannot be assimilated by plants in this form it must be changed to sugar before it can be transported and used in building up plant tissues.   Hence the leaves have to perform the office of a stomach in order to digest the food they have made for the use of the tree; they change the starch to sugar, and they take from the sap nitrogen, sulfur, phosphorus, and other substances which the roots have appropriated from the soil, and to these they add portions of the starch, and thus make the proteids which form another part of the diet of the tree. It is interesting to know that while these starch factories can operate only in the sunlight, the leaves can digest the food, transport it, and build up tissues in the dark.

Fig. 287.   The bole of a sugar maple grown in a wood.

The autumn leaf, which is so beautiful, has completed its work. The green material which colors the pulp in the leaf cells is withdrawn, leaving there material which is useless, so far as the growing of the tree is concerned, but which glows gold and red, thereby making glad the eye that loves the varying tints in autumn foliage. It is a mistake to believe that the frost makes these brilliant colors : they are caused by the natural old age and death of the leaf, and

where is there to be found old age and death more beautiful ?
When the leaf turns yellow or red it is making ready to depart
from the tree ; a thin corky layer is being developed between its
petiole and the twig, and when this is finally accomplished the
leaf drops from its own weight, from the touch of the lightest
breeze, or from a frost on a cold night.

OBSERVATIONS ON THE MAPLES.

We want you to know the maples from actual observation.

Discover the characteristic forms of the tree, the character of
bark, fruits, and leaves. Verify the pictures in this lesson.

Though the fruit of the sugar maple matures in midsummer, yet
you may perhaps find beneath your tree some of the keys or seeds

Fig. 288. Leaves and fruits of Norway maple.

now partially planted. If the tree stands alone you may per-
chance see how well she has strewn its seeds, and how many of
its progeny have been placed in positions where they can grow
successfully.

We have in New York State seven species of maple common in
our forests. Two of these are dwarf species rarely attaining
thirty-five feet in height, more often found as mere bushes. These
two are the mountain maple and the striped maple or moosewood.
This latter is sometimes called goose-foot maple, because its leaf
is shaped somewhat like the foot of a goose. Of the maples that
attain to the dignity of tall trees we have four species : the sugar

maple, the silver or white maple, the red or swamp maple, and the
box elder. The leaf of the box elder does not look like the leaf
of a maple at all ; it has a compound leaf of three or five leaflets,
but the flowers and fruits are those of the maples. There is also
a variety of sugar maple that is called black maple. We have
planted in our parks the sycamore and Norway maples introduced from Europe, and also ornamental species from Japan. Our
native species are easily distinguished from these and from each
other ; just a little observation as to the shape of the leaves, the
form of the trees, and the character of the bark enables a person
to tell all these species at a glance. I hope that you will become
familiar with the seven native species. Such knowledge is not
only of practical use, but gives real zest and pleasure. When a

Fig. 289. Leaves and fruits of striped maple.

person walks in the morning he should be able to call his tree
acquaintances as well as his human acquaintances by name.

QUESTIONS ON THE MAPLES.

1. How many species of maple trees do you know and what
are they ?

2. How do you distinguish the red maple and the silver maple
from the sugar maple ?

3. What is the shape of the one tree you have chosen to study ?

4. What is there in its shape to tell you of its history, *i. e.*, did
it grow in the open or in the forest ? Was it ever shaded on either

side ; if so, what was the effect ? How have the prevailing winds affected its shape ?

5. How old do you think the tree is ?

6. Was the tree injured by storm or insects during the past season ; if so, how ?

7. Study the leaves on this tree and note any differences in shape and color.

8. What is the use of the skeleton of the leaf ?

Fig. 290.   Leaves of mountain maple, sugar maple, red maple.

9. Is there always a bud in the axil where the leaf stalk joins the twig ?

10. How are the leaves arranged on the twig ?

11. What is the color of the tree this autumn ?

12. When did the leaves begin to fall ? Place in your note book the date when the tree finally becomes bare.

13. Have you found any seeds from your tree? If so, describe them.

14. How are they dispersed and planted?

15. Are both seeds of the pair filled out?

16. How high is your tree?

17. How large an area of shade does it produce? If it stands alone, measure the ground covered by its shadow from morning until evening.

18. How has its shadow affected the plants beneath it? Are the same plants growing there that grow in the open field?

19. Make a sketch of the tree you are studying, showing its outline.

20. Make a sketch of the leaf of the sugar maple.

THE MAPLE IN FEBRUARY.*

By ANNA BOTSFORD COMSTOCK.

SAP.

Strong as the sea and silent as the grave, it ebbs and flows unseen :
Flooding the earth,— a fragrant tidal wave, with mists of deepening green.
— JOHN B. TABB.

APPING the sugar bush " are magical words to the country boy and girl. The winter which was at first so welcome with its miracle of snow, and its attendant joys of sleighing and skating, begins to pall by the last of February. Too many days the clouds hang low and the swirling flakes make out of-door pursuits difficult. Then there comes a day when the south wind blows blandly and the snow settles into hard, marble-like drifts, and here and there a knoll appears bare, and soggy, and brown. It is then that there comes just a suggestion of spring in the air ; and the bare trees show a flush of living red through their grayness and every spray grows heavy with swelling buds. Well do we older folk remember that in our own childhood after a few such days the father would say, " We will get the sap buckets down from the stable loft and wash them, for we can tap the sugar bush soon if this weather holds." In those days the buckets were made of staves, and were by no means so easily washed as are the metal buckets of to-day. Still do we recall the sickish smell of musty sap that greeted our nostrils when we poured the boiling water in to cleanse those old, brown buckets. During the long winter evenings we had all had something to do with the fashioning of the sap spiles made from selected stems of sumac ; after some older one had removed half of the small branch lengthwise with a draw-shave we younger ones had cleared out the pith, thinking thirstily meanwhile of the sweet liquid which would sometime flow there.

---

*Home Nature-Study Course, Vol. V, No. 5, February, 1904.

With buckets and spiles ready when the momentous day came, the large, iron caldron kettle was loaded on a stoneboat together with the sap cask and log chain, the axe and various other utensils, and as many children as could find standing room ; and then the oxen were hitched on and the procession started across the rough pasture to the woods where it eventually arrived after numerous stops for reloading almost everything but the kettle. When we came to the boiling-place we lifted the kettle into place and flanked it with two great logs, against which the fire was to be kindled. Meanwhile the oxen and stoneboat had returned to the house for a load of buckets ; and the oxen blinking with bowed heads or with noses lifted aloft to keep the underbrush from striking their faces "geed and hawed" up hill and down dale through the

Fig. 291.   Sugar making in New York.

woods, stopping here and there while the man with the auger bored holes in certain trees near other holes which had bled sweet juices in years gone by. When the auger was withdrawn the sap followed it and enthusiastic young tongues met it half way though they received more chips than sweetness therefrom. Then the spiles were driven in tightly with a wooden mallet.

The next day after "tapping," those of us large enough to wear the neck-yoke donned this badge of servitude and with its help brought pails of sap to the kettle, and the "boiling" began. As the evening shades gathered, how delicious was the odor of the sap steam permeating the woods farther than the shafts of fire-light pierced the gloom ! How weird and delightful was this night experience in the woods ! and how cheerfully we swallowed the smoke which the contrary wind seemed ever to turn toward us ! We poked the fire to send the sparks upward and now and then we added more sap from the barrel and removed the scum from the boiling liquid with a skimmer which was thrust into the cleft end of a stick to provide it with a sufficiently long handle. As the evening wore on we drew closer to each other as we told the stories of the Indians and the bears and panthers that had roamed these woods when our father was a little boy ; and there came to each of us a disquieting suspicion that perhaps they were not all gone yet, for everything seemed possible in those night-shrouded woods ; and our hearts suddenly jumped into our throats when nearby there sounded the tremulous, blood-curdling cry of the screech owl.

It was the most fun to gather the sap in the warmer mornings, when on the mounds the red squaw-berries were glistening through a frosty veil ; then we looked critically at the tracks in the snow to see what visitors had come sniffing around our buckets. We felt nothing but scorn for him who could not translate correctly those hieroglyphics on the film of soft snow that made white again the soiled drifts. Rabbit, skunk, squirrel, mouse, muskrat, fox : we knew them all by their tracks.

After about three days of gathering and boiling the sap, came the "syruping down." During all that afternoon we added no more sap, and we watched carefully the tawny steaming mass in the kettle ; and when it threatened to boil over we threw in a thin slice of fat pork which seemed to have some mysterious, calming influence. The odor grew more and more delicious, and finally the syrup was pronounced sufficiently thick. The kettle was swung off the logs and the syrup dripped through a cloth strainer into the carrying pail. Oh ! the blackness of the material left on that strainer ! but it was "clean woods-dirt" and never destroyed our faith in the maple sugar any more than did the belief that our friends were made of "dirt" destroy our friendship for them.

Now the old stave bucket and the sumac spile are gone, and in their place a patent galvanized spile not only conducts the sap but holds in place a tin bucket carefully covered. The old caldron kettle is broken or lies rusting in the shed. In its place are evaporating vats placed over furnaces with chimneys, built in the new-fangled sugar houses. The maple molasses of to-day seems to

28

us a pale and anæmic liquid and lacks just that delicious flavor of the rich, dark nectar which we, with the help of cinders and smoke and various other things, brewed of yore in the open woods.

While sugar-making interests us chiefly as one of our own industries, yet we must not forget that it is based upon the life processes of the maple tree, and in studying about it we may be able to learn important facts about the tree which we have chosen for our study.

QUESTIONS ON THE MAPLE TREE.

1. How does the maple tree look in winter? Describe it or sketch it.

2. Are the buds on the twigs opposite or alternate?

3. Are the tips of the twigs the same color as the bark on the larger limbs and trunk?

4. If you can draw, make a pencil sketch, natural size, of three inches square of bark of the maple tree trunk.

5. How does the bark on the trunk differ from that on the branches?

6. How does the bark on the trunk of a maple tree differ from that on the trunk of a soft maple or an elm?

7. What work for the tree do the trunk and branches perform?

8. Is the tree tapped on all sides? If not, why?

9. How deep must the spiles be driven successfully to draw off the sap?

10. Would you tap a tree directly above or at the same spot tapped last year; or would you place two spiles one above the other? Give reasons.

11. Why does the sap flow more freely on warm days after cold nights?

12. Is the sap of which we make sugar going up or down?

13. How does the sugar come to be in the sap?

14. Why is the sugar made during the "first run" better than that which is made later? Why cannot you make sugar in the summer?

15. Does it injure trees to tap them?

16. Do the holes made in earlier years become farther apart as the tree grows?

17 What other trees besides the sugar maple give sweet sap?

18. What animals, birds, and insects are to be seen in the woods during sugar-making time?

19. Have you ever seen the tracks of animals on the snow in the woods? If so, make pictures of them and tell what animals made them.

LEAFLET XLIX.

THE RED SQUIRREL OR CHICKAREE.*

By ANNA BOTSFORD COMSTOCK.

" All day long the red squirrels came and went, and afforded me much entertainment by their manœuvres. One would approach at first warily through the shrub-oaks, running over the snow crust by fits and starts like a leaf blown by the wind, now a few paces this way, with wonderful speed and waste of energy, making inconceivable haste with his "trotters" as if it were for a wager, and now as many paces that way, but never getting on more than half a rod at a time; and then suddenly pausing with a ludicrous expression and a gratuitous somerset, as if all the eyes in the universe were fixed on him,— for all the motions of a squirrel, even in the most solitary recesses of the forest, imply spectators as much as those of a dancing girl,— wasting more time in delay and circumspection than would have sufficed to walk the whole distance,— I never saw one walk,— and then suddenly, before you could say Jack Robinson, he would be in the top of a young pitch-pine, winding up his clock and chiding all imaginary spectators, soliloquizing and talking to all the universe at the same time,— for no reason that I could ever detect, or he himself was aware of, I suspect." — THOREAU.

FROM contact with civilization some wild animals flourish while others are soon exterminated by association with man. To this latter class belongs the black squirrel. Within my own memory this beautiful creature was almost as common in the rural districts of New York State as was the red squirrel; but now it is seen no more except in most retired places; while the red squirrel, pugnacious and companionable, defiant and shy, climbs on our very roofs and sits there scolding us for daring to come within his range of vision. One reason for the disappearance of the black squirrel is, undoubtedly, the fact that its meat is a delicious food. The red squirrel is also good food at certain times of the year, but because of its lesser size, and its greater agility and cunning, it has succeeded in living not merely despite of man, but because of man, for now he rifles corn cribs and grain bins and waxes opulent by levying tribute on man's own savings.

---

* Home Nature-Study Course, Vol. V, No. 2, November, 1903.

Although the red squirrel is familiar to us all, yet, I think, there are few who really know its habits, which are as interesting as are those of bear or lion. Note, for example, the way he peeps at us from the far side of the tree, and the way he uses his tail as a balance and a help in steering as he leaps. This same tail he uses in the winter as a boa by wrapping it around himself as he lies curled up in his snug house. His vocal exercises are most entertaining also ; he is the only singer I know who can carry two parts at a time. Notice some time this autumn when the hickory nuts are ripe that the happy red squirrel is singing you a duet all by himself,— a high, shrill chatter, with a low chuckling accompaniment.

We usually regard nuts as the main food of squirrels, but this is not necessarily so ; for they are fond of the seeds of pines and hemlocks, and also hang around our orchards for apple-seeds. In fact, their diet is varied. The red squirrel is a great thief and keeps his keen eye on chipmunks and mice, hoping to find where they store their food so that he can steal it if he can do so without danger to his precious self.

QUESTIONS ON THE RED SQUIRREL.

We want you to make some original observations on the red squirrel.

1. In summer, what is the color of the red squirrel on the upper parts ? Beneath ?

2. What is the color along the side where the two colors join ?

3. Do these colors change in winter ?

4. Tell how and where the squirrel makes its nest.

5. Does it carry nuts in its teeth or in its cheeks ?

6. Has it cheek pockets like the chipmunk ?

7. Does the red squirrel store food for winter use ? If so, where ?

8. Does it spend its time sleeping in winter like the chipmunk, or does it go out often to get food ?

9. Name all the kinds of food which you know it eats.

10. Did you ever see a red squirrel disturb birds' nests ?

11. How does a squirrel get at the meat of a hard-shelled nut like a black walnut, or a hickory nut ? (Answer this by a sketch, if you can draw.)

12. Do the squirrels of your neighborhood have certain paths in tree-tops which they follow ?

13. How many emotions does the squirrel express with his voice ?

14. What kind of tracks does the red squirrel make in the snow ? (Show this by a sketch if possible.)

LEAFLET L.

THE IMPROVEMENT OF COUNTRY SCHOOL GROUNDS.*

By JOHN W. SPENCER.

My Dear Teacher :

Despite all that is said and done the average school ground is far short of its possibilities in an artistic way. Of this you are well aware, and no doubt you have often wished that you might remedy this defect. Your hours are full of arduous work. Perhaps, however, you can interest your children to help you to clean and to improve the grounds, without much extra care or work on your part.

This illustration of a schoolhouse (Fig. 292) is taken from Bulletin 160, published by the College of Agriculture of Cornell University. The title of the bulletin is "Hints on Rural School Grounds." I wish you would send for the bulletin. It will be mailed you free if you request it.

The picture is not an imaginary sketch, but a faithful representation of what stood in a prosperous rural community less than five years ago. To one familiar with country school buildings it will not be considered as a solitary "awful example," but rather as a type of many that are scattered over the State. I hope it is not your misfortune to be teaching in such a house, even though it is my desire to reach every teacher who is that luckless. However, to make my talk more real let us "make believe," as children say, that you are the priestess in a similar temple of learning. Together we will plan how we can make the most of very uncongenial surroundings.

---

*Supplement to Junior Naturalist Monthly, February, 1902.

It would be safe to wager a red apple that the inside of the
building is every bit as dilapidated as the outside. A community
that tolerates such a building would not be likely to have anything
but the rudest furniture and most of that on crutches. It would
be something out of the usual if the box stove is not short a leg
or two, with brick-bats being used as substitutes. You will be
fortunate if the stove door has two good hinges and if the wood is
not green. At the last school meeting, did the patrons instruct
the trustees not to pay more than six dollars per week for your
services? Was the proposition that the district raise five dollars,
to which the State would add five more for the purchase of books

Fig. 292.   A country school property.

for a library, unanimously voted down and the poor man who
introduced the resolution expected to apologize for his temerity?
The leading man in the district each Sunday during summer
drives two miles to salt his young stock, inspect fences, and see
how the yearlings are prospering; but he never thinks of visiting
the school to see how his children are progressing. Yet the people
of this district are not bad. They are counted good citizens by
the bar and judge, when they are drawn on juries. The public
buildings at the county-seat are models of their kind and these
gentlemen do not remonstrate as to the expense. Perhaps it has
not occurred to them that school buildings and grounds should
have as high a standard as those of the county. A correct public

ideal is everything.   It is not a hopeless undertaking to advance
such an ideal in the community of which we are speaking.

I suggest to you as teacher in this school to undertake some
improvements in the grounds.   I consider the above sketch to be
a zero case.   If improvements can be developed here, it is reasonable to suppose that the same can be repeated where conditions
are primarily better.   The possibilities are sufficient to warrant
the undertaking.   The victory will add to your strength.   The

Fig. 293.   " The girls organized themselves into a tug-of-war team."

lives of the children will be better filled for the part they may do,
and you will have started a public improvement.

I should not appeal to the parents for help.   You have a fountain of power in the children.   It is necessary only to inspire and
guide them.   This is no theory of mine.   It is a result that has
been worked out in many instances.

The beautiful city of Rochester is proud of its schools.   The
development of the town made the construction of new school
buildings necessary to such an extent that little money remained

for the improvement of the grounds. Some of them were located in the breadwinners' districts. The grounds were as the contractor left them ; your imagination can picture their condition. The interiors were well nigh perfect. The exterior was sometimes a Sahara of mud and builders' rubbish. The principal of one of the schools — a woman, by the way,— knowing the force in children, set about to apply it to the improvement of the surroundings. Her method was first to inspire, and then to direct. Her success was ample. Both boys and girls participated. The girls organized themselves into a tug-of-war team (Fig. 293). By fastening ropes to sticks and beams, these things were hauled out of sight. The boys leveled the hummocks and brought fertile soil from some distance. This principal confined her improvements to small areas — so small that the children wanted to do more when they were through. From the time school opened until the rigors of winter stopped the juvenile improvements, only part of the space from the front of the building to the street was graded. Some of the boys brought chaff from a haymow, which was raked in as lawn grass seed. The following spring quite as many weeds appeared as grass, but the children gave the weeds the personification of robbers and made their career short. The promoters had a just pride in what they had accomplished ; and that meagre bit of lawn meant vastly more to them than had it been made by a high-salaried landscape gardener.

I am acquainted with another instance, where the patrons are largely Polish Jews. I am credibly informed that the average head of a family does not have a gross annual income to exceed three hundred and fifty dollars. This necessitates that the mother go out for work and that the children leave school as soon as the law allows to take up work. Yet with all these unfavorable circumstances the pupils have a pride in their school grounds that is glorious to see. In the fall of 1901 prizes were offered for the greatest improvement of school grounds made by children. Nothing daunted, the principal entered his grounds in competition with those in the more wealthy part of the city. The committee of awards gave him the third prize. To judge from the mere physical side, the decision was no doubt just ; but when judged on the score of getting the greatest results from the least material, the principal and his school may have deserved the first prize, plus a reward.

The chances are that your fuel is wood, and perhaps not very dry at that. It is in a pile in the open. Sometimes the sticks are scattered over half the lot. This you can prevent by properly appealing to the pride of your pupils. You will find that they wish to be more tidy than is the school over in Whippoorwill Hollow or in some other district that is considered to be a little more in the back country than your own.

About the time you hear the first spring notes of the bluebird and the robin, prepare public opinion in your little school community for a spring furnishing. You can devise many ways to inspire them. Tell them about Col. George R. Waring and his white brigade and what they did to make New York City cleaner than it had been for many decades before. After the Spanish war, when Cuba became a responsibility upon the United States, the question arose as to what could be done to make filthy Havana cleaner and freer from yellow fever. No one was thought by the Federal government so competent to solve the problem as Colonel Waring. He went, spared not himself, and did his duty, did it so fearlessly that he died the victim of the filth he had fought so valiantly. He had done much during previous years to commend his memory to posterity ; but probably nothing will stand out so prominently as his great ability to correct municipal untidiness. Ask your pupils to be Warings in their own neighborhoods.

By this time the ground will be bare of snow and it will be soft. Ask some of the pupils to bring rakes, and have them gather up the rubbish. You can all play gypsies when you gather about the bonfire. This will be a favorable time to sow grass seed ; for I have no doubt the school lot will need it. A lawn mixture of seed would be ideal, but I hardly expect you to pay for it. At this stage of your improvements, I scarcely expect that any of the patrons of your school would do so either. Later some of them may feel differently. Your pupils can at least follow the plan of those spoken of in Rochester — get chaff from a haymow. It will inevitably be a mixture of grass and weeds, but the latter can be pulled out after germinating. It is barely possible that some farmer will give you some clover and timothy, such as he uses in seeding his meadow ; and this will be far better.

Next, I should put out a hitching-post. When your school commissioner calls it will be appreciated. If that functionary does not publicly compliment your school for even such small improvements, I wish you would report such indifference to me, giving his full address, and I will request him to explain this forgetfulness.

Good results in landscape-gardening depend on observing certain principles, the same as with our wardrobe. Many a clever girl will accomplish more in dress with twenty-five dollars than others can do with twice that amount. Among the first and most important efforts is to make a frame or setting for the house by planting around the borders of the place. Sometimes the location will make this inconvenient if not impossible, when, for instance, the building is placed near the street or crowded between other buildings. Even in such cases, however, it is well to keep the idea

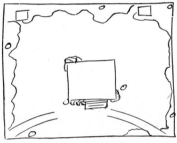

Fig. 294. Showing how the borders may be planted.

clearly in mind and to approach it as nearly as circumstances will permit. An illustration of a normal location to which this principle can be applied is shown in Fig. 294. The trees and the higher shrubs are planted first and on the extreme borders of the lot, with shorter shrubs, roses, and the like in front of them. This frame can be given a finish by planting flowers or very low things next the grass. If the area be ample, let the edges be irregular (Fig. 294); but if very limited, straight lines become necessary.

The open space within the boundaries should be a mat of green carpeting, for nothing can be more beautiful than sward. Fight all influences to bedeck it with beds of flowers in forms of stars and moons and other celestial and terrestrial designs. The demands for such capers may be great, but hold out against them boldly. Certain small shrubs, ferns, and flowers may be planted along the walls of the building, particularly in the angles; but I beg of you to leave the green plat unscalloped and unspoiled, only as is necessary for drives and walks. When the buildings are unsightly, cover with vines and plant bushes against them. Fig. 295 illustrates how Fig. 292 may be improved with very little effort.

Now I will speak of the actual planting. In the light of unnumbered thousands of Arbor Day trees put out to struggle a few weeks for life and then die, this may seem the most important feature of my article. To the unsuccessful planter, let me suggest that he select shrubs and trees which take care of themselves under adverse conditions.   We have a number of such.   If they were imported from Japan and sold at fancy prices, they would be greatly appreciated.   The common sumac is one of them.   For a shrub I know of nothing of its class so sure to bear the ordeal of transplanting or to make more vigorous growth under adverse conditions.   It can be pruned to suit, and nothing can rival its blaze of color in late autumn ; yet as a farmer, I know the experience of fighting against its existence in fence corners, about stone piles, and on steep hillsides.   I do this even though I am fond of the shrub and admire it.   It encroaches on my vineyard and injures the crop.   Grapes will help pay taxes and sumac will not.   In my cherry orchard it is a weed.   In my back yard and on

Fig. 295.   How the grounds in Fig. 292 may be improved.

the borders of my lawn it is an ornamental shrub.   The same can be observed of people.   When in their proper sphere they are helpful factors in a community ; when out of it they are nuisances.

If you ask me to mention a tree most likely to live when planted by unskilled hands, I should name the willow.   I mean the most common kind to be found in the northern States — the kind that stands beside the roadside watering-trough.   The impression is common that willows will thrive only in wet places.   It is true that a willow is very comfortable in places where many other trees will suffer from wet feet ; yet it will give good results elsewhere. It is reasonable to suppose that poor soil goes with a poor school building, and a refined tree would probably find life hard in such a place. I should certainly plant a willow in such cases. It will thrive where a goat can, and where a sheep cannot. For city places, the Carolina poplar is to be recommended. If the soil is good enough, plant maples, elms, or other trees.

A judicious planting of Virginia creeper helps the appearance of buildings both good and bad. I should surely plant it about the main building and the outbuildings and fences, if the patrons of the school did not object. The probabilities are that when the vines have begun to cover some of the deformities of the place, some finicky resident of the district will cut them out on the plea that they promote decay of the weather-beaten clap-boards ; but do not be discouraged by such a possibility. Vines, too, usually interfere with the painting of a building. Although they may be taken down and put back after the painters are through, the first effect is not regained unless the process of putting back has been done with unusual care.

Do not make the mistake of planting too much. A small lawn can be overdressed as is sometimes the case with women. Lilac, Japan quince, syringa, hydrangea, and like common shrubs, could be planted if the opportunities of space seem to warrant.

I hope it will be your taste to allow the limbs of the trees to start low and those of the shrubs to begin as near the ground as possible. I am aware that among country people it is the practice to tolerate only the higher limbs. I can give a reason for this only on the supposition that they must do something in pruning, and the lower limbs are the most convenient to reach. I know a man who came into possession of a place having a fine lot of evergreens with the lower branches at the ground. By way of proclaiming a change of ownership he cut away the lower branches, leaving a bare trunk of about five feet. Before he touched them they were beautiful green cones and when passing the place I always turned my face in their direction to enjoy the beauty. When he was through they were standing on one leg, and a wooden leg at that. I have never felt kindly toward the man since.

In the matter of planting I know of no better method than that of the experienced orchardist. As a rule he buys his trees of a nurseryman. They are often dug in the fall, and are planted the following spring. During the interval they are stored in specially constructed cellars, and at no time are the roots permitted to become dry. When packed for shipment damp moss is placed about the roots. When the orchardist removes them from the packing box he "heels" them in, which is a kind of probationary planting in shallow furrows where they stand until ready to be set out permanently. When that time comes the trees are taken from the trench and the roots plunged in a tub of thin mud or doused with water and covered with a blanket. An orchardist counts a tree lost if the roots have been allowed to remain in the sun until the small rootlets have so dried that they have a gray appearance

In taking the young tree from the nursery row only a fraction of the original roots go with the tree, and these are badly bruised at the point of cleavage. These ragged ends should be dressed smoothly by means of a slanting cut with a knife. All mutilated roots should be removed. You must bear in mind that the roots you find with the trees are capable of performing but a small part of what was done by all the roots when growing in their native place.

The hole in which the tree is set should be large enough to accommodate the roots without cramping them out of their natural positions. It is important that the earth used for filling should be fertile, and it is doubly important that it should be fine — even superfine. Clods, even small clods like marbles, will not snuggle up to the bark of the root as closely as is absolutely necessary. Set the tree about an inch deeper than you think it originally stood, so that when planted and the earth settles, it will really be about the same depth. All the earth should not be dumped in at once and then the surface pressed firm with the feet. A close examination will show that the soil has "bridged" in places, leaving many roots in tiny caverns. It is important that fine soil should be snuggled close to each little rootlet, not for warmth but for moisture. Fill the hole by installments of one-third at each filling. Sprinkle the fine earth about the roots. Then dash in a third of a pail of water. This will give the roots much needed moisture and, best of all, will wash the earth about each root fiber. I urge the adoption of this careful method for all trees and shrubs, not excepting the sumac and willow. Even willows will show their gratitude for such considerate treatment, even though they are able to survive rougher usage. They will pay for it when the drought and neglect of summer come.

The most common mistake made in the selection of trees is in taking those that are too large. For the conditions that we have under consideration, I suggest that a tree no larger than a broom-handle be chosen. I know that the common feeling is, " we shall have to wait too long for our shade." Unless the larger tree is in the hands of an expert, the smaller will be the more desirable at the end of five years. I much prefer, moreover, the selection of a tree or shrub growing in the sunshine, rather than one from the shade.

I have one final request to make, which to the novice will be the most difficult of all and one which he is quite likely to fail in performing because of lack of moral courage. I mean the cutting back of the top of the tree or shrub after planting. Before the removal of the tree, the roots probably found pasturage in a cart load of soil. After planting, the root pasturage is not more than half a bushel of soil. What follows when the forces of plant growth begin ? A demand for soil products, with a very much restricted means of supply. The top must be cut back to match the shortened root system. Thousand of trees die every year because this principle is not duly observed and the failure is often attributed to the nurseryman. The amount necessary to cut back differs with different trees and shrubs. No hard and fast rules can be given. With willows and sumacs one-third to one-half of everything bearing leaf buds can be cut away. With a maple having a diameter of one and a half inches at the butt, I should suggest that about one-third of the branch area be left to grow.

In this article I have had in mind the improvement of school grounds where all the conditions are at zero — where the building would be a discredit to any owner, where the patrons are totally indifferent, and where the only resource is to awaken a public spirit on the part of the children. With better school buildings, more ample grounds, and a small number of patrons favorable to improvement, the foregoing ideas need not be followed closely. However, they do contain principles and some details that deserve careful consideration, even in landscape planting of the highest form. The first step should be the development of local pride. Something may be accomplished among the parents ; but it is a problem as to what extent that may be done. To the true teacher the pupils may be counted upon as the mainstay in such an undertaking. To such a teacher I should say, Do not for a moment believe that the improvements seen about the school grounds will be all the good that is wrought. Fifty years from now there will be a few gray-haired men and women who take more interest in the appearance of their "front-door-yard," and give their children encouragement in having a posy bed "all their own," and who extend sympathy and service to the better appearance of the school grounds, because of your altruism when you taught district school.

We have some aids that may be helpful to you and to which you are welcome. Bulletin 160, spoken of at the beginning, specifically treats of this work, and Bulletin 121, on "Planting of Shrubbery," has been very popular. We have published a number of articles on children's gardening, all of which will be sent you free if you request it. If you have specific problems we shall be glad to have you write and we will help you all we can by correspondence.

The most efficient help we can give you is through the organizing of your pupils into Junior Naturalist clubs. We give these clubs especial instruction in gardening and the improvement of home and school grounds. Children receive great inspiration from large numbers doing the same thing, while we can give instruction to ten thousand as easily as to one child. Many hundreds of teachers and thousands of children find the study of nature a beam of sunshine in the schoolroom and a great aid in the English period without being a burden to the teacher.

PART II.

CHILDREN'S LEAFLETS.

Designed to Open the Eyes of the Young.

Most of these leaflets were published as companions to the Teachers'
Leaflets and Lessons,— the teachers' lessons written in one vein and the
children's in another. Even though the subject-matter may be largely dupli-
cated in the two, it seems worth while to keep these separate as showing a
simple method of presentation and as suggesting a means of procedure to
those who would reach small children.

29   449

THE CHILD'S REALM.

By L. H. Bailey.

A little child sat on the sloping strand
  Gazing at the flow and the free,
Thrusting its feet in the golden sand,
  Playing with the waves and the sea.

     I snatch'd a weed that toss'd on the flood
       And parted its tangled skeins ;
     I trac'd the course of the fertile blood
       That lay in its meshèd veins ;

     I told how the stars are garner'd in space,
       How the moon on its course is roll'd,
     How the earth is hung in its ceaseless place
       As it whirls in its orbit old :—

The little child paus'd with its busy hands
  And gaz'd for a moment at me,
Then dropp'd again to its golden sands
  And play'd with the waves and the sea.

LEAFLET LI.

A SNOW STORM.*

By ALICE G. McCLOSKEY.

(Compare Leaflet VII.)

A chill no coat however stout,
Of homespun stuff could quite shut out,
   *   *   *   *
The coming of the snow storm told.
                      — WHITTIER.

"SURELY, it is going to snow," says Grandfather, as he puts an armful of wood into the old box beside the fire ; and a happy feeling comes over you, and you like Grandfather a little better because he has promised you a snow storm. "What a wise old Grandfather he is ! " you think. He always seems to know what is going to happen out-of-doors and you wonder how he learned it all. Perhaps I can tell you why Grandfather is so wise. When he was a boy he lived on a farm and was in the outdoor world summer and winter. There he learned to know Nature day by day. This is why he can consult her now as to wind and weather, and why he nearly always understands what she tells him. He is a good observer.

If you hope ever to be as weather-wise as Grandfather, you must begin right away to see and to think. The next time you hear him say, "It is going to snow," put on your fur cap and mittens and go out-of-doors. Is the air clear, crisp, and cold — the kind you like to be out in ? Or is it a keen cold that makes you long for the fire-place ? Can you see the sun ? If so, how does it look ? In what direction is the wind ? How cold does the thermometer tell you it is ?

All the time that you are learning these things the storm will be

---

*Junior Naturalist Monthly, December, 1903.

coming nearer. Then on your dark coat sleeve something soft and white and glistening falls — a snowflake. You touch the bright thing and it disappears. Where did it come from and whither did it go? Others follow faster and faster, jostling each other as they whirl through the air. Look at them closely. Are the crystals large and flowery or small and clear? Put your head back and let them come down on your face. Is their touch soft or do they hurt as they fall?

Perhaps by this time you are very cold and think that supper must be nearly ready. You go into the house, and you find the gray kitten snoozing comfortably on the hearthrug. You snuggle down beside her "to warm your frozen bones a bit," and still the storm and outdoor world are near; for is it not splendid music that the wind is making as it roars down the old chimney or sways the tall pine trees?

SUGGESTIONS FOR STUDY.

Answer as many of the following questions as you can from your own observations:

1. How did the sky look before it began to snow? During the storm? After the storm? It is always a good thing to look up at the sky.

2. In what direction did the old weather-cock tell you the wind was blowing as the storm came on? Did the wind change during the storm? If so, did the snow change in any way?

3. Look at snow crystals through a tripod lens if you have one. How many points do they have?

4. After supper go to the window, raise the shade, and look out on the stormy night. Tell Uncle John all that you see.

5. On your way to school the next day after a snow storm, have the following in mind to write to us about:

(a) The tracks in the snow. How many do you find? Did Rover make them? the gray kitten? a snow bird? an old crow? a rabbit? a squirrel?

(b) The way the trees and small plants receive the snow. Some hold it, others cast it off: why?

(c) Notice the snow drifts. Where are they highest? Why does the snow pile up in some places and not in others? Is the drift deepest close to buildings or a little way from them? Are the drifts deepest close to the trees, or is there a space between the tree and the drift?

LEAFLET LII.

A PLANT AT SCHOOL.*

By L. H. BAILEY.

I DROPPED a seed into the earth. It grew, and the plant was mine.

It was a wonderful thing, this plant of mine. I did not know its name, and the plant did not bloom. All I know is that I planted something apparently as lifeless as a grain of sand and that there came forth a green and living thing unlike the seed, unlike the soil in which it stood, unlike the air into which it grew. No one could tell me why it grew, nor how. It had secrets all its own, secrets that baffle the wisest men ; yet this plant was my friend. It faded when I withheld the light, it wilted when I neglected to give it water, it flourished when I supplied its simple needs. One week I went away on a vacation, and when I returned the plant was dead ; and I missed it.

Although my little plant had died so soon, it had taught me a lesson ; and the lesson was that it is worth while to have a plant. I wish that every Junior Naturalist would have a plant. It matters little what the plant is. Just drop the seed, keep the earth warm and moist, watch the plant "come up," see it grow. Measure its height at a given time every day. Keep a record of how many times you water it. Make a note of every new leaf that appears. See whether it leans towards the light. If it dies, tell why. Four weeks from the time when you plant the seed, send Uncle John your notes.

A sheet of foolscap paper contains about twenty-eight lines, one line for the notes of each day, and space enough at the top to write your name, date of sowing, kind of seed, and nature of the soil. Open the sheet and on each line at the left side write all the dates for four weeks ahead ; then fill in these lines across the two pages day by day as the plant grows. For the first few days there will not be much to write, but you can say whether you watered

---

* Junior Naturalist Monthly, February, 1903.

the earth or not, and where you kept the pot or box. It will be good practice to get into the habit of taking notes. I suppose that the record of the first few days will run something as follows :

MYRON JOHNSON, name of school, age —.

———, Teacher.

Feb. 2. Monday. Planted six cabbage seeds in loose soil from the chip yard. I put the earth in a small old tin cup, and pressed it down firmly. I made it just nicely moist, not wet. I planted the seeds about equal distances apart and about one-fourth inch deep, and pressed the earth over them.

Fig. 297. An egg-shell farm. The plants, from left to right, are : cabbage, field corn, pop-corn, wheat, buckwheat.

Feb. 2. Did not water to-day, for the soil seemed to be moist enough.

Feb. 3. Watered at 10:30 A. M. Teacher told me to be careful not to make the soil too wet.

Feb. 4. Watered at noon.

Feb. 5. Put the cup nearer the stove so that the seeds would come up more quickly.

Feb. 6. The earth is cracking in two or three places. Watered at noon.

Feb. 7. Went to the schoolhouse and found some of the plants coming up.

Feb. 9. Four of the plants are up. (Here tell how they look, or make a few marks to show.)

When your month's record is all complete, send the sheet, or a copy of it, to Uncle John, and this will be your club dues. See how many things you can find out in these four weeks.

Fig. 298. A window plant that is easy to grow. It is a common garden beet. The end of the beet was cut off so that it could be got into the tin can. A very red beet will produce handsome red-ribbed leaves. In all cases, be sure that the crown or top of the plant has not been cut off too close, or the leaves may not start readily. The beet starts into growth quickly and the growing plant will stand much abuse. It makes a very comely plant for the school-room window. Try carrot, turnip, and parsnip in the same way.

Before the four weeks are past write to Uncle John and he will tell you what next to do. By that time your plants will need transplanting, and he will tell you how to do it. Perhaps you can set some of the plants outdoors later on and see them grow all summer ; whether you can or not will depend on the kinds of plants that you grow. If you want to grow asters or cabbages next summer, you can start some of them in February and March.

Quick-germinating seeds, fit for starting in the schoolroom, are wheat, oats, buckwheat, corn, bean, pumpkin and squash, radish, cabbage, turnip. Perhaps some of these require a warmer place than others in which to germinate. If you find out which they are, let Uncle John know.

You can grow the plants in egg-shells, wooden boxes (as cigar boxes), tin cans, flower pots. If you use tin cans it is well to punch two or three holes in the bottom so that the extra water will drain out. Set the can or box in a saucer, plate, or dripping-pan so that the water will not soil the desk or table. It is best not to put it in a sunny window until after the plants are up, for the soil is likely to "bake" or to become hard on top ; or if you do put it in such a place, throw a newspaper over it to prevent the earth from drying out.

SUGGESTIONS FOR PLANT STUDY.*

Last year hundreds of children sent us records of their plants. This kind of work is most satisfactory to Uncle John. Following is a record which we received in March, from a girl in the fourth grade :

Feb. 16 — Monday. I planted seven cabbage seeds in an egg-shell. I did not water it.

Feb. 17 — Did not see anything.

Feb. 18 — Saw a little brown thing.

Feb. 19 — Saw a little seed lying on top.

Feb. 20 — Saw little sprout.

Feb. 21 — Holiday.

Feb. 22 — Holiday.

Feb. 23 — Holiday.

Feb. 24 — Saw two little sprouts.

Feb. 25 — The egg-shell was full of sprouts.

Feb. 26 — The plant was coming up and the earth was very wet, so I did not water it.

Feb. 27 — Saw six sprouts.

Feb. 28 — Holiday.

March 1 — Holiday.

March 2 — Turned the plant around, so it would look toward the light.

---

* Alice G. McCloskey, Junior Naturalist Monthly, January, 1904.

March   2 — That afternoon I planted the cabbage in a tin can with tissue paper around it, because the cabbage outgrew the egg-shell some time ago.

March   3 — I put the plant out of the window.

March   4 — I did not look at it.

March   5 — One of the sprouts began to droop.

March   6 — I dug the dirt up around it. Then it was put in the air out of the window.

March   7 — Holiday.

March   8 — Holiday.

March   9 — I put it out of the window.

March 10 — It was put out of the window. It was brought in at the close of school.

March 11 — Dug the dirt out from the plant and patted it down

March 12 — Watered.

March 13 — Put out of the window.

March 14 — Holiday.

March 15 — Holiday.

March 16 — Watered and put out of the window.   HELEN.

Was not this a good record for a little girl to make? I wish that she had told something about the soil in which she planted the seeds. This is always important. In winter you may have some difficulty in getting soil, but in the village a florist will let you have some, and in the country you may be able to get it in the cellar of a grocery store or from your own cellar. Perhaps you can find some in the potato bin. When there is a "thaw," get some soil, even if it is very wet; you can dry it near the stove. Perhaps your schoolhouse will be too cold over Sunday in mid-winter to allow you to grow plants. If so, plant the seeds at home.

Fig. 299. Radish seeds germinating between blotting-paper and the side of a tumbler.

When you have planted your seeds, unless you take them up every day, you cannot see how the little plants are behaving down under the soil. I want to tell you how you can know some things that the plants are doing without disturbing them.

Choose an ordinary glass (Fig. 299), roll up a piece of blotting paper so that it is a trifle smaller than the glass, and place it inside. Between the blotting paper and the glass, put a few radish seeds or any kind of seed such as you planted in the soil. Keep the blotting paper moist and watch what happens. In four or five days the plants should be "up." Here are some things to think about as you watch them :

1. Note any change in the seeds when they have been moist for a few hours.

2. What happens to the outer coat of the seed?

3. In what direction does the little root grow? The stem?

4. Notice the woolly growth on the root? Does this growth extend to the tip of the root?

5. When the little plant has begun to grow, turn it around so that the root is horizontal. Does it remain in that position?

6. How soon do the leaves appear?

It may interest some of the Junior Naturalists to see the effect of much water on seeds. Suppose you experiment a little along this line. Choose three glasses. In one put seeds into water, in another put them into very wet or muddy soil, and in the third plant the seeds in moist soil, such as seeds are ordinarily planted in. Tell us the results of the three experiments.

A THIRD-GRADE RECORD.

Following is a fac simile reproduction of a spontaneous and unpruned record made by a child in the third grade. The child grew beans in a tumbler against blotting paper, as shown in Fig. 299. I hope that this will illustrate to both teacher and children the value of simple note-taking.

Jan. 14, 1904.

I planted a bean.
I watered it

Jan.
15, 1904.

No change.

Jan. 16, 1904.
No change.

Jan. 17, 1904.
No change.

Jan. 18, 1904.

No change.

Jan. 18, 1904.
No change.

Jan. 19, 1904
No change

Jan. 2 0, 1 9 0 4.
No change

Jan. 2 1, 1 1 0 4.
A been was
getting ready
to sprote.
Jan. 2 2,
1 9 0 4.
I saw
four beautiful
sprotes ——

Jan. 2 4, 1904
No change.

Jan. 2 5, 1904.
No change

Jan. 26, 1904.
No change

Jan. 27, 1904,
No change.

Jan. 28, 1904.
No change

Jan. 29, 1904.
My skin was
all off.
and the
sprotes are
getting
larger.

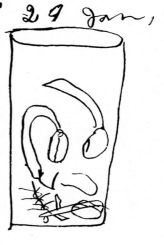

29 Jan,

Jan. 30, 1904.
Saturday

Jan. 31, 1904.
Sunday.

Feb. 1, 1904.
My been has
two little
leaves and they
all had a
long things
that look like
three little
stenns.

Feb. 2, 1904.
No change.

Feb. 3, 1904.
My been had
some pretty
little leaves.
Feb. 4, 1904.
My been
had more
leaves.
Feb. 5, 1904
No change.

Feb. 1. 1904.

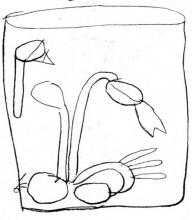

30

Fig. 300.   *The bean plants that were grown by the third-grade child.*

LEAFLET LIII.

AN APPLE TWIG AND AN APPLE.*

By L. H. BAILEY.

(Compare Leaflet XXXI.)

YESTERDAY I went over into the old apple orchard. It was a clear November day. The trees were bare. The wind had carried the leaves into heaps in the hollows and along the fences. Here and there a cold-blue wild aster still bloomed. A chipmunk chittered into a stone pile.

I noticed many frost-bitten apples still clinging to the limbs. There were decayed ones on the ground. There were several small piles of fruit that the owner had neglected, lying under the trees, and they were now worthless. I thought that there had been much loss of fruit, and I wondered why. If the fruit-grower had not made a profit from the trees, perhaps the reason was partly his own fault. Not all the apples still clinging to the tree were frost-bitten and de-

Fig. 301. This is the branch that tried and failed.

cayed. I saw many very small apples, no larger than the end of my finger, standing stiff on their stems. Plainly these were apples that had died when they were young. I wondered why.

I took a branch home and photographed it. You have the engraving in Fig. 301. Note that there are three dead young apples

*Junior Naturalist Monthly, January, 1903.

at the tip of one branch.   Each apple came from a single flower.
These flowers grew in a cluster.   There were three other flowers
in this cluster, for I could see the scars where they fell off.

   But why did these three fruits die?   The whole branch on
which they grew looked to be only half alive.   I believe that it
did not have vigor enough to cause the fruit to grow and ripen.
If this were not the cause, then some insect or disease killed the
young apples, for apples, as well as people, may have disease.

*Fig. 302.   These are the flowers that make the apples.   How many clusters are
there?*

   Beneath the three dead apples, is still another dead one.   Notice
how shrivelled and dried it is, and how the snows and rains
have beaten away the little leaves from its tip.   The three uppermost apples grew in 1902 ; but this apple grew in some previous
year.   If I could show you the branch itself, I could make you see
in just what year this little apple was borne, and just what this

branch has tried to do every year since. This branch has tried
its best to bear apples, but the fruit-grower has not given it food
enough, or has not kept the enemies and diseases away.

The lesson that I got from
my walk was this : if the
apples were not good and
abundant it was not the fault
of the trees, for they had done
their part.

In the cellar at home we
have apples. I like to go into
the cellar at night with a lantern and pick apples from this
box and that — plump and big
and round — and eat them
where I stand. They are crisp
and cool, and the flesh snaps
when I bite it and the juice is
as fresh as the water from a
spring. There are many kinds
of them, each kind known by
its own name, and some are
red and some are green, some
are round and some are long,
some are good and some are
poor.

Over and over, these apples
in the cellar have been sorted,
until only the good ones are
supposed to remain. Yet now
and then I find a decayed
heart or a hollow place. The
last one I picked up was fair
and handsome on the outside,
but a black place and a little
" sawdust " in the blossom end
made me suspicious of it. I
cut it open. Here is what I
found (Fig. 306). Someone
else had found the apple
before I had. Last summer a

*Fig. 303.   The apples are usually borne one
in a place, although the flowers are in
clusters.   Why?*

little moth had laid an egg on the growing apple, a worm had come from the egg and had eaten and eaten into the apple, burrowing through the core, until at last it was full grown,

as shown in the picture. Now it is preparing to escape. It has eaten a hole through the side of the apple, but has plugged up the hole until it is fully ready to leave. When it leaves it will crawl into a crack or crevice somewhere, and next spring change into a pupa and finally come forth a small, dun-gray moth. This moth will lay the eggs and then die; and thus will be completed the eventful life of the codlin-moth, from egg to worm and

Fig. 304. The Baldwin apple. How many kinds of apples do you know?

pupa and moth. But in doing all this the insect has spoiled the apple. The insect acts as if the apple belonged to him; but I think the apple belongs to me. I wonder which is correct?

Some of these apples are sound and solid on the inside, but they have hard blackish spots on the outside (Fig. 307). This is a disease — the apple-scab. This scab is caused by minute plants and these plants also claim the apple as their own. There are ways by means of which the apple-grower is able to destroy the

Fig. 305. The same Baldwin apple cut in two.

codlin-moth and the apple-scab; and thereby he secures fair and sound apples.

Insects and diseases and men are all fighting to own the apple.

TEN THINGS TO LEARN FROM AN APPLE.

When you write your dues to Uncle John on the apple, answer as many of the following questions as you can. You can get the answers from an apple itself. He does not want you to ask any-one for the answers :

1. How much of the apple is occupied by the core ?

2. How many parts or compartments are there in the core ?

3. How many seeds are there in each part ?

4. Which way do the seeds point ?

5. Are the seeds attached or joined to any part of the core ? Explain.

6. What do you see in the blossom end of the apple ?

7. What do you see in the opposite end ?

Fig. 306. *This is an apple in which a worm made its home.*

8. Is there any connection between the blossom end and the core ?

9. Find a wormy apple and see if you can make out where the worm left the apple. Perhaps you can make a drawing. To

Fig. 307. These are the apples on which other plants are living.— The apple-scab.

do this, cut the apple in two. Press the cut surface on a piece of paper. When the apple is removed you can trace out the marks.

10. When you hold an apple in your hand, see which way it looks to be bigger — lengthwise or crosswise. Then cut it in two lengthwise, measure it each way, and see which diameter is the greater.

Fig. 308.   Here is where city boys and girls buy their apples.

LEAFLET LIV.

TWIGS IN LATE WINTER.*

By ALICE G. McCLOSKEY.

ALONG a country road, through a drifted field, over a rail fence, and into the woods I went, gathering twigs here and there as I passed. A February thaw had come and these first messengers of spring, reaching out from shrub and tree, were beginning to show signs of life. Many young people do not believe that spring is near until they hear a robin or a bluebird. The bare little twigs tell us first. Look at them as you go on your way to school. Are they the same color in February that they were in the short December days?

When I reached home with my bundle of twigs, it was "fun" to sit by the window and study the strange little things. They were so different one from another, and so interesting in every way, that I decided to ask our boys and girls to gather some winter twigs and tell us about them. Select your twigs from the butternut, willow, hickory, horsechestnut, apple, plum, plane-tree, maple, or any other tree that you come across. Here are some suggestions that will help you in your study :

1. How many colors do you find in one twig? Count the tints and shades. I found eight colors on a small maple branch (Fig. 309).

2. Notice the differences in several twigs as they lie on the table. What makes them look so dif-

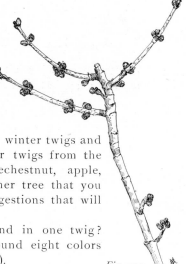

Fig. 309.
Red or swamp maple.

*Junior Naturalist Monthly, February, 1904,

ferent : size, shape, color, arrangement of buds, the size or shape of the buds ?

3. On how many twigs are the buds opposite each other ? Note the opposite buds on the horsechestnut (Fig. 310). On how many are they alternate ? Are the buds opposite on the butternut (Fig. 311) ?

4. Which twigs bear the buds singly ?

5. When you find two or more buds growing together on a stem, is there any difference in the size of the buds ?

6. On how many of the twigs can you see a scar left by the leaf when it dropped off (Fig. 310 and Fig. 311 *a, a*) ? Compare the leaf scars on different twigs. Notice the strange scar on the butternut (Fig. 311). It looks like the face of an old sheep.

7 Do you see any cocoons on your twig ?

Fig. 310. Horse-chestnut.

8. You all know the rings on an apple twig that tell how much it grew each year. Do you find rings on other twigs ? Do you see them on any of these pictures ?

9. What do you suppose makes these rings ? Do you think there was once a large terminal bud where these rings are ?

*Fig. 311.
Butternut.*

LEAFLET LV.

PRUNING.*

By ALICE G. McCLOSKEY.

(Compare Leaflet XLVI.)

FIRST snow, then sleet, and then a downpour of rain — it stormed all day. At nightfall it grew colder. The wind blew fiercely. The twigs and branches fell on the white crust which covered the earth. Nature was pruning the trees.

Have you ever seen your father go into the orchard and prune his trees? Why did he do it? Compare the work done by nature and that which your father does. Which seems to be the more careful pruner?

Let us experiment a little. It will please Uncle John. He always wants his boys and girls to find out things for themselves. Select a branch of lilac or some other shrub. Mark it so that you will always know it. Count the buds on the branch. Watch them through the spring and the summer. Note the number that become branches. You will then know that nature prunes the trees.

If you think a minute, you will see that pruning is necessary in the plant world. Suppose a branch has thirty buds, and that every bud should produce thirty branches, each of which in turn should produce thirty more,— do you think there would be any room left in the world for boys and girls? Would a tree be able to hold so many branches?

You certainly have noticed decayed holes in trees. Did you ever wonder why they were there? I suppose that most persons never wonder about it at all; or if they do give it any passing thought, they say it is only "natural" for trees to have rotten spots. But these rotten spots mean that once the tree was injured. Perhaps the injury was the work of a careless or thoughtless man

---

* Extended from Junior Naturalist Monthly, February, 1901.

who pruned the tree. Very few persons seem really to know how
to remove the limbs of a tree so that the wound will heal readily.

As you go and come, observe how
the trees have been pruned. Do you
see long "stubs" left, where limbs
have been cut? Yes ; and that is the
wrong way to cut them. They should
be cut close to the main branch or
trunk, for then the wounds will heal
over better (Fig. 312). If we abused
our cows and horses, as we sometimes
abuse our shade trees, what would
become of the animals?

*Fig. 312.   The wrong way
and the right way to remove
a limb.*

Did you ever see trees that were
mutilated to allow of the stringing of
telephone and telegraph wires?

Who owns the shade trees along a street or public highway?

LEAFLET LVI.

THE HEPATICA.*

By ALICE G. McCLOSKEY.

(Compare Leaflet XL.)

OMETHING new and pleasant happened in my life this year. In February, while the wood was snow-covered and the roadsides piled high with drifts, I saw hepaticas in bloom.

Oh, no! I did not find them out of doors. I had all the fun of watching them from my warm chimney-corner. Then when winds blew fiercely I often went to the window where they grew and buried my head in the sweet blossoms. What do you suppose they told me? If some winter day you feel their soft touch on your face, and smell their woodsy fragrance, you will hear the message.

Perhaps you want to know how the hepaticas found their way into my window-box. Last fall as I walked through a leafy wood I gathered a few plants, roots and all, that I had known and loved in spring and summer days. Among them were hepaticas. These I laid away in the cellar until the first of February. Then I planted them in a corner of the window-box that I had left for them.

Since the little woods plants have come to live with me I have learned to know them well. Perhaps the most important lesson they have taught me is this : The blossoms may be the least interesting part of a plant. Will you find out what hepaticas have to tell as the seasons pass?

Even before you hear the first robin, go into the woods, find one of the hepaticas, and mark it for your own. You will know it by the old brown leaves. Then watch it day by day. The following questions will help you to learn its life story :

1. Where do hepaticas grow, in sunny or shady places? During which seasons do they get the most sunlight?

---

*Junior Naturalist Monthly, March, 1903.

2. Watch the first sign of life in the plant. Do the new leaves or the flowers come first?

3. Look at the hepatica blossom a long time. How many different parts can you see in it? Whether you know the names of these parts now does not matter. I want you to see them.

4. Notice the three small, green, leaf-like parts that are around the flower bud. As the flower opens see whether they are a part of it, or whether they are a little way from it on the stem.

5. Observe the stem closely. Is it short or long? Hairy or smooth?

6. As the new leaves appear find out whether they are fuzzy on the inside as well as on the outside. Notice how they are rolled up and watch them unroll.

7. In how many different colors do you find hepaticas?

8. Do some smell sweeter than others? If so, does color seem to have anything to do with it?

9. Look at a hepatica plant at night or very late in the afternoon. Also watch it early in the morning and in cloudy weather. Then look at it in bright sunshine. Do you see any change in the flowers? I think you will discover something of much interest.

10. Seed-time among hepaticas is very interesting. Notice what becomes of the three small, leaf-like parts that were underneath the flower. How many seeds are there?

11. How long do you think the leaves of hepatica remain on the plant? Do you suppose they remain green all winter?

12. What becomes of the hepatica plant after it blossoms? Did you ever see one in summer? Describe.

LEAFLET LVII.

JACK-IN-THE-PULPIT.*

By ALICE G. McCLOSKEY.

(Compare Leaflet XLI.)

HEY call him Jack-in-the-Pulpit, he stands up so stiff and
so queer
On the edge of the swamp, and waits for the flower-folk
to come and hear
The text and the sermon, and all the grave things that
he has to say;
But the blossoms they laugh and they dance, they are wilder than ever
to-day;
And as nobody stops to listen, so never a word has he said;
But there in his pulpit he stands, and holds his umbrella over his head,
And we have not a doubt in our minds, Jack, you are wisely listening,
To the organ-chant of the winds, Jack, and the tunes that the sweet birds
sing!

LUCY LARCOM.

"It is Indian turnip," said I.

"No," said Grandmother, "it's memory root. If you taste it
once you will never forget it." And what Grandmother said to
me so long ago, I say to every boy and girl, "If you taste it once
you will never forget it."

But of all the names for this strange little wood plant, I like Jack
in-the-pulpit best. Though never a word has it said in our life-
long acquaintance, it has been a helpful little "country preacher"
to me. As we go into the woods this year, let us make up our
minds that we will know more than we ever have known before
of its interesting life.

Where do you find the Jack-in-the-pulpit? In what kind of
soil does it grow? How does it first come up?

What is the shape of the root? One is enough for the whole
class to study and it should be planted again. We do not want the
Jack-in-the-pulpit to disappear from our woods.

Does the little hood fold over at first?

The hood or "umbrella" is not the flower. You will find the
flowers on the little central stalk that you call "Jack." See

---

*Junior Naturalist Monthly, April, 1903.

whether the blossoms are alike.   Look at the blossoms on several
plants.   Place a stick by the side of one of these plants so that
you will know it later in the year when the Jack-in-the-pulpit has
disappeared.

Notice whether there are insects in the lower part of the flower
stalk.   If so, can they get out?

When the blossom has gone, look for the seeds.   What color are
they in June?   In August?

Have you any house plant that you think is related to Jack-in-
the-pulpit?

Fig. 313.   Tubers of Jack-in-the-pulpit, or Indian turnip.

LEAFLET LVIII.

THE DANDELION.*

BY ALICE G. McCLOSKEY and L. H. BAILEY.

HE first warmth of spring brought the dandelions out of the banks and knolls. They were the first proofs that winter was really going, and we began to listen for the blackbirds and swallows. We loved the bright flowers, for they were so many reflections of the warming sun. They soon became more familiar, and invaded the yards. Then they overran the lawns, and we began to despise them. We hated them because we had made up our minds not to have them, not because they were unlovable. In spite of every effort, we could not get rid of them. Then if we must have them, we decided to love them. Where once were weeds are now golden coins scattered in the sun, and bees revelling in color ; and we are happy ! L. H. BAILEY.

SUGGESTIONS FOR STUDY.

I. Ask your teacher to let you go out of doors for ten minutes to look at dandelions. In your note books write answers to the following questions :

1. At what time of day are you looking for the dandelions ? Is the sun shining, or is the sky overcast ? Make up your mind to notice whether dandelions behave the same at all hours of the day and in all kinds of weather.

2. How many dandelions can you count as you stand on the school-ground ? The little yellow heads can be seen a long distance.

3. Where do they prefer to grow, — on the hillsides, along the roadsides, in the marshes, or in your garden ?

II. Gather a basket full of blossoming dandelions, roots and

---

* Supplement to Junior Naturalist Monthly, May, 1904.

all, take them to school, and ask the teacher to let you have a dandelion lesson. Here are some suggestions that will help you:

1. Each pupil should have a plant, root and all. Describe the plant. Is it tall or short? How many leaves are there? How many blossoms?

2. Hold the plant up so that you can see it well. How many distinct colors do you find? How many tints and shades of these colors?

3. Look carefully at the blossom. How many parts has it? How much can you find out about the way in which the yellow head is made up?

III. Mark a dandelion plant in your garden. Watch

Fig. 314. Blow the dandelion balloon!

it every day. Keep a record of all that happens in its life. Later in the year send Uncle John a little history or account of the plant you have watched.

DANDELION.

Dear common flower, that grow'st beside the way,
   Fringing the dusty road with harmless gold,
First pledge of blithesome May,
   Which children pluck, and, full of pride uphold,
High-hearted buccaneers, o'erjoyed that they
   An Eldorado in the grass have found,
Which not the earth's ample round
   May match in wealth, thou art more dear to me
Than all the prouder summer-blooms may be.

                 — LOWELL.

LEAFLET LIX.

MAPLE TREES IN AUTUMN.*

By ALICE G. McCLOSKEY.

(Compare Leaflets XLVII and XLVIII.)

The hills are bright with maples yet,
    But down the level land
The beech leaves rustle in the wind,
    As dry and brown as sand.
The clouds in bars of rusty red
    Along the hill-tops glow,
And in the still sharp air the frost
    Is like a dream of snow.— ALICE CARY.

THE hills are bright with maples about the time Jack Frost appears, and many people say that he makes the leaves turn red and yellow. Wise folk tell us, however, that Jack Frost is not the artist ; that leaves change to autumn tints when their work is completed.

Boys and girls may not know that leaves "work ;" yet all through the long summer days when you have been playing in the shade of some old maple, the leaves over your head have been very busy. Uncle John says that each leaf is a "starch factory," and this is true. Starch is necessary for plant food and it is manufactured in the leaves. The green leaves and stems are the machinery, which is run by sunlight. Look at a large branch of maple and see how the leaves are arranged to catch every sunbeam. The more light the green parts of the tree get, the more plant food can be made and the sturdier and handsomer the tree.

But the story of the way in which the plant food is made is a long one and not easy for young people to understand. This can come later when you have become familiar with the many interesting things that you learn by watching the tree and by studying with the microscope.

---

* Junior Naturalist Monthly, November, 1903.

If I should to go into your school-room and should ask how many boys and girls know a sugar maple, I suppose every hand would be raised. But if I should ask: "When does the sugar maple blossom?" "What do the blossoms look like?" "When do the winged seeds fall?" I wonder how many could give me satisfactory answers to my questions!

Choose some fine old maple for study. The one that stands near the door will be best, since you can see it every day. Write in a note book all that you can find out about it as the weeks go by.

SUGGESTIONS FOR FALL STUDY.

1. Notice how the leaves turn to the sunlight.

2. Try to find two leaves exactly alike in color, form, size, length of stem, etc. If you succeed send them to Uncle John.

3. How many different tints can you find in a single leaf?

4. As you look at two sugar maple trees, do they seem to be colored alike?

5. Are all sugar maples that you know the same shape?

6. How are the leaves arranged on the branch?

7. Can you find any winged seeds near the tree? If so, plant one in a box of earth and see whether it will grow.

8. If you find any plants growing beneath the maple tree, describe them or tell what they are.

9. Do you know any other kinds of maples? How do you distinguish them?

Child's drawing of a maple leaf. Fifth grade. (Reduced.)

LEAFLET LX.

A CORN STALK.*

By ALICE G. McCLOSKEY.

(Compare Leaflets XLII and XLIII.)

"TOM," said I to a young friend who stood by the window tossing a ten-cent piece into the air, "what plant is used for part of the design on that coin?"

The boy did not answer right away. I do not believe he had ever looked at it closely; yet this is one of the prettiest of our silver pieces. After a few minutes he said, "It is corn, isn't it?"

Hearing a note of surprise in his voice, I told him something about corn-raising in this country. We then decided that it is a good thing to represent corn on one of the United States coins, since it is a source of much of our wealth.

But aside from its value, Indian corn should interest us because it is a wonderful plant. Boys and girls do not know much more about it than does any old black crow. You have watched the farmer plant corn and you like to eat it. Jim Crow has watched the farmer plant corn and he likes to eat it, too. The time has come, however, when you can get ahead of him if you care to; and to get ahead of crows on the corn question is worth the while. Let me tell you how to do it.

1. Secure a kernel of corn, cut it in halves, and note the food inside it. This food was stored in the seed by the parent plant. Uncle John would say that it is the "lunch" that the mother puts up for her children. What must happen before the food can be used by the little plant?

2. Place some moist soil in a tumbler, and put a kernel of

---

*Junior Naturalist Monthly, May, 1903.

corn in it near the side so that you can watch it grow. How soon does the root appear? The leaves? How many leaves come up at one time?

3. Ask your father to give you a small piece of ground in the garden. Plant a few kernels of corn so that you will have some plants of your own to study this summer. Other people's plants are never so interesting as our own.

4. As your corn plants push their way up into the light and air, watch them every day. Notice how the new leaves are protected by the next older ones.

5. Is the stem hollow or solid? In which way would it be stronger?

6. Notice the joints. Are they the same distance apart throughout the length of the stem? Does the distance between the joints always remain the same? Measure them some day; then in a week measure them again.

7. Where does the stalk break most easily?

8. Where does the leaf clasp the stalk?

9. Notice how strong the leaf is. In what direction do the ribs extend? If these long narrow leaves were not strong what would happen to them as they wave back and forth in the wind?

10. Have you ever noticed the ruffled edges of the leaves? As you bend them you will see that the edges do not tear.

11. There are two kinds of blossoms on a corn plant. The ear bears one kind, the tassel the other. If you were to cut all the tassels from the plants in your garden, the kernels would not grow on the ears. Later on you will learn why.

12. Watch the ear closely as it grows.

13. Follow a thread of silk to the place where it is attached. Notice whether there is one silk for each kernel.

14. When the corn is in the milk stage it is preparing to store up food for the young plants. How does it taste at this time?

15. Look closely at the base of the corn stalk and you will see roots extending obliquely into the soil. These are the brace roots. Of what use do you think they are to the corn stalk?

LEAFLET LXI.

IN THE CORN FIELDS.*

By ALICE G. McCLOSKEY.

(Compare Leaflets XLII and XLIII.)

CAW caw!" said Jim Crow as he flew over our heads "Was he jeering at us?" we wondered, the children and I. Perhaps he was inquisitive to know what business we had in the open country and in the fields of corn. Perhaps he was not concerned with us at all. Very likely crows are less concerned with us than we think they are.

Jim Crow flew on out of sight, but we stayed among the ripening corn. The ears were filling out. The ends of the silk were turning brown. We saw many things that we had planned to look for in vacation : the tall stem, the brace roots, the long strong leaves and the way the ribs extend in them, the ruffled edges of the leaves, the two kinds of blossoms, and where each silken thread is attached. The whole story was before us.

Fig. 315.   Over the fields in corn-harvest time.

But this is the harvest time and we are ready to learn a new lesson from the corn fields. As we watch them now let us answer the following questions :

1. How is the corn cut?

---

* Junior Naturalist Monthly, October, 1903.

2. How many ears do you find on a stalk?

3. Are the ears on the same side of the stalk or on opposite sides?

4. Take into the school room as many kinds of corn as you can find and describe each as follows :

   a — The shape and color of the kernel.

   b — Number of rows of kernels.

   c — The number of kernels in each row.

5. Perhaps the girls will pop some corn and bring it to the Junior Naturalist Club meeting. Let them try to pop field corn. Cut kernels in two of field corn and pop-corn, and report whether they differ. Why does pop-corn pop?

6. Make a list of the foods for which corn is used.

7. Why are pumpkins planted among corn?

8. Why not make for your school room some decorations from ears of corn?

LEAFLET LXII.

THE ALFALFA PLANT.*

By L. H. BAILEY and JOHN W. SPENCER.

(Compare Leaflet XXXIV.)

ALL the things that the farmer sells are produced by plants and animals. The animals live on the plants. It is important that we know what some of these plants are.

Some plants are grown for human food. Such are potato, wheat, apple, lettuce. Some are grown only to feed to animals. Such are grasses and clover,—plants that are made into hay.

Hay is the most important crop in New York State. In fact, New York leads all the States in the value of the hay and forage. This value is more than 66 millions of dollars.

Hay is important in New York also because there are so many dairy cattle in the State. There are more than one and one-half millions of dairy cattle in New York. In the value of the milk and butter and cheese, New York also leads all other States.

Fig. 316. Sprig of the alfalfa plant.

* Junior Naturalist Monthly, October, 1904.

489

There are also great numbers of beef cattle, horses, mules, and sheep. All these millions of animals must be supplied with hay in our long cold winters.

Hay is made in New York State from grasses and clover. Suppose we could find some plant that would yield twice as much hay as clover yields, and yet be as nutritious,— you can readily see how valuable such a plant would be to the State. It would be better than a gift of millions of dollars. Such a plant is alfalfa.

Now that you know something about alfalfa in a general way, I want you to know how the plant looks and how it grows. It is not yet very well known even among farmers, but its cultivation is increasing every year. You will probably know where there are fields of it. Sometimes it grows along roadsides as a weed. Last spring Uncle John offered to send a small packet of alfalfa seeds to any Junior Naturalist who wrote for it. He sent about 5,000 packets. But if you do not know the plant or cannot find it, *write at once to Uncle John and he will send you some by mail from the University farm.*

Let us see how many school children in New York State will know what alfalfa is between now and Thanksgiving time. When writing to Uncle John about alfalfa, try to answer as many of the following questions as possible from your own observation :

1. Does the plant remind you of any other plant that you ever saw ? Of what ?

2. How does it grow,— straight up or spreading out on the ground ?

3. How many stalks come from one root ?

4. What are the leaves like ? Mark out the shape with a pencil.

5. What are the flowers like ? Do you know any other flowers of similar shape ? What is the color ?

6. If possible, dig around a plant and describe how the root looks. Does it branch into many fibres, as grass roots or corn roots do ?

UNCLE JOHN'S LETTER ABOUT THE ALFALFA GARDENS.

My Dear Boys and Girls :

Do you know much about the alfalfa plant ? Do you remember that last spring we promised to send a packet of seed to each of you who asked for it ? Did you send your name asking that you be served ? We received the names of several thousand children

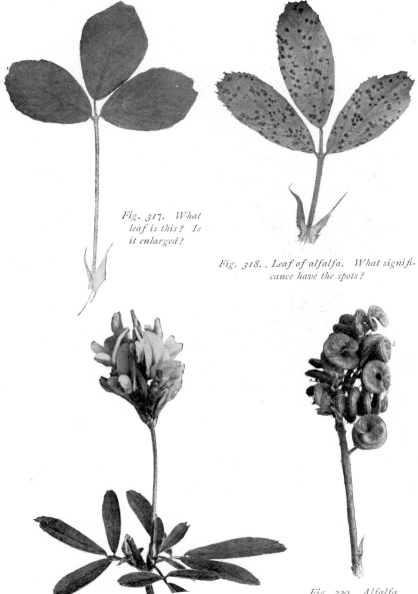

Fig. 317. What leaf is this? Is it enlarged?

Fig. 318. Leaf of alfalfa. What significance have the spots?

Fig. 319. Flowers of the alfalfa. Are they natural size?

Fig. 320. Alfalfa pods. How much enlarged?

asking for seed and I am wondering whether you are one of them. If so, did you sow the seed? Will you write me a letter telling me what became of it?

I am very fond of children's letters. Each year I receive more than thirty thousand of them. I sometimes wonder whether there is another man who is honored by so many letters from young people, for I count it an honor to be so remembered.

As large as that number is, I cannot spare one letter. I always want a few more. All your letters are read and I take great pains to answer all questions. If, by any oversight, you have been missed I am sorry. I know what it costs a boy or girl to write a letter. I never open one without feeling that the writer is a friend of mine, otherwise he would not have expended so much hard work to write it.

Fig. 321. *Crown of the alfalfa plant, showing how root and top start off.*

School has now begun and of course you are very busy, and so is your teacher. One of the best opportunities to write letters is in school. Please ask your teacher whether you may not write me during your language period. You may say that she may make authors of all of you if she can, but I will do all I can to help you become good letter writers. Ask her whether a letter to me may not be a substitute for a composition.

In your letter you may tell me your experience with alfalfa. Tell me your failures as well as your successes. Even though you received your seeds and did not sow them, tell me that. I shall never find fault with you for telling me the truth. If you sowed the seed and the plants did not do well, tell me that also. The plants may look very small and uninteresting to you this year, but next year they may surprise you.

In some parts of the United States the alfalfa crop is of great value and the loss of it would bring distress to many farmers. I am wondering whether the crop, as raised in all parts of our country, is not worth more money than all the gold found in the Klondike, taking the two year by year. I do not know how that may be. I am wondering. Men by the thousand have gone to the gold mines and endured many hardships and later returned with less money than those who had remained at home and took care of their alfalfa.

It may be that a mine of wealth lies very near you, and to get it you may have to ask alfalfa to find it and bring it to you. Gold cannot be found in all places in a gold country and alfalfa may not feel comfortable and grow in all parts of a good farming country. What we asked of you last spring was that you become alfalfa prospectors and later tell us what you found.

JOHN W. SPENCER.

LEAFLET LXIII.

THE RED SQUIRREL.*

BY ALICE G. McCLOSKEY.

(Compare Leaflet XLIX.)

*The squirrel came running down a slanting bough, and as he stopped
twirling a nut, called out rather impudently, " Look here ! just get
a snug-fitting fur coat and a pair of fur
gloves like mine and you may laugh at a north-
east storm." —* THOREAU.

FOR a cheery companion give me
the red squirrel ! I enter the
woods and there the little fellow is, ready to welcome me.
" What a fine day it is for gathering nuts ! " he seems to say,
and straightway, as I listen to
his merry chatter, I think it is a
fine day for any sport that includes him and the brown November woods.

Young naturalists may think it is a difficult thing to become
acquainted with red squirrels, but you will often find them willing to be sociable if you show them a little kindness. I have
many times watched two or three squirrels playing about a friend as
she sat in her garden. They seemed to find her nearly as interesting as the old pine tree near by. They are inquisitive animals.

" How did you tame them ? " I asked.

" I fed them occasionally," she replied. " At first I put some
nuts on the grass several feet away from me. Then I gradually
placed a tempting meal nearer and nearer until the little fellows
seemed to lose all fear of me."

If we care to, you and I, we can learn a great deal about red
squirrels before another year has passed. If you live on a farm
you should know the habits of all the wild creatures about you.

---

*Junior Naturalist Monthly, November, 1903.

You can then be just to them, and decide whether or not you can afford to let them continue to be tenants on your farm. You will find that all of them have interesting lives.

THE RED SQUIRREL.

A. B. C.

Just a tawny glimmer,
   A dash of red and gray,—
Is it a flitting shadow,
   Or a sunbeam gone astray?

Fig. 322. In the haunts of the red squirrel.

It glances up a tree trunk,
 And from some branch, I know
A little spy in ambush
 Is measuring his foe.

I hear his mocking chuckle ;
 In wrath he waxes bold,
And stays his pressing business
 To scold and scold and scold.

QUESTIONS ABOUT THE RED SQUIRREL.

1. What is the color of the red squirrel ? Is he really red ? Is his entire coat of one color ? Does he wear different colors in winter and summer ?

2. Did you ever see a red squirrel's nest ? If so, describe it.

3. Does the red squirrel hibernate ; that is, does he sleep all winter as the chipmunk does ?

4. What does a red squirrel eat ? Did you ever see him getting the winged seeds out of a pitch pine cone ?

5. Do you believe a squirrel ever planted an oak ? Give a reason.

6. If you live in the country, you have seen red squirrels running on the rail fences. Why do they like rail fences ? Do you see them so often on other kinds of fences ?

7. Notice the tracks made in the snow in winter woods. Try to find whether the red squirrel's is among them.

8. If you know any other kinds of squirrels, tell how they differ from the red squirrel.

32

LEAFLET LXIV.

ROBIN.*

By L. H. BAILEY.

HE drifts along the fences are settling. The brooks are brimming full. The open fields are bare. A warm knoll here and there is tinged with green. A smell of earth is in the air. A shadow darts through the apple tree : it is the robin !

Robin ! You and I were lovers when yet my years were few. We roamed the fields and hills together. We explored the brook that ran up into the great dark woods and away over the edge of the world. We knew the old squirrel who lived in the maple tree. We heard the first frog peep. We knew the minnows that lay under the mossy log. We knew how the cowslips bloomed in the lushy swale. We heard the first soft roll of thunder in the liquid April sky.

Robin ! The fields are yonder ! You are my better self. I care not for the birds of paradise ; for whether here or there, I shall listen for your carol in the apple tree.

* * *

Our lesson on robin shall be a lesson out of doors. We shall leave the books behind. We shall see the bird. We shall watch him and make up our minds what he is doing and why. We shall know robin better ; and robin lives in the fields.

Perhaps you think you know robin. Suppose that one of your friends never saw a robin ; do you think you could close your eyes and describe him so that your friend would know how the bird looks ?

Then tell me where robin builds its nest, and of what materials ; and how many eggs are laid and their color ; and how long the mother bird sits ; and how long the fledglings remain in the nest. You can readily find a family of robins in some near-by tree, or perhaps even on the porch ; and you can learn all these things without ever disturbing the birds.

---

* Introduction printed in Junior Naturalist Monthly, March, 1901.

I want you to watch a bird build its nest. You may think that you know how robin builds, but can you really tell me just how the bird carries the mud, and where it finds the other materials, and how long the building operation continues? Do both birds take part in the building?

Then I want to know whether you can tell the difference between father robin and mother robin. Did you ever notice whether robins that come first in the spring have brighter breasts than those that come later? And can you explain?

Tell me, too, what robin does with his year. You know when he comes in spring and when he builds and when the speckled young ones fly. But where is he in summer and fall and winter? And what is he about all this time? Does he build another nest and rear another family, or does he go vacationing? And does he gather the same kind of food in spring and summer? Does he gather cherries for his family or for himself? Did you ever see robin in winter in New York?

What can you tell me about the song of robin? Does he sing all the year? Or does he have a different note for summer? Not one of you can tell how many different notes and calls robin has. I sometimes think that robin knows several languages.

I have seen many more springs than you have seen: and yet I always wait for robin on the lawn. I often wonder whether the same robins come back to my lawn. They seem to go to business at once. They hop with the most confident air, and day after day pull strings out of the ground. You know what these strings are: but do you know how robin finds them? Is it by smell, or sight, or feeling, or hearing? Do you suppose he is listening when he cocks his head to one side and then to the other? Or is he merely making motions? And I wonder whether birds and animals usually make motions just for the sake of making them?

I have asked you many questions, and not one of you can answer. Perhaps I cannot answer. You ask, " What's the use?" If you can see robin, and learn why, you can also learn other things. But I like robin just because he is robin.

There is one thing more. You will read about robin redbreast. Who is he? Find out for me whether robin redbreast of Europe and of English poetry is the same as our American bird.

LEAFLET LXV.

CROWS.*

By ALICE G. McCLOSKEY.

(Compare Leaflet XXIV.)

T a wigwam in the Adirondack Mountains a tame crow lives with a family of Indians. These Indians make baskets of birch bark and other things that they find out of doors, and sell them to visitors who spend their summer in the mountains. The little crow helps in the business. He makes himself so interesting to the passers-by that they stop to watch him. The Indians then have an opportunity to show their baskets, and very often sell them.

But we need not go to the Adirondacks to find a crow that earns his living. Mr. F. E. L. Beal, who has studied crows a long time, speaks of them as valuable farm hands ; and Neltje Blanchan says that they are as much entitled to a share of the corn as the horse that plows it. This may surprise boys and girls who have heard crows spoken of as thieves and rascals. Let us look into their story so that we can find out for ourselves whether to the farmer the crow is a friend or an enemy.

How Jim Crow does harm : —

1. By killing toads, frogs, small snakes, and salamanders ("lizards"). Why are these little creatures first rate farm hands ?

2. By pulling up sprouting corn. Some farmers prevent this by tarring the corn.

3. By stealing eggs, small chickens, and tiny birds. It is said that the crow is rarely guilty of these wrongs. What do you know about it ?

How Jim Crow does good : —

4. By eating large numbers of insects : grasshoppers, caterpillars (including army worms and cut worms), June bugs, and other insects. So many insects does he devour that he earns more than

*Junior Naturalist Monthly, February, 1904.

he destroys. A half bushel of corn scattered on a field is said to be sufficient in many cases to prevent Jim Crow from pulling the growing corn.

To study crows : —

Watch the crows to find out just what they do. Do you ever see them flying in large numbers? If so, at what time of day do they fly? Where are they going? Notice how they use their wings.

Do they come from the same direction each morning? Would it not be a great experience to make up a party and visit the place from which they come? What do you think you would find there?

Fig. 323.   *Who's afraid!*

When you see crows feeding in a field try to learn what they are eating.

You can often find crows' tracks in the snow. There the prints of their feet and wings may be seen. What do you think interested the crows in the snow-covered field?

Determine whether the caw is always the same. Is it sometimes short, sometimes long? Can you associate these differences with the actions of the birds?

I wish you would read John Hay's poem, "The Crows at Washington."

LEAFLET LXVI.

A FRIENDLY LITTLE CHICKADEE.*

By ALICE G. McCLOSKEY.

(Compare Leaflet XXIV.)

This scrap of valor just for play
Fronts the north wind in waistcoat gray.
— EMERSON.

O NE cold December day a chickadee found himself alone in a wood. He looked very much like other chickadees, a small, gray bird, wearing, as someone has said, "a black hood with white side pieces and a black vest." He was like others of his kin, too, in that he was a skillful acrobat. He could stand right side up on a twig or cling to it upside down — one position seemed as easy as the other.

But I am not sure that this little chickadee was like his fellows in one respect. I have wondered whether they are all as friendly as he. I shall tell of something that he did, and leave it to young naturalists to find out whether other chickadees will show as friendly a spirit.

It happened on the cold December day when the chickadee was alone in the "snow-choked wood" that a Senior Naturalist wandered along that way. Whether or no the little bird knew that the tall man was there I cannot say. At any rate, he called out "phœ-be," the plaintive little pipe of two notes, clearer and sweeter than the real phœbe bird can make. The tall man answered the call, whistling two notes as plaintive and sweet as the chickadee's own. Again and again the whistle was repeated and every time it was answered. Nearer and nearer came the fluffy midget, until finally he alighted on a tree directly over the tall man's head.

---

* Junior Naturalist Monthly, December, 1903.

And then a remarkable thing happened! You will scarcely believe it, yet it is true. Knowing how near the chickadee was, the tall man whistled "phœ-be" very softly, and the little bird flew down and rested on his arm. How pleased the Senior Naturalist must have felt when he had gained the confidence of this wild bird! I wish that our boys and girls would try to do the same thing and tell Uncle John whether the experiment is successful.

STUDY OF A CHICKADEE IN WINTER.

1. Keep a sharp lookout for chickadees. Can you tell one when you see it? They are often with nuthatches and downy woodpeckers. If you tie a piece of suet in a tree near your house these winter birds may visit you.

2. Listen to the notes of all the winter birds. Some day you will hear one say "Chick-a-dee-dee-dee-dee." Then he may sing "phœ-be," and you will try to imitate the notes. He may answer you. Tell us how near you can get to one of these friendly little birds.

3. Watch a chickadee searching for his breakfast on a twig. What kind of a bill has he? What do you think he is finding to eat?

4. If I lived on a farm I should have suet hung in my orchard to encourage the chickadees to stay there. Can you tell why?

5. Do you see chickadees in summer? Where are they then?

6. If I were to ask you to find a deserted chickadee's nest, where would you look?

THE FAMILY OF WOODPECKERS.*

By ALICE G. McCLOSKEY.

(Compare Leaflet XXIV.)

I. THE RED-HEADED WOODPECKER.

THE story goes that, once upon a time, a naturalist found a great many grasshoppers wedged into an old fencepost. They were alive but could not get away. Bye and bye their jailor appeared. He was neither somber nor ugly, as you might suppose, but a merry red-headed woodpecker. With never a thought of cruelty in his little red head, he had used the fencepost as a cold-storage place, and had filled it with a good supply of food.

Now I am sure our boys and girls will ask, "Is this story true?" I cannot say. The best way to decide whether it may be true is to study the habits of a red-headed woodpecker. Do you think that we shall find him capable of so clever a trick?

The red-head is not uncommon. Keep on the lookout for him. His head, neck, throat, and upper breast are red ; the rest of his body is blue-black and white. He is a handsome fellow, a bright bit of color in wood, garden, orchard, or field. Let us see what we can learn about him.

SUGGESTIONS.

1. Try to get a nearer view of any bird that you see sitting on a telegraph pole or fencepost. It may be a red-headed woodpecker.

2. Is this little fellow as good a drummer as his relatives?

3. His mate likes his music. If she comes near, the better to hear him drum, notice whether she has a red head.

4. Do you find beech-nuts or other food stored in decayed trees? Under a bit of raised bark? In cracks in bark? In gate posts? If so, a red-head may be about.

* Junior Naturalist Monthly, January, March, April, and May, 1903.

5. These woodpeckers eat more grasshoppers than any of the others. Find out whether they eat them on the ground.

6. Have you ever seen one fly into the air after a passing insect?

Fig. 324.   The red-headed woodpecker.

7. Do red-headed woodpeckers ever visit your chicken yard? Watch them closely and find out why they are there.

8. Do you see them later in the year eating fruit on your farm?

9. It has been found that they eat ants, wasps, beetles, bugs, grasshoppers, crickets, moths, spiders, and caterpillars. If you

find them doing harm on your farm will you not compare it with the good they do ?

10. What plants do they visit ?

11. Where is red-head's nest ?

II. DOWNY WOODPECKER.— A LITTLE ORCHARD INSPECTOR.*

Rap ! rap ! rap ! the little inspector has come to look at our apple trees. "You are welcome, downy woodpecker," say we every one. "Stay as long as you like. We want to look at you closely so that we shall know you every time we see you."

A bird about three inches shorter than a robin, black above, white below, white along the middle of the back, and the male red on the nape of the neck : this is the way downy looks. A hardworking, useful, sociable tenant of the farm : this is what downy is.

Let us see how this little woodpecker is useful. If you live on a farm, you have probably heard of borers — grubs that get into trees and injure them. Your father does not like these grubs, but downy does. He seems to like any kind of grub. Watch him on a tree sometimes when he is looking for one. He knows where to find it, although neither you nor I might suspect that an insect is living beneath the smooth bark. Then he bores into the tree, and spears the grub with his long tongue. His tongue is a remarkable weapon. He can stretch it

Fig. 325. Cocoons of the codlin-moth as they were found attached to a piece of loose bark, natural size.

two inches beyond the tip of his bill, and it is barbed on both sides.

Downy does not stop work, you must remember, when borers are not plenty. Beetles nibble no more plants after his eyes light on them. They are trespassers, and as judge, jury, and execu-

---

*Junior Naturalist Monthly, January, 1903.

tioner, he proves his right to be considered a most useful farm hand. Ants, too, provide him with a good meal occasionally.

Among the helpful deeds of the downy woodpecker, we must not forget to mention that he destroys great numbers of the larvæ or worms of the codlin-moth in winter, when these worms have tucked themselves away in the crevices of the bark, all wrapped in their cocoons. (Figs 325, 326.) Perhaps your father has shown you these little cocoons along the body and in the crotches of the apple tree. If not, you can find them yourself. Open some of them and see whether the worm is still there. If he is not, downy has probably taken him. I suppose you know that the larvæ of the codlin-moth are the worms you find in apples. See Leaflet LIII.

You must not confound the downy woodpecker with that other

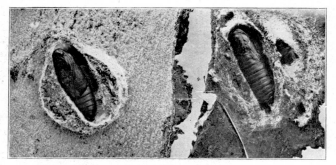

Fig. 326. Pupæ of the codlin-moth in cocoons, enlarged.

woodpecker, the sap-sucker, that often drills rings of holes in the trunks of apple trees. The sapsucker has yellow on his under parts. I shall tell you about him some other time.

You have learned that insects and apple-scab and yourselves all try to see who shall own the apple fruit. Now you know that birds, and insects that feed on leaves and in the wood, are also concerned in this quarrel about the apple.

A FEW THINGS TO OBSERVE.

1. Does the downy woodpecker travel down a tree head first or does he hop backward?

2. Try some day to see his feet. You will find that two of his toes are turned forward and two backward. Are there other birds that have this arrangement of toes?

Fig. 327. The downy woodpecker.

3. Notice that he braces himself with his tail as he works.

4. Do you ever see the downy woodpecker eat seeds of plants that the farmers do not like to have on their land?

5. Hang a bone or piece of unsalted suet out of doors for the woodpeckers. They will enjoy an unexpected feast.

6. Where does downy make his nest?

III. THE SAPSUCKER.*

If you are walking through an orchard or wood and see a jolly little woodpecker with red on its head, do not say at once that it it is a downy woodpecker. Look again. Has it yellow on the underparts, black on the breast, a red throat, and red on the crown instead of on the nape? Then it is a sapsucker, a new arrival. (Fig. 328.) It is larger than the downy. The female has no red on the throat.

And to think that such a merry little fellow has such a bad reputation among farmer-folk! You will be surprised to find how unkindly woodpeckers are treated throughout the country, because of the misdeeds of the sapsucker. Even the downy has suffered much abuse. This is unfortunate, for I am sure downy woodpeckers have done much more good than sapsuckers have done harm.

I wish that all Junior Naturalists would try to find out whether even the sapsucker deserves all that has been said against him. He does harm by boring holes in trees, but how much? Let us learn. As woodpeckers are not shy, it is not difficult to get near them. I have stood within a few feet of a sapsucker, and he did not mind a bit. He kept on boring holes in a tree without a thought that any one might object.

1. How many trees can you find that have holes bored by the sapsucker?

2. How are the holes arranged; here and there on the trunk, or in rings around it? Have you ever found a complete ring of holes?

3. Keep a record of the months in which you find the sapsucker.

4. Notice how the sap runs down into the holes that have been newly made by a sapsucker.

5. It is said that this woodpecker eats the inner bark of the tree as well as the sap. What can you find out about this?

*Junior Naturalist Monthly, March, 1903.

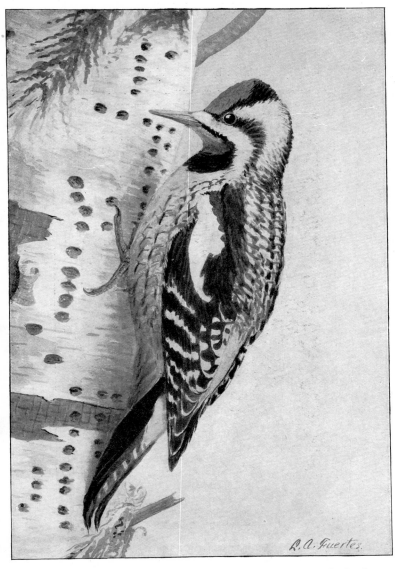

Fig. 328. The sapsucker. Compare this picture with that of the downy woodpecker in Fig. 327.

6. Do you ever find insects near the holes made by the sapsucker? Do you think he eats them?

7. Find out where the sapsucker has his nest.

IV. THE FLICKER.*

Three woodpeckers have been introduced to you in these leaflets : the red-head, the hard working downy (Fig. 327), the sap-

Fig. 329.   The flicker.

sucker (Fig. 328). There is one more that we ought to add to
the list for summer study, since he is very likely to cross our path,
— the flicker (Fig. 329).

---

*Junior Naturalist Monthly, May, 1903.

This woodpecker has a great many names, probably because he lives in a great many States. The most common are : flicker, highhole, yellow-hammer, and golden-winged woodpecker. I like the name flicker best of all.

He is a good-sized bird, about two inches longer than a robin. His colors are : brownish with black spots above, whitish spotted with black underneath, a black crescent on the breast, and a scarlet crescent on the back of the neck. When he flies you will notice two things : the rich golden color of the inside of his wings, and the white patch on the back just above the tail.

Now, since he is a woodpecker, you will probably expect to find the flicker in trees ; but you are quite as likely to find him on the ground. About half of his food consists of ants, and these he finds afield. He also eats other insects, as well as a good deal of plant food.

I hope that you will see a flicker this year and hear him call out, " a-wick-a-wick-a-wick-a-wick-a-wick-a." Possibly some of you may find a nest that these birds have dug out in an old apple tree. They do not always make new nests, however, but live in the deserted homes of other woodpeckers.

QUESTIONS.

1. Has the flicker a straight bill like the downy woodpecker?

2. Have you seen the flicker's mate? If so, in what way does she differ from him in color or marking?

3. Where does the flicker build its nest? What color are the eggs?

4. Try to watch a flicker feeding its young. Describe.

5. Do you know the call of the flicker? Can you imitate it, or write it so that Uncle John can recognize it?

6. Do flickers remain all winter? If not, when do they come? When do they leave?

33

LEAFLET LXVIII.

DESERTED BIRDS'-NESTS.*

By ALICE G. McCLOSKEY.

There is a wagon trail which I like to follow; it is always a pleasant walk. There is no foot path; so I do not think many people pass that way. Perhaps this is why many little wild creatures of the field and wood like to live there. I do not know any other place where the birds sing so sweetly, where the wild flowers grow so thick, and where the insects are so numerous.

By the side of this little vireo's nest which road I found the you see in the picture. It was about five feet from the ground, and hung near the end of a long branch. It was interesting to find out what it was made of, — grasses, strips of bark, hair, pine needles, plant fibres, and bits of paper. On the outside were lichens

Fig. 330. The vireo's nest.

and spiders' webs. The pieces of paper were dropped along the way, I think, by the leader in a cross-country run. Even the little vireos have an interest in the outdoor sports of the college men.

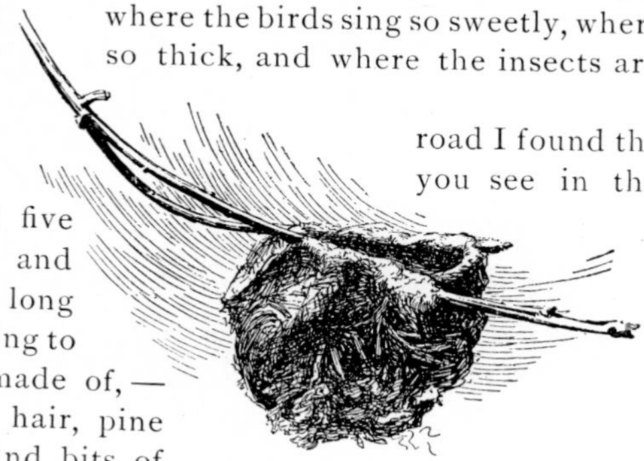

One of the most interesting bird homes is the oriole's nest. Uncle John will like to know whether you find one. The young orioles must have happy times in their cradle, which hangs between the earth and the sky.

Winter is the best time of year to hunt for birds' nests. It is hard to find them in the spring and the summer. The parent birds intend it shall be. If you succeed in getting a nest, take it into the school room so that the other members of your club can study it with you.

SUGGESTIONS.

Where did you find the nest? What is its size and shape? Name it, if you can.

---

* Junior Naturalist Monthly, February, 1901.

Was it built on the horizontal crotch of the branch, or on an upright crotch?

How was it fastened to the branch?

Notice the materials of which it is made.

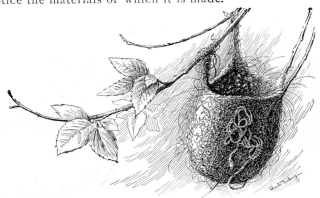

Fig. 331.   The hanging nest of the oriole.   A cord is woven into the nest.

In the oriole's nest you will see that there is a difference in the way in which the upper and lower parts are made.   What is it?

How deep is the oriole's nest which you find?   Compare the material on the outside with that on the inside.

How is the nest fastened to the twigs?

Where does a catbird build its nest?   Robin?   Bluebird? Swallow?   Hen?   Turkey?

What?

LEAFLET LXIX.

THE POULTRY YARD: SOME THANKSGIVING LESSONS.*

By ALICE G. McCLOSKEY and JAMES E. RICE.

ROSY–CHEEKED girl, a freckled-faced boy and a little bald-headed baby were the only young persons at the Thanksgiving dinner. The baby was not old enough to be invited, but we were so thankful to have her with us that we could not resist drawing her chair up to the table.

The turkey was a big one and "done to a turn." We old folks thought so, the freckled-faced boy thought so, and the rosy-cheeked girl thought so. The baby, so far as I could judge, thought not at all. She chewed energetically on a spoon and left the discussion of the turkey to her elders.

Having known for a long time that children like to chatter, I decided that I would give the little lad and lassie opposite me an opportunity to talk about turkeys, ducks, chickens, and the like. "These," thought I, "are good Thanksgiving topics, and a boy and girl who have lived on a farm all their lives can tell me some interesting things about them."

But this world is full of many strange surprises! It was not long before I learned that those little folk could not answer some very simple questions about poultry. They did not even know why a chicken does not fall off the roost when it sleeps. To be sure, they could tell the exact moment when, in the process of carving, the wish-bone would appear: but you will admit that this is very little. I certainly was disappointed. The bald-headed baby cheered things up a bit, however, by crowing lustily. I rejoiced in the fact that apparently she had heard sounds from the barn-yard.

Now there are many reasons why children, Junior Naturalists especially, should know something about poultry. It may be that

* Extended from Junior Naturalist Monthly, November, 1902.

you live on a farm and will want to raise chickens, ducks, and turkeys some day ; and the farmer who knows his poultry best will be most successful in raising it. But whether you live in country or city you will like to study these interesting birds. Let us see what we can find out about them in the next three or four weeks. November, the month of Thanksgiving, is a good time to begin.

TURKEYS.

Let us first pay our respects to the king of the poultry yard. We may never know His Royal Highness, the old gobbler, very well, because it is said he will not often permit folks to meet him on his own ground. I am told that a visitor is more sure of a welcome within his domain if he wear sombre garb. Although gaily dressed himself the old fellow objects to bright colors on others.

There is one thing that we can do if the gobbler does not let us near him,— we can peek at him through the fence. Then, too, at Thanksgiving time many a slain monarch will hang in a nearby market. Following are a few suggestions that will help us to learn something about turkeys. I hope that you know all these things now, and, therefore, will not need to be asked. If you do, please write Uncle John. How many letters do you think he will get from such persons ?

In the study of any bird, learn to describe it fully : the size, the shape, the bill, the length of legs, the feet, and the color. Is there more than one color of turkey ?

Observe the head, face and wattles of the turkey gobbler.

Notice the strong, curved beak ; the bright, clear, hazel eyes.

How many colors does he wear ?

When the turkey is being prepared for the Thanksgiving dinner, ask mother for the foot. Are there any feathers on it ? Has it the same number of toes that you find on a rooster's foot ? Is the arrangement of the toes the same ?

Perhaps you find scales on the legs of the turkey. Do you find them also on hens' legs ? On which side of the leg, — front or back — are the scales the larger ?

When I was a little girl I liked to pull a tendon that I found in the turkey's foot after it had been cut off. It was amusing to see the toes curl up. I did not know then that when birds roost at night this tendon is stretched as they bend their legs. Then the toes grasp the perch and hold the bird on. When it stretches its leg to leave the roost the toes spread out, but not until then Because of this birds can go to sleep without the least fear of falling. What kind of perch do they choose, a wide one or a narrow one ? Why ?

Can you tell which is the hen turkey and which the gobbler ? Explain. On which one do you find a hairy tuft on the breast ?

Did you ever hear of the caruncle on the head of the turkey ? Compare this with the comb in domestic fowls. Does it differ in shape ? Do ducks and geese have combs ?

What is the color of the turkey's face ? Does it change color ?

Fig. 332. A turkey likes to roam through the fields.

Do you notice any difference in color when the turkey is angry ? What are the turkey's wattles ?

Notice the fourth toe. Why is it placed in opposite direction to the others ? I wonder whether it enables the fowl to grip the perch ; and whether it gives the turkey a wide span for support in running over loose brush.

Turkeys and chickens and other animals have habits, as boys and girls do, only that they are not bad habits. Did you ever watch turkeys hunting grasshoppers ? And did they go in flocks or alone ? How do chickens hunt,— in flocks or alone ? Which

roams farther from home, turkeys or chickens? Do turkeys lay
their eggs in the barn or poultry house, as chickens do? Did you
ever see a turkey's nest, and where was it?

We have Junior Naturalists in many parts of the world: England, Scotland, Australia, Egypt. Will they have an opportunity
to study turkeys? See what you can find out in answer to this
question.

A TIME-HONORED RACE — GEESE.

Geese, as you know, come of a very distinguished race. This is
no advantage to them in a social way in the poultry yard, however.
There is not a duck nor a turkey nor even a wise rooster, that
knows or cares whether in times gone by geese saved a Roman
city, or whether they were recognized in ancient Egypt.

Fig. 333.   Geese ; " a very distinguished race."

The story of the old gray goose was the one I liked best long
ago,— the goose that died before Aunt Nabby had enough feathers
to make a bed. How often you and I have listened to mother
sing about her! And what an inconsiderate old gray goose we
thought she was, to die before the feather bed was finished.

Some things for Junior Naturalists to think about come into my
mind in connection with Aunt Nabby's goose and others of its
kind :

Why do goose feathers make the best beds?

Do you think an old grandmother goose would give enough

feathers in her lifetime to make a good bed ? I have heard of one that lived sixty years.

Are feathers ever taken from live geese for beds?

Compare the feathers of land-fowls and water-fowls.

Probably one or more of our Junior Naturalists will have a goose for his Thanksgiving dinner. If so, I wish that the wing feathers might be brought to school. See whether you can find out why the wing feathers of a goose were preferred for making quill pens. Make a pen if you can and write a letter to Uncle John with it. The five outer wing feathers are most useful for writing, and of these the second and third are best. Why ? Do

Fig. 334. A happy family.

you think that the Declaration of Independence was signed with a quill pen? Do goose quills make good holders for artists' brushes?

What kind of food do geese like best ?

Is the tongue of a goose similar to that of a turkey or chicken ?

Is the old gander as cross as the turkey gobbler ?

Have you ever seen a flock of wild geese flying northward or southward ? Which way are they going in the fall ? Observe that nearly always they keep their V-shaped ranks unbroken. There is, of course, a leader whose call the flock follows. Whether the leader is some chosen member of the number or whether he takes his position by chance I do not know. What time of day do the wild geese fly ? Do you like to hear them honking as they go on their way? I wish you would find out whether our farmyard geese are only these common wild geese tamed.

CHICKENS AND DUCKS; AND THE STORY OF TWO MOTHER HENS.

One mother hen had her own brood of fluffy little chicks (Fig. 334). When they were old enough they scratched for worms and ate gravel as obediently as any one could desire. How happy they were underneath the hemlocks in the long afternoons!

The other mother hen had to take care of ducks (Fig. 335). Pretty as any chicks they were, but troublesome as only little ducks can

Fig. 335.   Mother hen amd baby ducks.

be with a nervous old hen for their adopted mother. The family in the picture looks very contented. Do you suppose that the photographer told them to look pleasant? When we come to know ducks and chickens better, we shall learn why the little ducks are often such a trial to the hen mother.

It may be that when we ask boys and girls to study chickens and ducks they will say that there is nothing new to learn about them. I am not so sure. The freckled-faced boy thought he knew all about them, too. Let us see whether we can suggest some new things to think about, as you look over the fence into the poultry yard, or watch the cook preparing a hen or duck for the Thanksgiving dinner.

As I looked at the chickens in a barn-yard the other day, I was interested in the different kinds that I saw : some brown, some white, some black, some speckled ; some had feathers on their feet, others had not ; some had combs with many points, in others the comb was close to the head ; some had long tails, some short tails, some no tails at all to speak of. If I were to name the differences that I noticed you would not get through reading them in time to write your November dues. How many unlike marks or characters can you find in chickens or ducks ?

Have you ever seen two chickens or two ducks exactly alike ?

Compare the feet of a hen and a duck. Their bills. Do you think that a duck can scratch for worms ?

What do ducks eat ? What kind of food do hens like best ?

How do a hen's feathers differ from a duck's ?

Note the scales on a hen's foot. Snakes have scales on their bodies, too. Some day you may learn a wonderful story that these similar features of hen and snake suggest.

Touch a hen's eye lightly with a pencil. Does she cover it with a thin eyelid ? A turtle does this. Has a turtle scales also ? If so, may be it will come into the wonderful story connected with hens and snakes.

Look closely at a hen's ear.

Watch chickens as they make their toilet. A farmer told me that among the tail feathers of barn-fowls there is an oil sac that they find useful in cleaning their clothes. I wonder whether this is true ?

While I was watching some chickens the other day, I saw one jump up into the air several times. She was a skillful little acrobat. What do you think she was trying to catch ?

Watch the cook as she prepares a chicken or turkey for dinner. Find the crop into which the food passes after it has been swallowed. From the crop it passes on to the gizzard. Look closely at the gizzard. See what strong muscles it has. It needs them to grind the grain and gravel stones together. It is a very good mill, you see.

Try to find out whether a duck has a crop and a gizzard. Do not ask any one. Wait until there is to be a duck for dinner some day. Would you suppose from the kind of food ducks eat that they need a crop and a gizzard ?

Do little chickens have feathers when they are hatched? What is the cover of their bodies called? Are they always of the same color when they are hatched that they are when they are grown up? What kinds of poultry change their color when their feathers grow? Notice the chickens of Black Minorcas (if you know any one who has that kind), then write Uncle John about their color. Did you ever see fowls without feathers? When you go to the fair be sure to look for some "Silkies." Did you ever see fowls whose feathers were all crinkled up toward their head? Look for "Frizzles" when you go to the fair.

A LESSON ON EGGS.

What is the color of the turkey's egg? Do the first-laid turkey's eggs differ in color from those that are laid later? How do these

Fig. 336.   A coop of chickens.

eggs differ in color from the eggs of ducks, geese, and hens? Do eggs from different breeds of hens differ in color? Do eggs from different kinds of poultry differ in shape? Can you not make some drawings of eggs showing how they differ, and send to Uncle John? Not one of you can tell how much a turkey's egg weighs, nor a hen's egg. Do you think that eggs from all kinds of hens weigh the same? And if they do not, do you think that they are worth the same price the dozen?

Did you ever look through an egg at a strong light? What did you see? Was there an air space? Was it on the big end or the little end ?   Leave the eggs in a dry room for a few days.   Does the air space increase in size ?   Boil an egg.   Remove the shell carefully over the air space.   Do you notice a membrane ?   Are there two membranes ?   Boil an egg until it is very hard ; does the white of the egg separate in layers ?   Break the yoke carefully ; do you notice layers of light and dark color ?   Is there a little soft light colored spot in the centre ?   Write to Uncle John and ask him what this is.

Some Questions in General.

How many varieties of fowls can you name ?   How do they differ in size and color ?

Fig. 337.   What kind of hens are these?

Have you ever seen ducks, geese, hens, and turkeys standing on the snow or ice ?   If so, how did they behave ?   Which seemed to enjoy it ?   Why should a duck or goose be able to swim in ice water without apparently suffering from cold ?   When mother dresses a duck or goose for dinner, ask her to let you see the layers of fat under the skin and inside the body.   Write to Uncle John and tell him what the fat in the body is for.   Ask him how this fat came in the body ; also whether there is such a thing as fat in the food which the ducks eat.

Did you ever see hens and ducks out in the rain ?   Did they all enjoy it? Did you ever see anything wetter than a wet hen? Why do they look so disconsolate?

Examine the feathers of different kinds of poultry. How do the feathers of ducks, geese, turkeys and fowls differ? Try wetting the various feathers, then let them dry out. Make drawings of these feathers, showing, if you can, the different colors and shapes.

Do turkeys think? Did you ever watch a turkey steal her nest? Where did she go? How long did you watch her before you found the nest? Did she cover up her eggs? With what? Why do they cover the eggs when they leave the nest? Do ducks, geese, turkeys, and hens all cover their eggs? Why do hens differ in this respect from the turkeys? Do all kinds of ducks cover their eggs?

Did you ever watch ducklings and little chickens eat? Did you notice any difference in their appetites? Which grow faster, little chickens or little ducks?

Do you know that some hens do not pay their board? Sometimes hens eat more than they are worth. It may be the fault of the hen or it may be that she is not provided with the proper kind of food or given the proper care. A hen cannot make eggs unless she has the proper kind of food. Some persons so feed and handle their hens that they are able to produce eggs for six cents the dozen; other persons expend more than a dollar to get the dozen.

How does the farmer make his money from fowls (that is, what kind of products does he sell)?

You should learn to classify chickens according to the uses for which they are grown. (1) Some kinds of hens excel in egg-laying. These kinds are known as the "egg breeds." One of the leading egg breeds is the Leghorn. (2) Others produce much meat, and are known as the "meat breeds," as the Brahma. (3) Others are fairly good fowls for both eggs and meat, and are called "general-purpose breeds", of which Plymouth Rock and Wyandotte are good examples. (4) Then there are "fancy breeds," grown as pets or curiosities or as game birds. Now, try to find out whether there are any general differences in form and looks to distinguish one class of breeds from another. And find out whether turkeys, geese, and ducks may be similarly classified.

HOW FRANK AND HENRY RAISED CHICKENS.

Frank and Henry wanted to keep chickens all by themselves. They thought they might sell the eggs and the fowls and get spending money. They knew little about chickens, but then, it did not matter, for chickens will take care of themselves. All there is to do is to give them corn and water every day,—at least, so the boys thought.

Both boys had a hard time the first year, but they kept at it. Frank finally made a success. Henry lost money ; his hens died or did not lay, and he had to give up. One boy turned out to be a good farmer and the other a poor farmer. You have seen such farmers living side by side.

I will tell you why Frank succeeded. 1. He provided warm and pleasant quarters for the chickens, so that the fowls were comfortable and contented. 2. He learned to like the chickens, so that he spent many of his extra hours watching them and caring for them. 3. He learned that something more is required in feeding a hen than merely to satisfy her appetite. Some kinds of food may be best for growing chicks and others for laying hens. 4. He soon found that some hens lay more and larger eggs than others, and he saved eggs from these hens for hatching. Henry said that "eggs are eggs" and that there was "no sense in being so fussy." 5. He learned that eggs and poultry sell best when they really are best and when they are carefully cleaned and neatly packed. Frank had learned the first lessons in good farming.

Fig. 338. At the drinking fountain.

LITTLE HERMIT BROTHER.*

By ANNA BOTSFORD COMSTOCK.

IN far Thibet exists a class of Buddhist monks who are hermits and who dwell in caves. I was told about these strange people by a Senior Naturalist, who has spent his life going around the world and finding the countries upon it as easily as you Junior Naturalists find the same countries on the globe in the schoolroom. A real naturalist is never contented with maps of places and pictures of things, but always desires to see the places and things themselves.

The Senior Naturalist told me that he found Thibet a dreary land inhabited by queer people ; and the hermit monks were the queerest of all. Each one dwelt in his solitary cave, ate very little, and worked not at all, but spent his time in thought. Could we read his thoughts we should be none the wiser, since they are only mysterious thoughts about mysterious things.

Now it is a surprising fact that we have hermits of similar habits here in America ; only our hermits are little people who dress in a white garb and live in cells underground ; they also eat little and work not at all, and probably meditate upon mysteries. However, they are equipped with six legs while the monks of Thibet have only two, a difference of little importance since neither hermit travels far from his cave.

*   *   *

There are in eight or nine counties in New York State places that may surely expect visitors on certain years. The connection between these guests and the hermits of Thibet may not seem very close at first sight ; but wait and see.

The reason why these New York counties expect company is that they entertained a large number of similar guests in 1882,

---

* Nature-Study Quarterly, June, 1899.

1865, 1848, 1831, 1814, in 1797, and probably at intervals of seventeen years long before that; in 1797, however, was the first record made of the appearance of these visitors. Every time they came they probably outstayed their welcome; yet they had the good quality of allowing their hosts sixteen years of rest between visits.

In order that the Junior Naturalist may recognize these visitors I will describe their methods of arrival. Sometime in the latter part of May or in early June you may hear a great buzzing in some trees, as if there were a thousand liliputian buzz saws going at once. If you examine the trees you will find on them many queer-looking insects, with black bodies about an inch long, covered with transparent wings folded like a roof. Naturally you will wonder how such great numbers of large insects could appear one day when they were nowhere to be seen the day before. But if you look at the ground beneath the trees you will find in it many small holes. You will also find clinging to the trees many whitish objects, which at first sight seem like pale, wingless insects, but which on closer examination prove to be merely the cast skins of insects (Fig. 339). These are the cowls and robes which our little American hermits cast off after they come out of their underground cells, and which they must shed before they can free their wings. Our little American hermits we call the seventeen-year locusts. However, this name is a most confusing one, since we also call our grasshoppers locusts, and to them the name truly belongs. These seventeen-year locusts are really cicadas, and they belong to a different order from the locusts. The real locusts have mouth-parts formed for biting, while the cicadas have mouth-parts grown together in the form of a tube, through which they suck juices of plants. So we hope the Junior Naturalists will call our little hermits by their right name, cicadas; and will not permit them to be spoken of as locusts.

In order that you may know the mysterious lives of these wonderful insects, I will tell you the story of one of them.

THE STORY OF LITTLE HERMIT BROTHER, CICADA SEPTENDECIM.

Once a cicada mother made with her ovipositor a little slit or cavity in an oak twig, and in this slit placed in very neat order two rows of eggs. Six weeks later there hatched from one of these eggs a pale, lively little creature, that to the naked eye looked like a tiny white ant. If, however, we could have examined him through a lens we should have found him very different from an ant ; for his two front legs were shaped somewhat like lobsters' big claws, and instead of jaws like an ant, he had simply a long beak that was hollow like a tube. After he came out of his egg he ran about the tree and seemed interested for a time in every-thing he saw. Then, suddenly, he went to the side of a limb and deliberately fell off. To his little eyes the ground below was invisible ; so our small cicada showed great faith when he practi-cally jumped off the edge of his world into space. He was such a speck of a creature that the breeze took him and lifted him gently down, as if he were the petal of a flower ; and he alighted on the earth unhurt and probably much delighted with his sail through the air. At once he commenced hunting for some little crevice in the earth ; and when he found it he went to the bottom of it and with his shovel-like fore-feet began digging downward. I wonder if he stopped to give a last look at sky, sunshine, and the beauti-ful green world before he bade them good-bye for seventeen long years ! If so, he did it hurriedly, for he was intent upon reaching something to eat. This he finally found a short distance below the surface of the ground, in the shape of a juicy rootlet of the great tree above. Into this he inserted his beak and began to take the sap as we take lemonade through a straw. He made a little cell around himself and then he found existence quite blissful. He ate very little and grew very slowly, and there was no perceptible change in him for about a year ; then he shed his skin for the first time, and thus, insect-wise, grew larger. After a time he dug another cell near another rootlet deeper in the ground ; but he never exerted himself more than was necessary to obtain the little food that he needed. This idle life he found entirely satisfactory, and the days grew into months and the months into years. Only six times in the seventeen years did our hermit change his clothes, and this was each time a necessity, since they had become too small. Judging from what the Senior Naturalist told me, I think this is six times more than a Thibetan hermit changes his clothes in the same length of time.

What may be the meditations of a little hermit cicada during all these years we cannot even imagine. If any of the Junior Naturalists ever find out the secret they will be very popular indeed with the scientific men called psychologists. However, if we may judge by actions, the sixteenth summer after our hermit buried himself he began to feel stirring in his bosom aspirations

toward a higher life. He surely had no memory of the beautiful
world he had abandoned in his babyhood; but he became suddenly possessed with a desire to climb upward, and began digging
his way toward the light. It might be a long journey through the
hard earth; for during the many years he may have reached the
depth of nearly two feet. He is now as industrious as he was
shiftless before; and it takes him only a few weeks to climb out of
the depths into which he had fallen through nearly seventeen
years of inertia. If it should chance that he reaches the surface
of the ground before he is ready to enjoy life, he hits upon a device
for continuing his way upward without danger to himself. Sometimes his fellows have been known to crawl out of their burrows
and seek safety under logs and sticks until the time came to gain
their wings. But this is a very dangerous proceeding, since in
forests there are many watchful eyes which belong to creatures who
are very fond of bits of soft, white meat. So our cicada, still a
hermit, may build him a tall cell out of mud above ground. How
he builds this " hut," " cone," or " turret " as it is variously called,
we do not know; but it is often two inches in height, and he keeps
himself in the top of it. Under ordinary circumstances our cicada
would not build a hut, but remain in his burrow.

Finally there comes a fateful evening when, as soon as the sun
has set, he claws his way through the top of his mud turret or out
of his burrow and looks about him for further means of gratifying
his ambitions to climb. A bush, a tree, the highest thing within
his range of vision, attracts his attention and he hurries toward it.
It may be he finds himself in company with many of his kind
hurrying toward the same goal, but they are of no interest to him
as yet. Like the youth in the famous poem, "Excelsior" is his
motto and he heeds no invitation to tarry. When he reaches the
highest place within his ken he places himself, probably back
downward, on some branch or twig, takes a firm hold with all
his six pairs of claws, and keeps very still for a time. Then his
skeleton nymph-skin breaks open at the back and there pushes
out of it a strange creature long and white, except for two black
spots upon its back; on he comes until only the tip of his body
remains in the old nymph-skin; then he reaches forward and
grasps the twig with his soft new legs and pulls himself entirely
clear from the old hermit garb. At once his wings begin to grow;
at first they are mere pads on his back, but they soon expand
until they cover his body and are flat like those of a miller. The

many veins in the wings are white and he keeps the wings fluttering in order that they may harden soon. If, in the moonlight of some June evening, a Junior Naturalist should see a tree covered with cicadas at this stage he would think it had suddenly blossomed into beautiful, white, fluttering flowers.

As the night wears on, the color of our hero changes and his wings harden; until when the sun rises we behold him in the glory of a black uniform with facings of orange and with beautiful glassy wings folded roof-like above his body. (Fig. 339.) Great is the change wrought in his appearance during this one marvelous night, and greater still the change wrought in his habits! He is now no longer a hermit; there are thousands of his kind about him, a fact which he realizes with great joy.

Fig. 339. *The cicada is full grown at last, and his empty nymph skin is hanging to a branch.*

So happy is he that he feels as if he must burst if he does not find some adequate means for expressing his happiness in this beautiful world of sunshine. Then suddenly he finds in himself the means of expression and bursts into song. Yet, it is not a song exactly, for he is a drummer rather than a singer. On his body just behind each of his hind wings is a kettle drum. The head to this drum

Fig. 340.
The cicada's drum.

is of parchment thrown into folds and may be seen with a lens if you lift his wings and look closely. (Fig. 340.) Instead of drum sticks he uses a pair of strong muscles to throw the membranes into vibration and there is a complex arrangement of cavities and sounding boards around these drum heads so that the noise he gives off is a great one indeed for a fellow of his size. So fond is he of making music that he has no time to eat or to do aught else but to sound fanfares all the sunshiny day. He is not the only musician on the tree ; there are many others and they all join in a swelling chorus that has been described as a roar like that made by the "rushing of a strong wind through the trees."

If our cicada could talk to one of you Junior Naturalists he would tell you that there was a good reason for all this music. He would explain that only the men of the cicada world possess drums and that the object and reason of all their music is the entertainment of the lady cicadas, who are not only very fond of this drumming, but are good critics of cicada music as well. He would perhaps tell you also that he had his eye on a certain graceful maiden perched on the leaf between him and the sun ; but she, on the other hand, seemed to give about equal attention to him and three other drummers situated near by. Excited by the competition and by her indifference, he rattled his drum faster and faster until he rose to the heights of cicada melody and harmony that left his rivals far behind. Then the lady of his choice listened spellbound and pronounced him the greatest of all musicians, and thus he won his bride. However, we may safely predict that their wedded life will be too full of happiness to last. After a few weeks the sunshine, the music, the happiness of wooing and winning will prove too much for our hero and one day he will beat his drum in a last mad ecstacy and fall to earth and die from happy exhaustion. His little wife may survive him only long enough to cut slits in some of the twigs of the home tree and place in them rows of eggs from which shall develop a family of hermits which shall come forth and fill the world with their music seventeen years hence.

*   *   *

There are many broods of cicadas in the United States, so that they appear in different localities in different years. New York State has five well-marked broods.

There are several other species of cicada peculiar to America. One is called *Cicada tredecim*, since it appears every thirteen years. However, this species is limited to the South.

The dog-day harvest fly, or lyreman, is the cicada that is best known to us through the northern and middle States. This appears in small numbers every year and is a distinct addition to the summer chorus of insect singers. He is larger and much more dignified in appearance than is his cousin *septendecim*. He wears a black suit embroidered with scrolls of dark olive green and the whole lower surface of his body is covered with white powder. His drums are situated above plates which may be seen on the lower side of the body, one behind each hind leg. He hides in trees and his shrill music is so associated with the heat of summer noons that the sound itself makes one drowsy. The hermit life of the lyreman in underground cells is supposed to last only two years.

While the cicadas of which we have spoken are the children of an ancient race which inhabits America, Europe also has her ancient races of cicadas, although they are not the kind which live hermit lives for seventeen years. We have evidence that their music was held in high esteem by the ancient races of men — especially the Greeks. When Homer complimented his orators he compared them with cicadas. Thus it may lend a special interest to the study of the cicada by our Junior Naturalists when they know that his kettle drums have been celebrated instruments of music by poets who wrote three thousand years before America was discovered by Columbus.

QUERIES FOR SHARP EYES.

1. When did you first see one of the cicadas?

2. What was it doing when you found it?

3. Did it do anything to attract your notice to it, or did you find it by accident?

4. Where did you find it?

5. See whether you can determine which are the father and which the mother cicadas.

6. Try to find where a mother cicada has laid eggs.

7. If you find where the cicada emerged from the ground, or from a hut, give a brief description of the location, as to kind of soil, etc.

8. Where did you find the most of the cast-off nymph skins?

9. Did you discover animals or birds feeding upon the cicada?

LEAFLET LXXI.

A HOME FOR FRIENDLY LITTLE NEIGHBORS.*

By ALICE G. McCLOSKEY.

(Compare Leaflet XVII.)

AST year when vacation days were over our young people found it hard to leave the acquaintances that they had made during the summer,—the garden-folk, the roadside-folk, and the wood-folk. Let us take them indoors with us this year. It will not be difficult to provide a home for some of the more friendly ones and they will help to make the schoolroom a cheerful place. How pleasant it will be in the long afternoons to hear the cricket's merry tune or see the flutter of a butterfly's wings! The quiet woods and the green fields will then seem nearer and we shall feel a little touch of their mystery and beauty.

It is not necessary to have a fine home for the outdoor-folk. They will not object if it is not an up-to-date dwelling. Fig. 341 illustrates a very convenient terrarium, as the home is called. The sides and top are covered with fine wire screening and the front is glass. By raising the cover, which is fastened to one side by means of hinges, new visitors can be admitted easily.

Another terrarium is shown in Fig. 126, page 208. This is made from an old berry crate. It does not look quite so well as the other, but, as I said before, the inmates will not mind a bit. The toads will give their high jump as gracefully and the crickets fiddle as merrily as in the finer one.

When the terrarium is ready to furnish, you can have some nature-study trips in search of materials for it. Cover the floor with stones and place about three inches of good soil over them. Then you will be ready to select the carpet. Let this be of soft green moss, the prettiest bits that you can find on the forest floor.

---

*Junior Naturalist Monthly, October, 1902.

Fig. 341.   A shower for the little neighbors.

Leave one corner free for sods on which tall grasses grow, so that there will be a cozy nook for the orchestra (crickets, grasshoppers, katydids, and the like). What a fine concert there will be ! Will the most conceited toad in the terrarium ever dare to raise his voice in song again after hearing it ? Perhaps next spring we shall know.

Even before the home is completed, you can gather your small guests about you. Temporary lodgings can be provided without much trouble. Fig. 342 illustrates a good insect cage, and a box containing da__p moss and covered with mosquito netting will make fairly comfortable quarters for salamanders ("lizards") and toads.

The first visitor that you welcome will probably be a little woolly-bear, a brown and black caterpillar that you see so often in your autumn walks (Fig. 343). He is one of my favorite insect friends, and I really like to have him snuggle up in a furry ball in my hand. You will find woolly-bear a very restless little creature. You never know what he is going to do next. He may spin a cocoon this fall or "he may curl up like a woodchuck," as Uncle John says, and sleep until spring. Then, if all goes well, he will spin his cocoon and come out an Isabella tiger-moth (Fig. 344). No matter how fast woolly-bear may be hurrying along the highway when you meet him, put him into the terrarium, for you will find that he is a most entertaining little fellow.

If you have an insect net, sweep it among shrubs and weeds. I am hoping that when you look into it you will find "golden-eyes" or the lace-winged-fly. When you see the pretty little green creature you will wonder that her children can be called aphis-lions, for they are not at all like their mother (Fig. 345) ; but when you have watched them among the aphids or plant-lice, you will understand how they have earned their name. They have very long jaws and very large appetites.

No one knows better than golden-eyes what her children are capable of doing when on a foraging tour. For this reason she places her eggs high on silken stalks (Fig. 345). If she laid them on the leaf close together, the first aphis-lion hatched would not give the other members of his family a chance to open their eyes, nor to know how pleasant it is to live on a green leaf. As it is he walks down the silken stalk and finds himself among the aphids. Then, when he has proved himself the gardener's friend by devouring a great many of the small green insects, he spins a pearly white cocoon and out of this comes a lace-winged-fly with glistening golden eyes. If one of these dainty creatures comes to live in your terrarium, you may notice some day that it has a disagreeable odor. This is a characteristic that many insects possess, and owing to it the birds do not like to eat them.

There is another insect out in the garden that ought to be an inmate of every terrarium this fall, the green cabbage-worm. Some Junior gardeners will object to calling this a friendly little neighbor, but you will find that he will teach you many new things, in this way proving himself friendly to you as a naturalist. You must remember that these green caterpillars did not know that you had planted the garden in which they worked destruction. They did not know that you wanted to send the very best cabbage to the State fair. They knew only that when they opened their eyes they were on a green leaf and it was good to eat.

Fig. 342. An insect cage.

Probably you will find the eggs of the cabbage butterfly on the under side of the leaves. Then you can feed the young caterpillars when they hatch. They will, of course, prefer cabbage leaves. If you miss them some day, search in the terrarium for the chrysalids into which they have changed. These chrysalids sometimes imitate the color of the support from which they hang, and you may have difficulty in finding them. For this reason it may be well to keep one of the caterpillars under a lamp chimney, the top of which has been covered with mosquito netting (Fig. 342), so that you may know how the chrysalids look.

The cabbage butterflies are familiar to most boys and girls ; yet as they come out of the chrysalid state in your terrarium, you will be able to observe them more closely. Notice that the wings are dull white on the upper sides, while on the under side the apex of the fore wings and the entire surface of the hind wings are pale lemon yellow. In the female you will find that there are two black spots besides the tip on each of the fore wings, and in the male there is but one.

Now that I have put you in the way to find a few members of the insect world for your terrarium, I am going to ask you to think about some other outdoor-folk that naturalists learn to like.

Have you ever turned over stones or broken off pieces of an old stump in the woods or along the bank of a stream? If so, you may have seen salamanders ("lizards") making their escape as quickly as possible. If you can get a few for your terrarium you will learn to like them, for they are harmless and have very interesting ways. Do not catch them by their tails as they try to get away, or you may find that you have captured the tails but lost the salamanders.

Let the excursion in search of these little fellows be one of the jolliest of the year. You will find them in moist places and should therefore, carry a box containing damp moss to put them in.

Fig. 343. Woolly-bear, natural size.

I would suggest that you take two boxes along, one for the smaller salamanders, the other for their larger brothers. Why? I will tell you.

It happened this summer that a party of little folks went out with me on a salamander hunt. We found three kinds: the *Spotted Salamander*, which is black with yellow spots on each side of the back; the *Red-back Salamander*, which usually has a reddish brown band along the back; and a black one covered with whitish spots. This black one with whitish spots was named "Freckles" by one of our number, a much more attractive name than his own, which is *Pleth'-o-don glu-ti-no'-sus.*

We placed the three in a box, and as I closed it the large spotted salamander seemed very well satisfied (no wonder !), while the other two raised their heads in a most appealing way. I was firm, however, and made them prisoners, feeling sure that they would be comfortable in the nice large terrarium.

When morning came we opened the box, for we were ready to put our little neighbors into their new home. What was our surprise to find the spotted salamander alone! As to countenance he was well content; as to sides he was much bulged out. Poor little "Freckles" and poor little Red Back! I wish I had listened to your appeal!

SUGGESTIONS FOR STUDY.

1. A terrarium is "an inclosed bit of earth on which things may live and grow." Do not think that it is necessary to have one as well made at first as that in the illustration. (Fig. 341.)

Fig. 344. Isabella tiger moths, male and female. The red and black woolly-bear is the larva or caterpillar of this moth. The smaller moth is the male.

Uncle John will be well pleased to know that you have made some arrangement for having outdoor-folk live in the schoolroom. Any such home will be a terrarium.

2. Every one can have grasshoppers for study. How many different kinds can you find? Do all have the feelers or antennæ the same length? Observe the growth of the wings in the nymph, as the young grasshopper is called. In the grown-up ones notice that the narrow wing is on the outside and the pretty ones underneath.

3. Every one can also find crickets, and no terrarium will be complete without them. In the warm schoolroom or home they

will make music until late in the year.   Watch the black cricket
make music with his wings.

Notice a tiny light speck near the elbow of the cricket's front
leg. This is the ear ; so you see the little fellows "listen with
their elbows."

The mother cricket has a spear at the end of her body. With
this she makes a hole in the ground in which to place her eggs.
She cannot chirp, but the father makes enough music for the
family. You will see that the mother seems to enjoy it.

Plant fresh grass seed and grain occasionally in the cricket corner of your terrarium.

4. If you do not own an insect net, try to find a lace-winged fly
without one. It will not be difficult for young naturalists to see

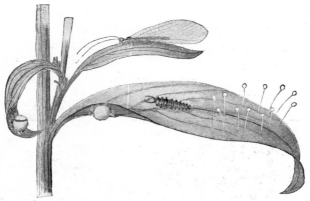

Fig. 345. Golden-eyes or lace-winged fly ; eggs, larva or
aphis-lion, cocoon, adult.

the flies resting on the bushes along the roadside. These insects
are valuable to farmers because their children, the aphis-lions,
eat so many plant-lice and other insects.

Look on the under side of the leaves for the cocoon illustrated
in Fig. 345. It has the appearance of a small pearl. The first
time I found one I did not know what it was. I left it on my
desk hoping that something interesting would come out of it. The
next morning there was a pretty green insect trying to get out of
the window and I wondered how it had come there. While thinking about it my eye fell on the cocoon lying on my desk. I
noticed that a lid had been raised on it and suspected at once
how golden-eyes had found her way into my room. Who will

succeed in getting the eggs, an aphis-lion, a cocoon, or a lace-winged fly? Let us know.

5. The larger the number of butterflies you can bring into the schoolroom, the gayer will be the terrarium world. Gather fresh thistles or other flowers from which they can suck the nectar or give them sweetened water in a dish. Notice their long mouth-parts as they eat.

One of the most common of all butterflies is the large brown and black one. This is called the monarch butterfly. Notice that many of these fly together on autumn days. They are going south with the birds.

6. Be sure to keep the moss damp for the salamanders and add occasionally fresh pieces in which they will get food. Perhaps you can teach them to eat raw meat after they have been with you awhile.

7. The terrarium will not be complete without a toad or two. You can feed them flies, other insects, and earthworms, and they may then leave the salamanders alone. You need not be afraid to handle the toads for *they cannot give you warts*. When they have been in the terrarium awhile they will show you how they like to spend the winter.

A terrarium in School No. 23, Buffalo.

LEAFLET LXXII.

MOTHS AND BUTTERFLIES.*

By ALICE G. McCLOSKEY.

O F all the insects that interest boys and girls, moths and butterflies seem to hold the first place. I find, however, that young people are not always able to distinguish these insects one from another, and do not know very much of the strange lives they lead. Perhaps you may have found out a few facts about them in books, but this is not *knowing*. To know, one must see some of the wonderful things that they do. When you have watched the whole life-story of a moth or butterfly, you will have a far greater interest in these animals than their handsome wings and graceful flight have ever given you.

The most important thing to remember in the study of moths and butterflies is that they appear in four different forms during their lives. These forms are :

The egg.   *The larva.*   *The pupa.*   *The adult.*

THE EGGS.

The eggs are laid singly or in clusters. They are usually found on the plant which is the favorite food of the young. Look for the shining masses of the eggs of the tent-caterpillar on apple and wild cherry trees ; also for the yellow eggs of potato beetles on potato leaves.

THE LARVA.

The larva or "worm" hatches from the egg. During this period in its history the insect *eats* and *grows*. If you doubt that they have good appetites, undertake to feed a few healthy caterpillars this spring. If you doubt that they are particular as to the kind of food they have, find out for yourselves whether the apple

---

* Junior Naturalist Monthly, March, 1902.

35   545

tree " worm " will eat milk-weed leaves or whether the milk-weed caterpillar will eat leaves taken from an apple tree.

One of the most interesting things to notice in the study of

larvæ or caterpillars is that they occasionally appear in bright new coats, and we find the old ones have been cast aside. It is necessity, not pride, that leads them to do this. You see, an insect's skeleton is on the outside of its body ; and if it could not be shed once in a while how would there be room for the little creature to grow ?

Fig. 346. Chrys'-a-lids of the mourning-cloak butterfly.

THE PUPA.

Of all the forms in which moths and butterflies appear, the pupa

Fig. 347.   Cocoon of the cecropia moth.   It is often attached to the twig of a fruit tree.

is the strangest. Although we speak of this period in the life of the insect as one of rest or sleep, it is the time when the most wonderful changes take place in its body.

The queer little objects that you see illustrated in Fig. 346 are the pupæ of the mourning-cloak butterfly. When the caterpillars were about to shed their coats for the last time, they hung themselves head downward from a twig by means of a silk button which they had spun. Then they cast off their skins, leaving the chrysalids or naked pupæ hanging ; protected from birds by their spiny form and protected from many enemies, even from young naturalists, by their wood-brown color which so closely resembles the support from which they are suspended.

Let us next look at the pupa of a moth. This is often inside a covering which is called a cocoon. If you look on the fruit trees or shade trees about your home you may find a cocoon of the

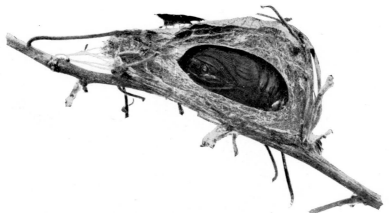

Fig. 348. The cecropia pupa inside the cocoon. Nearly natural size.

ce-cró-pi-a moth. You will see that it is made of silk. This covering was spun by the giant silkworm as a protection against the storms of winter. How snug the pupa is inside, and how firmly the cocoon is fastened to the twig on which you found it ! Figs. 347, 348, 349 show this interesting insect.

When you are studying pupæ remember that butterflies do not come out of cocoons. Their chrysalis or pupa is always uncovered. In the case of moths, however, the pupa is either inside a cocoon or protected by being underground or in some well sheltered place. These facts suggest a question. Is there any reason why the one should be better fitted to endure cold and storms than the other ?

THE ADULT.

We now come to the fourth period in the lives of moths and butterflies, a period which has ever had and ever will have an interest for young and old. Since there are many persons, little and big, who cannot distinguish the two groups, butterflies and moths, let us learn the marks by which they may be known.

Butterflies have uncovered pupæ. They fly by day. The wings are folded over the back when at rest. The antennæ or feelers have *knobs* on the ends. (Fig. 350 B.) The body is slender.

Moths have pupæ either inside cocoons or protected by being underground or in some sheltered place. Many moths fly at night. The antennæ are never knobbed. (Fig. 350 M M.) They leave the wings spread when they are at rest. The body is stout.

Fig. 349. Cecropia moth just emerged from the cocoon, on which it hangs. The moth comes from the pupa.

Occasionally you may come across insects that very closely resemble butterflies, yet have some characters that are similar to those of moths. They are the skippers, so named because of their strong and rapid flight. The antennæ have knobs, but these knobs are drawn out and turned back in the form of a hook. (Fig. 350 S.) The body is rather stout. The pupa is covered by a thin cocoon. In some species the wings are held vertically, in others horizontally.

SUGGESTIONS FOR STUDY.

Cocoons and butterfly chrysalids are very hard to find because they so closely resemble the withered leaves that cling to shrubs and trees.

You will probably find cocoons of the ce-cro-pi-a and pro-mé-the-a moths. The former, illustrated by Figs. 347 to 349, is commonly found on fruit trees; the latter swings loosely from a branch of ash, wild cherry, or lilac. The promethea cocoon is enfolded in a leaf which the caterpillar fastened to a twig by means of silk before it spun the cocoon. If you are rewarded for your s e a r c h by finding some of these w i n t e r homes, leave a few of them in a cool place and occasionally dip them in water that they may not become too dry. Look at them c a r e f u l l y from time to time and note any changes that take place. Following are a few suggestions that will help you in the study of cocoons :

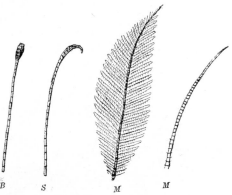

Fig. 350. *Antennæ or feelers.*

1. Observe the covering of the pupa closely. Is it made of other material beside silk? When the woolly-bear, that many of you have cared for all winter, spins his cocoon, he will use some of his own hair as well as silk.

Fig. 351. *Luna moth and swallow-tail butterfly.*

2. Open the cocoon. Is the pupa free from it? Are the threads of silk woven in the same direction in all parts of the covering?

3. Out of which end do you think the moth will come?

4. Describe the inside of the cocoon. Do you find anything in it beside the pupa?

5. The cocoons of the Chinese silkworm are soaked in hot water

or softened by steam before the thread can be unwound. Put one of the cocoons that you find in hot water and see whether you can unwind the silk. I wish you could secure some cocoons of the real silkworm.

Boys and girls often ask us what they shall feed moths and butterflies. Many of the adult insects do not eat at all. Some, however, sip the nectar of flowers or sap of trees. Oftentimes they will drink sweetened water or the juice of fruit. If you have an opportunity, watch one while it eats. Notice the long "tongue" through which it takes its food. This is made of two pieces grooved on the inner side, and when held together they form a tube. When the insect is not eating these mouth-parts are coiled.

Fig. 352. The life-story of an insect, the forest tent caterpillar. m, male moth; f, female; p, pupa; e, egg-ring recently laid; g, hatched egg-ring; c, caterpillar. Moths and caterpillars are natural size, and eggs and pupa are slightly enlarged.

LEAFLET LXXIII.

THE PAPER-MAKERS.*

By ALICE G. McCLOSKEY.

A Castle Made of Paper.

MANY school rooms in the State have a hornet's nest which some boy or girl has brought to show the teacher. It is usually hung on the wall or used as an ornament on top of the bookcase. Let us take it down some day this month and learn something about it.

Do you think the nest can be called a castle? Why not? Look inside. Is it not several stories high? Are there not spacious galleries in it? Is it not as well guarded when the wasps are at home as if an army of soldiers stood outside?

Let us see how this castle is built. You have heard that wasps were the first paper makers. In the early summer you will see them around wood that has been worn by the weather. They take off loose fibres and by means of their mouth-parts work them into pulp. Can the rain get through this paper? Find out whether it is waterproof.

Fig. 353.   The paper castle.

Some of the nests made by vespa (Fig. 353), as the hornets or yellow-jackets are called, are very large. Do you think a wasp could make one alone? No, these are social wasps; that is, a great many live together. There are males, females, and workers. Some day we shall tell you how the wasps form their colony, but for this lesson we want you to study the nest.

---

* Junior Naturalist Monthly, February and March, 1901.

Notice the envelope which covers the cells. How many layers of paper are there in it? We might call each layer a clapboard.

Can you see any difference in the direction of the outside layers on top of the nest and those which are below?

Fig. 354. Interior arrangement of white-faced hornet's nest.

How many stories high is the nest?

Note the difference in the size of the stories. Where do you find the smallest?

Count the rooms or cells in each.

You know, of course, that an egg is placed in each cell. When the larvæ, as the young of the wasps are called, are hatched, they still live in the cells.

How do they manage to keep in their cells? You see the nest is really turned upside down. Their little heads must hang where the worker wasps can feed them easily. I wonder whether you can tell me why the young wasps do not fall out?

The workers chew all the food which they give the little ones. When in summer you see hornets about your flower beds or feeding on other insects, it may be that they are preparing breakfast for the young. Notice the flowers which they visit.

POLISTES, THE PAPER-MAKER.

In the previous lesson I spoke of vespa wasps that make homes of paper. You learned that they bite off pieces of weather-worn wood with their jaws and chew it until it is made into pulp. Were you interested in these social wasps? If so, you may like to hear about another member of the same family.

Fig. 355. Home of polistes, the paper-maker.

Hiding in some crevice about your house or the school building there is probably a wasp which naturalists call po-lis'-tes.

She has been there ever since the cold weather came. In the spring you may see her tearing off pieces of wood from some unpainted building or weather-worn fence. Let us see what she is going to do.

This wasp is the founder of a colony. The first thing she does is to select a place for her home. Then she makes a few cells — only a few, for she has no help. When you find a nest like the one in the picture (Fig. 355), you will see how the comb is fastened to the roof or to a tree or to the under side of a stone.

As soon as the cells are completed, the mother lays an egg in each. From these eggs little grubs or larvæ are hatched. They are fed by the mother until they become pupæ. The cells are sealed over while the wasps are in the pupa state. They have to break open the seals before they can come out.

All members of the first brood are workers. As soon as they are hatched the mother has nothing to do but to provide eggs. They clean out the cells in which they passed their early days ; they make additions to the nests ; they take care of the young. Do you remember how the vespa workers prepared food for the larvæ in their colony and what they fed them ? The young polistes are cared for in the same way.

You may see the workers flying about in your garden this summer, getting the sweets from the various flowers that you have planted. You will know why they are so busy through the long sunny days. You will think of the hungry little wasps waiting for their dinner. You will wonder whether they put their heads out of the cells when the workers feed them.

Nest of Polistes.

1. Compare the nest of polistes with that of vespa.
2. In what ways do they differ?
3. Where did you find the nest?
4. How was it held in place?
5. How many cells are there in it?
6. Notice the pieces of the seals which still remain on the nest. Tell us whether they are made of the same material as the cells. Of what utility are the seals?

LEAFLET LXXIV.

SOME CARPENTER ANTS AND THEIR KIN.*

By ALICE G. McCLOSKEY.

(Compare Leaflet XXI.)

ONE bright August morning, as we were walking along the edge of a wood, we found an old tree trunk lying on the ground. I am sure it had been there a long time. Large pieces of bark were loose enough to be lifted up ; being naturalists, we took advantage of this fact to see whether anything was living underneath.

What queer little outdoor folk we found : " thousand-legged worms," sow-bugs, a black beetle that looked as if its back were made of patent-leather, and best of all a colony of ants ! These ants were large black ones known as carpenter ants. They had made very comfortable quarters in this old log. How alarmed they were when we so rudely exposed them to the light !

One brave ant impressed me more than any other member of the colony. I wish that all of our girls and boys might have seen it. With my knife I commenced to cut down the wall of one of the rooms to see what was inside. The soldier-like ant stood near and, instead of running away, it attacked the large steel blade with its jaws. Was not that a brave thing to do ? Are you surprised that I closed the knife and put it into my pocket ?

During all this time there was great commotion in the colony. The worker ants were scurrying off with the younger members of the family, trying to find a safe place for them. Some of these little brothers and sisters were tiny white legless creatures ; some were covered up in what looked like little bags ; others were ghost-like things, very white and apparently lifeless.

---

* Junior Naturalist Monthly, October, 1903.

Now before you can understand what is going on in an ant's nest, you must know four things :

1. The white oblong eggs are very small. You will not see them readily.

2. The little legless creatures, or larvæ, hatch from the eggs and are fed by the workers. Mrs. Comstock says that an ant larva looks like a crook-neck squash.

3. The larvæ either spin cocoons or rest awhile without any covering before they become fully grown ants. In their resting form they are called pupæ. Children usually think the little sack-like pupæ are the eggs.

4. The fully grown ants come from the pupæ.

Fig. 356. Making a home for ants.

We want every Junior Naturalist Club to have an ant's nest in the school room and to observe the following :

In time of danger do the ants look to their own safety first?

Watch the workers feed and clean the young.

Try to see an ant help a younger relative out of the pupa skin.

Notice how many uses the ants seem to have for their antennæ or feelers.

Has it ever seemed to you that ants carry on a conversation when they meet?

See how many different kinds of ants you can find out-of-doors. Tell us about their homes.

HOW TO MAKE AN ANT'S NEST.

In the illustration (Fig. 356) you will see an ant's nest. For this kind of nest you will need a plank, near the outside edge of which is a deep groove. The plank should be painted; can you tell why? In the center use two pieces of glass laid flat and separated by narrow sticks along each side, so that they are about one-eighth of an inch apart. The sticks should not come close together at one corner. This leaves a little doorway for the ants. Cover the top glass with black paper or cloth so that the space between the two pieces of glass may seem a nice, dark, safe room in which ants may live. It will be a good thing to keep a small piece of damp blotting paper in one corner of this room in case the workers want a moist place for the young ones. Fill the groove in the plank with water and the nest is ready.

The best ant colony to take indoors is the one that you find under stones in a pasture. With a trowel lift up the ants, pupæ, larvæ, and sand and put the contents carefully into a pint can. When you reach the schoolroom put the contents of the can on the plank and watch what happens. If the ants do not find the room you have made for them, place a few larvæ and pupæ within it. They will probably find them.

Do not neglect to provide food for the colony. Ants like to eat cracker soaked in sweetened water, bread, cake, berry jams, sugar, bits of raw meat, yolk of hard-boiled egg, and custard.

Junior naturalist museum in the school. District No. 2, Sheridan, N. Y.

LEAFLET LXXV.

A GARDEN ALL YOUR OWN.*

By JOHN W. SPENCER.

My Dear Nephews and Nieces:

WOULD you like to have a garden this summer — a garden all your very own? If so, you can surely have one. A man up in a balloon could have one if he were to try; a man living down in a coal mine could not, because there would be no sunlight. Plants must have light from the sun, which is the vital source of all light. I consider that anyone who cares for a plant, growing either in a window box or in a tomato can, has a garden. Yes; a plant growing in an eggshell constitutes a garden.

A Littte Girl's Garden.

Near my desk is a picture of a little girl, holding in her arms a big pumpkin that she raised in a garden all her own. I do not know how many pies could have been made from that pumpkin, but, at any rate, it was a big pumpkin. The seed from which the vine started was planted in an egg-shell in the school-room. When the bright May days came the egg-shell had become too small for the plant or the plant had become too large for the egg-shell, so the little girl planted it in the open ground at her home. She must have been a tiny girl or the soil in her garden must have been very hard, for without help she was unable to spade it and make it fine. She hired her father to do it for her and paid him by carrying his dinner every day for a week to the shop where he worked. When lunch time came, papa and she had a little picnic all by themselves. There is no prettier picture than is made by such strong comradeship between a little girl and her father.

Make a Bargain with Your Teacher.

I hope your teacher will permit you to have some boxes of earth (I mean *soil*) in the windows of your school-room, in which you

*Junior Naturalist Monthly, May, 1904.

may plant flower or vegetable seeds. In early June, just before the close of school, you can divide the plants among yourselves and set them out in the open ground or in window boxes at your

home. Ask your teacher whether you may have such a privilege. Promise that if she will grant this favor you will be just as good as the "little girl who had a little curl that hung in the middle of her forehead," and if at any time you become "horrid" the teacher may give your share of the plants to some one better behaved than yourself. If she is a wise teacher she will consent, but not until she has made a bargain with you that you are to

Fig. 357. Sweet peas.

do all the work and to ask nothing from her but advice when you need it.

A Plant Nursery.

Your first garden should be in a shallow box, called a "flat," which you may consider a kind of nursery for the plants. Let this nursery, or cradle, be as long and as wide as a soap box, and not more than three or four inches deep. You can make a "flat," as gardeners do, by sawing a soap box in two. In the bottom of the box make some small auger holes for drainage. Some of you may be so fortunate as to be able to gather from the woods and fields the material for fitting up the flat. Some moss,— say about an inch of it,— should first be laid in the bottom. When moss cannot be found, use stones or pieces of broken pottery to cover the drainage holes. This is to prevent the soil from washing through. The remainder of the flat should be filled with good woods earth. Pack the soil firmly. Fill the flat not even full, but to within half an inch of the top. Those who cannot go to the fields must get the best garden soil

Fig. 358. A nest of window pots.

to be found. A few children may be unable to get even garden soil. They will be obliged to go to the florist's for soil, as they must do when they fill their window boxes. Because of the frequent waterings required by all plants growing in boxes, it is important to get soil that is not sticky and that will not pack hard.

Sowing the Seed.

When the time comes for the sowing of seeds, you had better ask your teacher to look over your shoulder to see that you do it correctly. In sowing, put the seeds in straight rows. These rows may be made by denting the soil with the sharp edge of a stick or ruler. Let the rows extend the entire width of the flat. Into the dent, drop the seeds at regular intervals. If any seeds drop outside of the dent, gently push them into place with a toothpick. Half a dozen rows of one variety of flowers or vegetables having small seeds will give a large number of plants. One flat may accommodate a number of varieties.

At the point where one variety stops and another begins, a neat label of wood should be stuck. This affords a good chance for a boy to bring his new jack-knife into use. On the label should be written the name of each variety. This will give an excellent opportunity for one who writes a good vertical hand to make himself useful. Begin at the very top of the label and write towards the lower end ; then if the lower part of the label rots off or becomes discolored, you will still have the first and most important part of the name left. The label should never be disturbed, for a careless boy or girl might not put it back into the exact place where it was found, which would be indeed unfortunate. The Smiths and Joneses of that plant community would become so mixed that the Joneses would be called Smiths and the Smiths would be known as Joneses. It would be as bad as changing door-plates.

When the seeds have been evenly distributed in rows like houses along a street there comes another very important step,— the covering of the seeds. If seeds are covered too deep they will rot because of too much moisture ; if the covering is too thin, the soil will dry so rapidly that the seeds will fail because of insufficient moisture. The size of the seed usually determines the amount of covering necessary. As a broad general rule, the soil covering should be about four times the thickness of the seed.

Having been covered, the earth must be thoroughly watered. This must be done gently and carefully. If done with a rush, the water will wash the covering away and many of the seeds will be left bare. Whenever such an accident occurs, the seed may be pushed into the soil with a toothpick. At most times when watering, continue to apply the water until it just begins to drain

36

through the bottom of the flat. This should be practiced even after the seeds have germinated and become growing plants. Keep the flats shaded until the plants begin to push their heads

through the soil. After this time strong light should gradually be given them that the plants may not become tall and spindling, or "leggy," as gardeners say.

If the seed boxes are in a sunny or windy place, the soil may dry out too rapidly. This can be prevented by laying a newspaper over the flat when the sun strikes it. As the plantlets grow, care must be taken not to shade them too much.

Fig. 359.   Transplanted into a pot.

A PLANT KINDERGARTEN.

In some plants the first leaves are called the "seed-leaves," and, like children's milk teeth, soon disappear. The next set are the true leaves. After the true leaves appear, if the plants seem crowded and uncomfortable, like three boys trying to sleep in a narrow bed, transplant them into other flats prepared similarly to the one into which the seeds were sown. You may think of this as the promotion of the young plants from the cradle to the kindergarten. Here the plants should be placed about an inch from each other, in squares. Wet the plants thoroughly before taking them up and also the soil into which they are to make their second home. After this is done, the soil should be pressed firmly about the roots, as you snuggle the bedclothes about your neck on a cold winter's night. It is entertaining practice to transplant the plants into pots, if you happen to have any florist's pots of small size.

Fig. 360.   A soap box put to use.

This transplanting of plants in the school-room gives a quiet occupation to boys and girls who for a time may not be engaged in study. The disobedient child or the would-be "smart" one might better be denied the privilege. I say "privilege," because the wise teacher will make window gardening a privilege and not required work. After the transplanting has been completed and the plants thoroughly soaked with water, they must be shaded for about twenty-four hours, after which they had better receive the strong light once more, when they will resume their growth.

PLANTS NEED WATER.

If plants could feel and talk, they would tell of periods when they had endured great suffering because of thirst : suffering as great as that sometimes experienced by travelers in crossing a desert. Often it has been so great as almost to ruin a plant's constitution. I am often asked, "How frequently shall I water plants?" It is as difficult to give a fixed rule for watering as to determine how often a boy should be allowed a drink. During cool cloudy weather, plants do not require as much water as when the sun shines bright and hot on them. I can give no better general direction than this : — water plants when the surface of the soil seems dry and powder-like, when a pinch of it rolled between the thumb and finger does not form a little ball. Under conditions in which the drainage is good, plants should receive water until the surplus begins to trickle out of the holes at the bottom. If you follow these directions carefully, your school-room garden should afford a good lot of plants for cultivation at home in the open ground or in boxes.

WHAT YOU MAY PLANT.

As to the kind of seeds to sow, you must be governed by what you most desire to have in your home garden for summer cultivation. If you are able to have a garden in the open ground, I would have you make a selection of both flowers and vegetables. Do not choose a large variety of either, for children are but little men and women and must shape their tasks to fit their shoulders. It would be better to have a garden the size of a horse blanket and have it in good condition all summer than to have a larger one and allow it to become a wilderness of weeds.

In the vegetable line, you can have radishes and lettuce that may be harvested by the Fourth of July. After the first crop has been removed the ground should be spaded and wax beans planted in rows about eighteen inches apart and the beans six inches apart in the rows. These give the juiciest of pods, excellent for pickling. Kings and princes could have none better. This plan gives you two crops from the same ground in one summer. Plant radishes in rows twelve inches apart and about two inches apart in the row. Pull them for the table when the roots are three-quarters of an inch or a little more in diameter. Set lettuce about three inches apart in the row, which is twice or more as thick as the plants should be when full grown. When half grown or more every other plant may be pulled out for table use and the remaining ones will soon fill the vacancies.

Fig. 361. A window-garden of one's own.

In suggesting your selection of flowers, I shall mention but a few. I have chosen the following kinds because they are not too particular or exacting as to care, while some are equally well adapted for cultivation either in the open ground or in window boxes. I hope you will include sweet peas, dahlias, and gladioli in your selection. I have not named them in this list because they are not suitable for planting in flats, but are planted directly in the open ground where they are to spend their lives. Gladioli and most dahlias you will not raise from seeds.

The following is a list from which you may make a selection for planting in your school-room, to divide later with your mates for home planting : —

Petunia ⎫
Nasturtium ⎪ Suitable for planting either in
Sweet Alyssum ⎬ window boxes or in the open ground.
Mignonette ⎭

Bachelor's Button ⎫
Salvia (Flowering Sage) ⎪
Phlox ⎪ To be planted in
Aster ⎬ the open ground.
Marigold ⎪
Candytuft ⎭

Fig. 362. Plan of the improvement of the school ground, shown in Fig. 365.

MAKE A GARDEN IN A BOX.

There is no reason why you cannot have a window-box as attractive as the one shown in Fig. 361. Plants will grow as well for you as for the richest or the greatest man of whom you ever heard. All they require is to be made comfortable. The two things most necessary for their comfort are water as often as they need it, and fertile soil that will not become hard from frequent watering. Plants in boxes need water much oftener than those in the open ground. I once knew of a window-box on a tin roof on the south side of the house that was watered morning, noon, and night. Those plants must have been comfortable, for they made thrifty growth.

When you have learned how to make plants comfortable in a flat, you will know what is necessary for their comfort in a window-box. They should have the same kind of earth, but more of it. The box should never be less than eight inches wide and eight inches deep and as long as you can afford to fill with earth and plants. There must be holes in the bottom for drainage, and moss or small stones placed over the holes to prevent the soil from washing away.

The plants should be set four to six inches apart in the box. At first, this will seem too great a distance, but after a few weeks of growth, the plants will cover all bare spots. When transplanting either to window-boxes or to the open ground, do it the same way as when changing plants from the cradle flat to the kindergarten flat.

I know of a brother and a sister who found enough soil to fill some egg-shells. The shells had small drainage holes in the bottom. In time the plants grew and became too large for the egg-shells. Then the children went in search of more soil. They found enough to fill a few tomato cans. These cans also had drainage holes in the bottom. In each can they set a plant. They then put the cans into a soap box. Then they packed excelsior into all the vacant places in the soap box. The excelsior helped to hold the moisture. The box stood on a back veranda where the plants had plenty of sunshine. So long as they were comfortable they did their best, which is as much as they could have done if they had been in expensive vases in the grounds of the White House at Washington.

CONSIDER YOUR SCHOOL GROUNDS.

On the last page of this leaflet are two pictures of a school-house. The first shows how it looked when it had not a friend. The second shows what the friendship of the teacher and the children could do for it. In both cases the building remains the same. Look at one picture and then at the other. See, if you can, what one thing has been done to make the difference — a difference as

great as that between a tramp and a gentleman. A few shrubs
have been planted by the friends, but the greatest thing they did
was to clean up. They took away everything that looked untidy
and shabby.

At this time of the year you see many beautiful crocuses, tulips,
daffodils, and hyacinths. Nothing children can plant will give so
much for the labor as these bulbs. Why not have some on the
school grounds? When school begins next September, write me
for directions how to grow them.

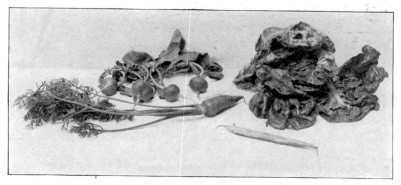

Fig. 363. Product of a child's garden.

Fig. 364. School premises before improving.

Fig. 365. School premises after improving.
Could you not do as much for your school grounds?

LEAFLET LXXVI.

THE GARDENS AND THE SCHOOL GROUNDS.

By JOHN W. SPENCER.

My Dear Boys and Girls :

OF course you believe that Co-lumbus discovered America, even though you were not with him. If you had been on the deck of his ship when San Salva-dor raised its head on the rim of the sea, you would be talking about it every day of your life. As it is, your knowledge comes to you through books, and you think you are fortunate if you are able to answer questions correctly on examina-tion. This leads me to remark that there is much more interest in things that we have helped to "make happen" than in things that we read about and that were "made to happen" by some one else.

There is a chance for each of you boys and girls, in a way, to become a Columbus. It is true that, not counting the north and south poles, all the continents are discovered, but there is much pleasure and "fun" in discovering facts. I am now speaking from experience. I think that James Buchanan was President when I learned, in such a way that I could explain to others, the principles of a suction-pump. Some of the suggestions led me to make a squirt gun from a bit of elder stalk. Sometimes when I made a demonstration the water would fly in the faces of my audience. I started a squirt gun factory, but the teacher stopped the enterprise because it made too much litter in the school-room.

I have a suggestion that will start you on a voyage of discovery. When you have gone as far as you can I wish you would write me, telling what you have learned. Writers of agricultural books sometimes use the expression, "There is fertility in tillage." Is that true ?

*Junior Naturalist Monthly, June, 1903.

By fertility is meant the power of the soil to furnish plant-food.
Fertile soil is "rich" soil.   By tillage is meant frequent stirring
of the soil.   For example, Billy Boy and his chum each have a
flower garden side by side of equal size.   Each boy sows seeds
from the same bag.   The same sunshine and the same rains give
vigor to each flower-bed alike.   Billy Boy spades the soil deep
and makes it fine.   His chum stirs the top and leaves clods on
the surface.   With the end of a sharp stick Billy makes a straight
drill for the seed.   On the bottom of the drill the soil is fine like
meal, and the seed is sown with great care and is covered with
the finest soil.   If the seed is small he makes the soil covering
very thin.   The last thing he does is to firm the soil by patting it
with either his hand or the flat part of a hoe, and he does it in an
affectionate way as if he were patting a dog.   His chum makes
the drill for the seed in a hasty way, leaving in the bottom little
clods of earth as large as hickory nuts.   He sows the seed as if
he were glad to get rid of it, and he covers it as if he wanted it
out of sight as soon as possible.

Which of the two boys gave the better tillage to the soil?   During the summer you will see how others care for their plants and
you will see instances of good tillage and poor tillage.   You must
observe and write me which of the two had the better success in
having the seed come up.   The difference between the two ways
does not end in sowing and germination of seed, but continues all
summer until the end of the season.   Billy Boy will care for the
soil by combing it with a rake several times a week, with the same
care and affection with which the lover of a horse will groom the
animal each morning.   The chum will think the plants are all like
goats, and ought to live with almost any chance.   Billy Boy will
have no weeds among his plants and his chum will have them in
great numbers.   The chum may say that weeds shade the plants
and thereby protect them from drought.   I have known grown-up
farmers to say that.   Is it true?   Go on a voyage of discovery
and find out.

I hope your garden may be of the Billy Boy kind, receiving
plenty of tillage.   You will have no trouble to find any number
of the other kind of gardens growing to weeds and receiving no
tillage.   It will please me very much if you will write me, giving as many reasons as you can why tillage makes the soil more
fertile (or "rich") and able to produce better plants and flowers.
Each letter will be carefully read.

AN EXPERIMENT.

Perhaps you can answer the questions by watching your garden or some one's else garden ; but you can answer them better if you will grow a few "hills" of corn. In the fall I shall have many questions to ask you about corn, and I want you to be able to answer by telling me what you have seen with your own eyes. Those of you who are Junior Naturalists have done well with your dues this year, but we must always do better next year than we did last ; so I want you to know many things about Indian corn when you come back to school in the fall. Your teacher has also been asked to study corn, and I am going to study it myself. I am a farmer and I have grown corn all my life. Once I thought that I knew all about it ; but frequently some one asks me a question about it that I cannot answer.

Now, I hope that you can plant at least ten "hills" of corn, or, if you do not plant it in "hills," you may make two rows, each of them five or ten feet long. I want you to plant part of these hills (or one of the rows) in good rich soil. Perhaps your father will let you plant them in the best part of the garden along with the cabbages or other crops ; or, perhaps, your mother will let you plant them at the back part of the flower garden. Then I want you to keep down the weeds and break or cultivate the ground often with a hoe or rake so that the soil is always loose. Then I want you to plant the other part of the corn in a poor or dry piece of ground, where the weeds grow. This part you need not cultivate. I think that before the summer is half over you will learn a very great lesson by looking at these two pieces of corn. Some of you will say that you know beforehand what will happen ; but I want you to grow the corn nevertheless.

By fall I hope you will be able to write me whether you can tell a rich soil when you see it, and also why you think it is rich. I want everyone of the Junior Gardeners to tell me that much when school opens.

To the Teacher : —

We must depend upon your courtesy to help in reporting what has been done by you and your pupils in improvement of school grounds. In addition to this we hope it may be your pleasure to ask all the children who are able to write to tell us in detail, at

some language period, what they have done. We are never able
to get reports of all this good work. Many teachers feel that
nothing but heroic deeds in the planting of school grounds are
worthy of mention. This is a mistake. Some grounds may be
more improved by attention to simple tidiness than by expensive
planting, and they are equally worthy of mention.

The attendance at some schools is small and the pupils are
young. Small efforts from them are relatively great when compared with what is done by schools with ample facilities. We
know a teacher who began her first teaching in the fall of 1902.
The pupils were eight in number and most of them were small.
The school was in the country. The interior of the building
was shabby. The teacher was courageous and resolute. With
her small handful of not over-competent pupils, she had school
"exercises" and the children sold tickets. By this means enough
paper was bought to cover the walls, and the teacher and the
children put the paper on. Then they made other sales, for which
they received as commission three pictures creditably framed.
They were hung on the walls of the school-house. By this time,
the tide of civic improvement in that community began to turn
towards the improving of the school building and grounds. We
are eagerly awaiting reports to know what was done on Arbor
Day. Under such conditions, it was no small thing that the
teacher and children accomplished.

Fig. 366. Making a school-garden in Massachusetts.

LEAFLET LXXVII.

SOMETHING FOR YOUNG FARMERS.*

By JOHN W. SPENCER.

My Dear Nephews and Nieces :

I WISH to make farmers of you all. I will try to tell you how to have farms all your own — farms on which you can plant seeds and see the plants grow. Once a little girl in Buffalo, who is one of my Junior Naturalists, asked me whether I would call at her home and see the harvest from seeds she planted on one of her farms the spring before. The principal of the school went with me, for he knew all about the little girl's success, and seemed proud of what she had accomplished. What do you think it was she had raised ? It was something that filled her lap and was good to eat. It was a fine pumpkin. It weighed twenty-two pounds. I wish I could have a photograph of her holding the pumpkin, her face glowing with pride and satisfaction.

You are surely able to do as much as this little girl did. Perhaps you would prefer some other crop to pumpkins, in which case you have many kinds of seeds from which to choose.

Last spring, in school, this little girl with other boys and girls began planting and caring for egg-shell farms. It costs no money and but little trouble to own several such farms. The greatest pleasure and profit is to be found in having them in school, for then you have the opportunity of seeing how others manage their farms, and there is a spur in doing what others are doing. When you have read all about my plan I wish you would ask your teacher whether you cannot have some egg-shell farms in your grade. When your plants are large enough to put permanently in the open ground, you can plant them in a garden or window-box at your

*Supplement to Junior Naturalist Monthly, April, 1902.

home. If it is not convenient to have egg-shell farms at school, ask your parents if you cannot have some at home.

Please give me your ears and your attention while I tell you how to get your farms.

In April you have eggs at some one of the three meals of the day, and the empty shells can be easily obtained. The end of the shell to be broken is the sharp or "peaked" end. Break away about a quarter or a third of it and pour out the white and the yolk that is inside. This empty shell is to hold the soil of your farm, and you can have as many farms as may be convenient to care for. On each egg-shell you may write your name, for the same reason that people have door plates on the doors of their houses or signs on their places of business. Some very methodical boys and girls write also the names of the kind of seeds sown, and the dates of planting and sprouting. Do not forget to put a hole through the bottom of each one of your farms for drainage. I wish I could be with you when you get your soil; we would go out to the pastures and the woods for a supply. I should be able to tell you much about different soils, and how they have been made. It is an interesting story that I must tell you when we are past the hurry of spring's work. If we could go afield we should find the best soil for your egg-shell farms about the roots of rotted stumps or in rotted leaves. It is necessary that the soil shall not bake hard because of frequent waterings, shall not dry out quickly, and shall have plenty of plant-food. I fancy the most convenient plan will be for all of you who wish soil to form a syndicate by contributing a cent each and go to a florist and buy your soil. Tell the florist you wish it for your use and the probabilities are that he will be so much interested in your plants that you will get more for the same amount of money than I could if I were to go for you.

The next difficulty will be to keep your farms right side up. That is easily accomplished by putting some sand or sawdust in a shallow box and making a dent where you wish each farm to stand. If you have your farms in the school-room, Tom, Dick, and Harry can have all their farms in the same box. There will be no trouble in separating them if the owner's name is written on each one.

Next comes the planting of seeds and the problem of the amount of earth to put over them. Big seeds require more covering than little seeds. Seeds like peas, beans, and corn may be thrust into the middle of your farm. Small seeds, like those of the petunia, which are almost like dust, require only the gentlest sprinkling of soil. Seeds as large as those of the aster and the balsam should be covered with a layer of earth as thick as a lead pencil. I advise you to plant twice as many seeds as you wish to have grow Many accidents may happen and if all grow, the surplus plants. can be replanted later or thrown away. The earth covering should be sprinkled or sifted over the seeds, and then it must be patted or pressed down firmly. By this means the particles of soil are snuggled close together, and the seed and the soil hold moisture much better than when the particles lie loose and far apart.

The next thing to do after planting is to sprinkle water over your farms. Do this as gently as possible, for with all your care some seeds may be uncovered. Look over the ground carefully, and those you find exposed poke into the earth with the point of a pencil or a stick.

The soil of your farms must be kept moist at all times. This is a point that will require your continued attention. When your Uncle John attended school, many years ago, there was a passage in his reader that taught him that " Eternal vigilance is the price of liberty." The attention required to keep plants suitably watered does not fall much short of eternal vigilance. This need not scare you. If you care for your farms you will find it a pleasure to wait on your plants.

If you have your egg-shell farms in the school-room, there will be no opportunity to water your plants Saturday or Sunday, when school is not in session. I think if you make your farms soaking wet Friday at the close of school, and then set them back from the window out of the direct rays of the sun, no harm will come from dryness before Monday morning.

You must watch to see whether all members of the same family do the same thing precisely alike. After sowing your seeds and watering your farms you will go to them many times to see whether anything has happened. You will not be able to see anything or hear anything, and you will conclude that nothing is going on in the soil.

In this you will be mistaken, for some active changes are taking place. They are of a kind that you can neither see nor hear. In days to come, when you are men and women, you will be able to appreciate the fact that some of the most important events come about silently and some of the least important come with a racket.

The first leaves that appear on most plants are called the seed-leaves. If your plants are comfortable, but a few days will pass before true leaves develop. You will find the latter very different from the seed-leaves. Before the first or seed-leaves appear it is not important that your farms have the strong sunlight. In fact I always put my egg-shell farms in the shade while the seeds are germinating, but at the first peep of a leaf or stem I put them in the full sunshine.

Most of you will no doubt have your farms on the window ledge. Among the first things you will observe is a way all the leaves have of looking out of doors. If you turn your farms around so the leaves are looking in the room, the time will not be long before all of them will be faced out of doors again. Once on a time one of my Junior Naturalists told me that plants take to sunshine as a duck does to water. A duck is never so comfortable as when in water ; and I am certain that sunshine is important to the comfort of most plants. Some of my nephews and nieces will understand why light is so necessary to plants, for I have spoken of this before.

I hope you will this moment decide to have some egg-shell farms, and sow some seed immediately after getting your soil. Later, when the plants are large enough to plant in the open ground, we will talk of what is best to do with them. In Leaflet LH you will find a picture of an egg-shell farm.

LEAFLET LXXVIII.

BULBS.*

By JOHN W. SPENCER.

A BULB GARDEN.

"It's rather dark in the earth to-day,"
Said one little bulb to his brother;
"But I thought that I felt a sunbeam ray—
We must strive and grow till we find the way?"
And they nestled close to each other.
Then they struggled and toiled by day and by
     night
Till two little snowdrops in green and white,
Rose out of the darkness and into the light,
And softly kissed one another.—*Boston Journal.*

To succeed with the cultivation of flowers, the first thing to have in mind is to make the plant comfortable. This condition should be not only the first thought, but also the last thought. If you can do this successfully, the plant will do the rest of the work and your results will be abundant.

What plant comfort is, is a question more easily suggested than answered, for it is a very large subject—about as large as the sur-

---

* Nature-Study Quarterly, October, 1899.

face of the earth. As a venture we will say that there are as many different kinds of plants as there are people. It is at least safe to say that plants have as many different notions as to their conditions of life as have the people of the different nations and tribes of the world.

If you were to have a birthday party and should invite as your guests the children from the four corners of the earth, and by magic could bring them to you in a jiffy, the boys and girls from Greenland would come enfolded in seal-skin, and those from Hawaii would bring only their bathing suits. You would have a busy time keeping them comfortable, for when you opened the door to cool off the little Greenlanders, the little Kanakas would complain of too much draft ; and at the table the former would ask if you happened to have some tallow candles for dessert, and the latter would ask for bread-fruit and bananas.

Fig. 367. The Snow-drop.

Many of our flowering plants have been brought together from such remote quarters as that. We have bulbs from Holland, and pansies from England, and phlox from the dry atmosphere of Texas.

There is as much difference in the conditions necessary for comfort in these different plants as there is in the requirements of the little Eskimos and little Polynesians. To some extent, plants can change their manner of living, but in the main they are happiest when they can have their own way, just as you and I are.

We cannot bring about the foggy, damp weather of Holland and England when we want it ; neither can we bring the dry atmosphere of Texas — air so dry that meat will cure hard in the hottest weather without tainting. It so happens, however, that from one Fourth of July to the next we have many kinds of weather, and if one could not find conditions suited to almost any kind of plant it would be strange. If we cannot make the weather accommodate itself to the best comfort of the plant, we must set the plant so as to accommodate itself to the weather.

Pansies from foggy England and bulbs from the lowlands of Holland should be planted to bloom in the cool days of spring, and the phlox from Texas will prosper in the heat and drought of July and August.

With this idea well fixed in your mind, you will easily see that when you know the country from which a plant has come, a knowledge of the physical geography of that country will be helpful in knowing how to make the plant happy and prosperous.

We must also make the plant comfortable in the soil. There is great difference in what plants require to make them comfortable. Some, like thistles or mullein or ragweed, will thrive on almost any soil and are no more exacting as to food than a goat or a mule ; but other plants are as notional as children reared in the lap of luxury. As a rule, flowering plants belong to the "lap-of-luxury" class.

Soil covers the land as thin skin covers an apple or as a thin coat of butter covers bread, and it holds more or less plant-food. When men erect school buildings and afterwards grade the ground they usually turn a part of the soil upside down. There is also considerable rubbish of the builders left scattered about, such as brick-bats, chips of stone, and the like, that go to make the place an uncomfortable one for notional plants. For this reason I wish particularly to call your attention to the manner in which you should prepare the ground on which you intend to plant. The first thing to do is to spade the ground thoroughly to the depth of at least ten inches. All stones as large as a big boy's fist should be thrown out, and all lumps given a bat with the back of the spade to break them into fine particles. This is to be a flower-bed and should be soft like your own bed. It would be better to make it up more than once. After the first spading it would be well to cover the bed with a coat of stable fertilizer to a depth of six to eight inches, which will give additional plant-food ; and in spading the second time, this fertilizer will become thoroughly mixed with the soil. The surface should next be raked smooth, and your flower-bed will then be ready for planting.

We all admire the bright bulb flowers that are among the first to blossom in the spring. These mostly come from Holland, or at least attain their perfection there. We have just spoken of the

importance of planting flowers at such a time that they may live
their career when our climate is most like that from which they
come.   In the case of bulbs, spring and early summer is the most
favorable time for them in this country, and fall is the proper
time for planting.

The exact time in the fall to plant, how to plant, what bulbs to
plant, when to put a winter overcoat on the bed, and other details,
I will leave for Mr. Hunn to tell in the followiug Leaflet.   He
has had many years' experience in the management of flowers, and
I advise you to read carefully what he says.

Fig. 36S.   A bulb bed at the school house.

LEAFLET LXXIX.

A TALK ABOUT BULBS BY THE GARDENER.*

By C. E. HUNN.

PERHAPS you would like to hear from the gardener. Your Uncle John has told you something about preparing a bed for your plants. His advice is very good ; but the bulbs we are to talk about are like those notional children whom he mentions and they do not want tallow candles for any part of their meal.

You should know that bulbs do not want to come into direct contact with the stable fertilizer. They want the fertilizer below them where the feeding roots may nibble at it when the bulb is hard at work developing the leaves and flower. You know that all the leaves and the flowers were made the year before, and the bulb simply holds them until the new roots have formed. No kind of treatment will make a bulb produce more flowers than were formed in the year it grew (last year) ; but the better the treatment the larger and finer the flowers will be.

If I wanted to make a bulb bed, I should choose, if possible, a sandy soil and throw out the top soil to the depth of six inches. Then I should put into the bottom of the bed about two inches of well rotted manure and spade it into the soil. Then I should throw back half of the top soil, level it off nicely, set the bulbs firmly on this bed, and then cover them with the remainder of the soil ; in this way you will have the bulbs from three to four inches below the surface. It is dark down there and in the fall months the top of the ground is cooler than at the depth of five or six inches and the top of the bulb will not want to grow, while the bottom, which is always in a hurry, will send out roots, to push out the leaves and flowers the next spring.

---

* Nature-Study Quarterly, October, 1899.

When the weather is cold enough to freeze a hard crust on the soil, the bed should have its winter overcoat. This may be straw, hay, cornstalks, or leaves spread over the bed to the depth of six inches if the material is coarse ; but if you use leaves, three inches will be enough, because the leaves lie close together and may smother out the frost that is in the ground and let the bulbs start. What we want is to keep them asleep until spring, because if they start too early the hard freezes of March and early April will spoil their beauty if the leaves or flowers are near or above the surface. Early in April the covering may be removed gradually and should all be off the beds before the leaves show above the ground.

Perhaps many of you cannot find a sandy place for your beds ; if not, make your beds as has been told you, leaving the stones in the bottom of the bed for drainage. Then, when you are ready to set the bulb, place a large handful of sand where your bulb is

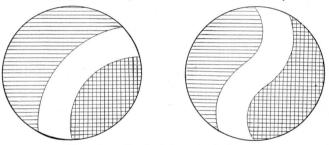

Fig. 369.   Simple designs for bulb beds.

to go and set your bulb on it ; this will keep the water from standing around the bulb. Very good results may be obtaiued on heavy soil by this method.

What kind of bulbs shall we put into these beds ? Choose hyacinths, tulips, narcissus, or daffodils, with snowdrops or crocuses of various colors around the edge.

If you use hyacinths you can have the national colors, red, white, and blue, or many shades of either color, as shown in the diagrams (Fig. 369). Of tulips you can have stars or ribbons of yellow, white, or crimson, or in fact almost any color except true blue. In narcissus, yellow, sulfur, and white are the colors. The little crocuses come in yellow, blue, white, and striped colors, and are in bloom and gone before the large flowers take your attention. Many other bulbs are fine for spring flowering ; but as most of them are more difficult to grow and many of them rather expensive, I do not think we will discuss them now.

Suppose we want a bed of red, white, and blue hyacinths (Fig. 369), and make it six feet in diameter : how many bulbs would you want ? Now, hyacinths should be planted six inches apart each way, and the outside row should be at least three inches from the edge of the bed. You see you will want a little over one hundred bulbs, which, if one person had to buy them, would cost him a considerable sum ; but if fifty or more boys and girls would club together it would be easy for everyone.

If you want a bed of tulips, they should be planted four or five inches apart instead of six inches. So you will need more bulbs ; but they are cheaper than hyacinths. The narcissus bulbs, being still smaller than tulips, may be planted three inches apart ; and the little crocuses, the first flowers of spring, should touch one another, as should also the snowdrops.

Perhaps many of you do not wish to wait until spring for your bulbs to flower, in which case we must try to persuade them to bloom through the winter, say at Christmas. Nearly all bulbs are good-natured, and may be coaxed to do things that nature never asks them to do ; so if we go at it right we shall find it very easy to make them think their time to bloom has come, even if the ground is covered with snow and the ice is thick on the ponds. Hyacinths, narcissus, and crocus can all be made to flower in the winter by starting this way. Get the bulbs so as to be able to pot them by the middle or last of October, or if earlier all the better. The soil should be rich, sandy loam if possible ; if not, the best you can get, to which add about one-fourth the bulk of sand and mix thoroughly. If ordinary flower pots are to be used, put in the bottom a few pieces of broken pots, charcoal, or small stones for drainage ; then fill the pot with dirt so that when the bulbs are set on the dirt the top of the bulb is even with the rim of the pot. Fill around it with soil, leaving just the tip of the bulb showing above the dirt. If the soil is heavy, a good plan is to sprinkle a small handful of sand under the bulb to carry off the water, the same as is done in the beds outdoors. If you do not have pots you may use boxes. Starch boxes are a good size to use as they are not heavy to handle ; and I have seen excellent flowers on bulbs planted in old tomato cans. If boxes or cans are used, care must be taken to have holes in the bottoms to let the water run out. A large-size hyacinth bulb will do well in a five-

inch pot.   The same size pot will do for three or four narcissuses
or eight to twelve crocuses.

   After the bulbs are planted in the pots or other receptacles,
they should be placed in a cool place, either in a cold pit or cellar or on the shady side of a building, or, better yet, plunged or
buried up to the rim of the pot in a shady border.   This is done to
force the roots to grow while the top stands still ; as only the
bulbs with good roots will give good flowers.   When the weather
gets cold enough so that a crust is frozen on the soil, the pots
should be covered with a little straw, and as the weather gets colder
more straw must be used.   From
six to eight weeks after planting,
the bulbs should have made roots
enough to grow the plant, and
the pots may be taken up and
placed in a cool room for a week or
so ; after which, if the plants have
started into growth, they may be
taken into a warmer room where
they can have plenty of light.
They will grow very rapidly now
and will want lots of water ;
after the flowers begin to show,
the pots may stand in a saucer
of water all the time.   When just
coming into bloom the plants
may have full sunlight part of
the time to help bring out the

Fig. 370.   Pot of tulips.

color of the flowers.   Fig. 370 shows a pot of tulips.

   I want to tell you of two bulbs that do not need so much
fussing with to get them to bloom for Christmas.   One of them is
called freesia (Fig. 371) and if I could have but one kind of bulb
to flower in the winter, I should choose this.   The little bulbs are
not half as large as crocus bulbs and you will be astonished at the
large leaves and flowers such a bulb can produce.   The bulbs are
about the cheapest of all winter bulbs and they grow without
putting them away to make roots, as the tops do not seem as
impatient to start as those of most other bulbs, but wait until
there are roots to help them along.   The flowers are borne on a
slender stem and look very graceful, either on the plant or in
bouquets.   They are also very fragrant, and a pot with five or six

bulbs will perfume a large room.   All they need is good light soil, sunlight, water, and warmth to make glad the heart of anyone who plants them.

The other bulb I should select is the oriental narcissus or Chinese sacred lily.   This grows in water without any soil what-

Fig. 371.   Pot of the freesia.

ever.   Just take a bowl or glass dish about three times the size of the bulb ; put some pretty stones in the bottom ; set in the bulb and build up around it with stones so as to hold it stiff when the leaves have grown ; tuck two or three small pieces of charcoal among the stones to keep the water sweet ; then fill up the dish

with water and add a little every few days, as it evaporates. Set
the dish in a warm, light place.   In about six weeks the fragrant,
fine white flowers will fill the room with perfume and you will
have the pleasure of watching the roots start and grow, the top
throw up long green leaves, and the flower clusters develop and
open their flowers.   Hyacinths may also be grown in water, but
not as easily as this narcissus, or in such inexpensive dishes.

Fig. 372.   Winter box of bulbs.

The picture (Fig. 372) of a bulb box was taken last winter from
a box of mixed bulbs grown at Cornell.   The calla in the center
and the Kenilworth ivy trailing over the front were planted in
the box in September, and pots of geraniums and other plants set
on the dirt to fill the space.   When the bulbs that were in pots
were ready to be started they were taken out of the pots and set

in the dirt in the box, where they grew and flowered ; the tall stems are paper white narcissus, the best variety for winter. On each side there is a hyacinth just starting and in front a little freesia in bloom. When these bulbs were done flowering, small pots of blooming plants were set on the box and a charming window box was obtained with many different things in it through the winter.

WHERE TO PLANT BULBS ; AND OTHER ADVICE FOR THE OUTDOOR GARDEN.

A large part of the beauty of the flower-bed lies in its position. A flower-bed in the middle of the lawn is usually out of place. It has no "setting," as the artists say. It lacks background. It is merely an incidental thing dropped into the sward. It is out of place. A flower-bed should belong to some part of the general planting of the grounds, or it should be a part of the border or boundary surrounding the place. The center of any grounds should be left open, or free from heavy planting. A few trees may be planted in the center, if one desires shade ; but all the masses of foliage and flowers should be somewhere near the sides or else near the foundations of the house or near other definite boundary lines. In such places the flower-bed is supported by other herbage. It has relation to something else. It forms a part of a general picture ; and every good yard should be a picture.

Along the borders the beds are usually more easily cared for than they are in the center of the lawn. In the latter place they are in danger of being trampled over, and the roots of the grass run underneath the bed and absorb the food and moisture which the flowers need. The beauty of a formal bed in the center of the lawn is destroyed if some of the plants are injured or do not develop. Symmetry is part of its merit. If, however, the bed is along the border, a few vacant places in the bed do not attract great attention. In school grounds it is well to have the beds somewhat near together or continuous, in order that the labor of taking care of them may be less.

It is always well to plant profusely. Much of the beauty of a flower-bed lies in an abundance of color. One must consider, also, that some of the roots, seeds, or bulbs may fail. Some of them may not grow in the first place, and others may be injured by weather or by accidents. It is well to provide for all these contingencies.

One of the best plants to use for the school bulb garden is the crocus, because the bulbs are cheap and very hardy. The mixed bulbs, comprising all the common colors, can be had for forty or fifty cents per hundred at retail, and if one should buy them in considerable quantities, they could be had for less than this. A thousand bulbs of mixed crocuses should be got for three dollars or a little more, and these would make a great display along the fence or walks of any school garden. One of the ways to grow crocuses is to plant the bulbs in the grass, not cutting out the grass where they are planted. That is, they grow right in the sod. By the time the lawn needs to be mown in the spring, the flowers are gone and the crocuses can be cut with the grass. The crocuses will not last so long in a mown sod as they will in beds which are especially prepared for them, but they will ordinarily give good results for two or three years if the land is good ; and they are so cheap that they can be renewed from time to time.

Other good, hardy bulbs for fall planting out-of-doors, aside from lilies, are hyacinth, snowdrop, snowflake, tulip, narcissus of various kinds (including daffodils and jonquils), grape hyacinth, squill. All these are early spring bloomers and will delight the children's eyes.

Fig. 373. A good arrangement of shrubbery and flower-beds.

LEAFLET LXXX.

HORSES.*

By ALICE G. McCLOSKEY and I. P. ROBERTS.

A FEW minutes ago I went into the stable to see Peg and Nan, the two bay horses. On the outside of each stall I found a door-plate, with *Nan* written in large, black letters on one, *Peg* on the other. I visited each old friend in turn.

They are quite different in disposition, these two horses. Nan is gentle, affectionate, patient; Peg is spirited, unfriendly, restless. I am very fond of them both and as yet have not been able to decide which I enjoy the more, quiet Nan or spirited Peg.

All horses are interesting to me. As I take my daily walk, I like to look at the different ones I meet along the way. There is the baker's horse and the butcher's; the doctor's horse, sleek and active; the heavy gray horses that haul loads of coal up the hill all through the winter weather; "Old Speckle," the postman's horse; and the friendly bay I so often see feeding in the meadow.

Fig. 374. Nan.

Of all these wayside acquaintances, I like best the one I meet in the meadow. Perhaps I associate him with the meadow-lark's song, the fresh, green grass, and the gay little dandelions that were about when I first crossed his path; or, perhaps our friendship progressed more rapidly than city streets ever will permit. He seems to know

* Junior Naturalist Monthly, December, 1904.

when I am approaching and raises his head in welcome. I always pet him and talk to him a bit, and we both know that two friends have met.

There are many things about horses that everyone ought to know. If we were to ask Junior Naturalists how coach horses differ from roadsters and how roadsters differ from draft horses, how many would be able to tell us?

Perhaps you will ask, "What is a draft horse?" The draft horse has short legs, a heavy body, a short, thick neck, broad deep chest and shoulders, strong hocks and moderately large feet. It may be that your father owns a draft horse. Ask him whether it

Fig. 375. A typical draft horse.

is a Percheron, a Clydesdale, or an English Shire. These are the most familiar breeds of draft horses. The Percherons came from France and at first they were gray. Now they are often black or dark brown. The Shires, commonly bay, brown or sorrel, came from England; and the Clydesdales, similar in appearance to the Shires but smaller and more active, came from Scotland.

All boys and girls know coach horses. As you stand by the school-room window, you may see one pass. They have long arched necks and fine heads. Their bodies are rounded and well proportioned.

Roadsters, trotters, and saddle horses are usually not so large as coachers. Their necks are inclined to be longer and their chests narrower than in the coach horse ; however, their muscles and tendons are strong.

Now you must not think that just because a horse is drawing a load he is a draft horse ; nor because a horse is hitched to a coach he is a coach horse ; nor because he is driven on the road he is a roadster. These three names,— draft horses, coach horses, road-sters,— represent types or classes. They mean kinds of horses that are supposed to be best adapted for drawing, or for coaches

Fig. 376. Welsh pony and its mother.

and carriages, or for fast driving, providing the horse has no other work to do. But the horses that you usually see are just mere common horses of no particular type, and are used for a great variety of purposes. They are "nondescripts," which means "undescribed" or "unclassified." You would not think of put-ting a true draft horse, like the animal in Fig. 375, on a light carriage ; nor of hitching a coacher like that in Fig. 377 to a coal wagon. Do you think there is any real roadster, or coach horse, or draft horse in your neighborhood ? If not, perhaps you can tell, as the horses pass you, whether they are nearest like one type or another. Try it.

If you will observe horses closely you will find that some are large, heavy, and strong, and that they are seldom made to move rapidly, while others may be nearly as tall but they are slim, and carry their heads high and their necks arched. You should also notice that the heavy draft horse does not lift his feet high nor walk with a proud and lofty tread, while the coach horse lifts his feet high, carries his head high, and moves very proudly.

There are several breeds of draft or heavy horses. Fig. 375

Fig. 377. A good coacher.

shows a fine Clydesdale horse imported from Scotland. Notice how nicely he is marked. The horseman would say that he has four "white stockings" and plenty of "feather" on his fetlock; strange, is it not, that this long hair should be called feather?

Is you should see a large, smooth gray horse similar to the Clyde, without the "white stockings" or the "feather," you may conclude that he is a Percheron horse. As we have said before, the Percheron breed of horses came from France. It is not always gray in color. It is slightly smaller than the Clydesdale.

After you have learned that a draft horse should be large and strong, study the picture of the coach horse (Fig. 377). Compare him with the draft horse. The coach horse is not a fast trotter nor even a fast roadster, but he is usually very beautiful, strong, and stylish.

Now I shall ask you to compare the neck shown in Fig. 380 with that shown in Fig. 381. Which do you think is the more beautiful? The horse with the long, slim neck is a noted trotter. If the neck and head were large, would it help or hinder the trotter? Compare the neck of the trotter with that of the

Fig. 378. Arabian horse.

draft horse and see whether you can explain why one is heavy and the other light. Can you explain to your parents why the draft horse should weigh more than the coach horse?

Do you admire the head and neck shown in Fig. 380? Wherein does it differ from the others? This type is called "ewe-neck."

Fig. 379. Shetland pony.

Can you tell why? Tell me whether you think this horse would be a safe driver.

What do you think of the head and neck of the Arabian horse (Fig. 378)? You like it, do you? Why? Can you imagine what kind of horse belongs to that head and neck? Describe it.

Probably the Arabian horse would be too spirited for you so I shall show you a Shetland pony. (Fig. 379.) Where is Shetland? Why are horses so small in the country where this little fellow came from? How does he differ from the other horses shown in the Leaflet? Note *all* of the differences.

In Fig. 376 you will see the picture of a Welsh pony, and she has a ponyette, a baby only a few days old. Which is the larger, the Shetland pony or the Welsh pony? Which one would you prefer if the baby were left out? Could you raise a calf until it became a grown cow and then trade it for a pony? Just a plain

38

little pony can be bought for the price of a good cow. It is part of a good education to know how to raise and handle cows and horses.

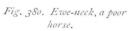

With this Leaflet in your hand, you should go to the stable, or, better still, out on the street, and see whether you can find as good horses and ponies as the pictures represent. As you study horses try to answer the following questions :

Fig. 380. Ewe-neck, a poor horse.

1. Where is the horse's knee joint? Which way does the knee bend?

2. Where is the hock joint? Which way does it bend?

3. Can a horse sleep when standing?

4. How are the legs placed when a horse lies down?

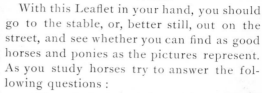

5. How does a horse get up, — front legs first or hind legs first? How does a cow get up?

6. When a horse starts, after standing, what foot does he put forward first, — the left or the right? Fore or back? What foot moves next?

Fig. 381. Neck of a trotter.

7. When a horse trots, do the two feet on one side move together? Or do lefts and rights move together?

8. What does a driver mean when he says that a horse "forges" or "over-reaches?"

9. Name the things that a horse commonly eats. What is a good feed for a day, — how much of each thing, and when given?

Fig. 382. At pasture.

INDEX.